Holistic Healing

Holistic Healing

Hildegard of Bingen

Manfred Pawlik
Translator of Latin text

Patrick Madigan, S.J.
Translator of German text

John Kulas, O.S.B.
Translator of Foreword

Mary Palmquist and John Kulas, O.S.B.
Editors of English text

A Liturgical Press Book

THE LITURGICAL PRESS
Collegeville, Minnesota

This book was originally published in German under the title *Heilwissen* by Pattloch Verlag, © Weltbild Verlag GmbH, D-8900 Augsburg. All rights reserved.

This translation of Hildegard of Bingen's *Causae et Curae* is based on a Latin text published in Leipzig by P. Kaiser in 1903 and translated into German by Manfred Pawlik in 1989 (Pattloch Verlag). This German text is the basis for this English translation by Patrick Madigan, S.J., which was edited by John Kulas, O.S.B., and Mary Palmquist.

Cover design by Greg Becker.

1   2   3   4   5   6   7   8

Library of Congress Cataloging-in-Publication Data

Hildegard, Saint, 1098–1179.
   [Heilwissen. English]
   Holistic healing / Hildegard of Bingen ; Manfred Pawlik, translator of Latin text ; Patrick Madigan, translator of German text ; Mary Palmquist and John Kulas, editors of English text.
      p. cm.
   "This translation of Hildegard of Bingen's Causae et Curae is based on a Latin text published in Leipzig by P. Kaiser in 1903 and translated into German [as Heilwissen] by Manfred Pawlik in 1989 (Pattloch Verlag). This German text is the basis for this English translation".
   ISBN 0-8146-2224-0
   1. Medicine, Medieval. 2. Holistic medicine—Early works to 1800. I. Madigan, Patrick, 1945- . II. Title.
R128.H513   1994
610—dc20
                                                         94-1902
                                                           CIP

Die Seele liebt in allen Dingen
das diskrete Mass.
Wann auch immer der Körper des menschen ohne Diskretion isst
und trinkt oder etwas anders
dieser Art verrichtet,
werden die Kräfte der Seele verletzt. . . .
In allen Dingen soll sich der Mensch selbst
das rechte Mass auferlegen.

Hildegard von Bingen

* * *

The soul loves moderation
in all things.
Whenever the human body lacks measure,
and eat and drinks or something like that
unbalances it, the powers of the soul are wounded. . . .
So in all things let people
maintain a proper balance.

Hildegard of Bingen

FOREWORD

As human being and saint, as a visionary and mystic, as abbess and homilist, as a woman thoroughly involved in societal and political issues, as a composer and a poet, as well as the "first published woman physician," Hildegard of Bingen (1098–1179) is one of the most fascinating personalities of the German Middle Ages. In her writings on scientific and medical matters, especially in her major work *Causae et curae,* she has made a significant contribution to the health sciences.

The biography of St. Hildegard, written at the end of the twelfth century by the monks Godfrey and Theodoric *(Vita sanctae Hildegardis auctoribus Godefrido et Theodorico monachis)* is an illuminating document with citations from contemporary sources, including many from Hildegard of Bingen herself. It is, to be sure, not a biography in the modern sense if by that one understands a comprehensive, unbiased, and well-documented historical work. The fifty-three chapters of this biography are arranged in three books which are each preceded by a foreword. In it a portrait of a saint is drawn who was reputed to be responsible for miraculous cures. It is a picture of a saint as her contemporaries saw her or, perhaps better, as her contemporaries desired to see her, a saint worthy of wondrous admiration and reverence. Subsequent painstaking research into the life, works, and influence of St. Hildegard has verified the details of her life revealed by this biography and has added more information. As a result, the following may be considered beyond dispute:

Hildegard of Bingen was born in 1098 on her parents' estate near Alzey in Rhenish Hesse. She was the tenth and last child of the noble couple Hildebert and Mechtild of Bermersheim. Seven of her brothers and sisters are known by name. In 1106, when she was eight years old, her parents consecrated her to God, entrusting her to Jutta of Spanheim (or, as in some records, Sponheim), who was living as a hermit at the Benedictine monastery at Disibodenberg. She instructed Hildegard in *The Rule of St. Benedict,* initiated her into the monastic life, taught her the psalms, and acquainted her with the liturgy and the Bible. This basic formation in the religious life was broadened and deepened through the activity of Volmar, a monk of Disibodenberg, who served as Hildegard's teacher *(magister)* and who later, until his death in 1173, functioned as her amanuensis as she authored her books. In this way Hildegard became thoroughly familiar with the Sacred Scriptures, especially the Hebrew Scriptures and with the patristic writings. However, she received systematic instruction in neither the classical languages of Greek and Latin nor in the "seven liberal arts," that is, in the *trivium* (grammar, logic, and rhetoric) and in the *quadrivium* (arithmetic, geometry, astronomy, and music). She modestly considered herself *indocta,* by which she meant that she was not the beneficiary of a systematic or scientific education.

Sometime between 1112 and 1115 Hildegard made her monastic profession, receiving the veil from St. Otto, bishop of Bamberg. According to her biography Hildegard attracted attention even as a young nun by virtue of the great patience she exhibited in her numerous illnesses. This allowed her to extend genuine sympathy and devoted care to those of her acquaintances who were sick, weak, or otherwise in need of assistance. After Jutta's death the community unanimously *(unanimiter)* elected her to be spiritual mother *(magistra).* Thereupon, Hildegard assumed the direction of the little convent which traced its origin to the hermitage which Jutta's father, Count Stephen of Spanheim, had founded at the Benedictine monastery at Disibodenberg.

According to her own testimony Hildegard was favored with visions from the time she was three years old. These she confided first to Jutta of Spanheim and later also to the monk Volmar. At the age of seventy-seven, she wrote to Wibert, a monk of Gembloux, that she invariably beheld these visions with eyes open during waking hours. They might occur by day or at night but never while she was experiencing an ecstatic trance. Thus, it was during a vision in the forty-third year of her life (1141) that she received the divine mandate: "O child of Adam and Eve, subject to all infirmity, ashes from ashes, corruption from corruption, tell and write the things you see and hear . . .!" *(O homo fragilis, et cinis cineris et putredo putredinis, dic et scribe, que vides et audis . . .).* After overcoming an initial hesitation and, in a manner of speaking, taking refuge in illness she accepted this calling which would transform her into a great visionary, the *prophetissa teutonica.*

Hildegard's first major work, *Scivias seu visionum ac revelationum libri III* (''Know the Ways of the Lord or Three Books of Visions and Revelations''), was begun in 1141 and was completed ten years later with the assistance of Dom Volmar and Richardis of Stade, who was also a nun. In the six visions described in Part One of this work, Hildegard depicts the history of the universe from creation to the sin of Adam and Eve. The seven visions of Part Two recount the redemption of humankind through Christ and the Church, while the thirteen visions of Part Three treat the acts of divine power *(virtutes)* up to the end of the world. This book of visions and allegorical interpretations was a prophetic work, in the sense that it sought to offer praise to God through the word. It brought her instant renown when Pope Eugene III personally read parts of it aloud to the fathers of the synod of Trier (30 November 1147 to February 1148). After rigorous investigation the pope authenticated Hildegard's charism as a visionary, certified her visions as legitimate private revelations, and encouraged her to continue writing. Her correspondence with Bernard of Clairvaux (1146–47) indicates how tentative and dubious she initially was in the face of these visions and how eagerly she sought and how gratefully she accepted the support and corroboration of the Church with respect to her prophetic gifts.

Hildegard's extensive correspondence, which she initiated at this time, reveals her as a valiant, competent, clear thinking and broadminded abbess and woman, who in the spirit of Christian care and concern had things to say about the most disparate ecclesiastical, political, and sociological problems. Her approximately three hundred letters were directed to influential ecclesiastical and secular personalities in the western world, e.g., Popes Eugene III, Anastasius IV, Adrian IV, and Alexander III (though not to any of the antipopes), to cardinals and archbishops (e.g., those of Mainz, Trier, and Cologne), to bishops and priests, to monks and nuns, to monasteries and convents. In her letters to abbots and abbesses she offered pointed advice and instructions based on her understanding of *The Rule of St. Benedict.*

She audaciously directed criticism at Emperor Frederick I (Barbarossa) and corresponded with his relatives. She wrote to distinguished princes and to King Henry II of England and Queen Eleanor. At about the time of the Synod of Trier, Hildegard determined to relocate her monastery from Disibodenberg, which had in the meantime become much too small for her nuns, to Rupertsberg situated directly across from Bingen. A variety of difficulties had to be overcome before she and her nuns were able in 1150 to move into the newly built monastery whose construction she had personally planned and supervised. Of critical importance in this move was the help provided by Margravine Richardis of Stade. On 1 May 1152, the archbishop of Mainz consecrated the new monastery church. Presumably the mystery play *Ordo virtutum,* which Hildegard had composed for that occasion received its premier performance on that day.

This "Dance of the Virtues" takes its place thematically alongside of *Scivias,* Hildegard's major theological work. After an introduction which recounts the author's gifts as a seer, a cast of heavenly powers and virtues appears allegorically, locked in mortal combat with the devil, whose manifold seductions directed at the human soul they are ultimately able to foil. Sixteen nuns played the parts of the *virtutes,* the divine powers. The only male role, that of the devil, was, it may be assumed, reserved for Dom Volmar. According to Hildegard's conception of music the words of the devil would have no melody but would only be some kind of *strepitus,* or noise. Only angels and human beings had the right to sing and to offer musical praise to God.

This religious musical production was not unique among Hildegard's poetic compositions. Seventy-seven songs (antiphons, responsories, hymns, and sequences, including very significantly thirteen songs in honor of St. Ursula and fifteen in honor of Mary) have been preserved. As has already been mentioned, Hildegard had no systematic training in music. She had the benefit solely of an early introduction to the choral singing of the Psalms and to Gregorian chant. Nonetheless, these artistic works contributed decisively to her reputation in spiritual matters. She offers this comment on her artistic talents in her autobiography: "I also composed and sang songs to the praise of God and the saints, even though I had received no human instruction and I had never learned the neums and the modes of Gregorian chant." According to a letter of the schoolmaster Odo of Paris, Hildegard's musical compositions were already well known by 1148. Wibert of Gembloux, who became Hildegard's secretary after the death of Volmar (1173) and that of Godfrey (1176), wrote in 1175: "These musical works which were composed for the praise of God and in honor of the saints are being performed publicly in church, an unheard-of accomplishment for a woman!"

Hildegard suffered greatly when several nuns, unwilling to accept the rigors of monastic life, left the monastery. But especially distressing was the loss of her cherished old friend, Richardis of Stade, who had provided such energetic support at the time of the relocation of the monastery to Rupertsberg and who was of great assistance to her in her literary work. At the behest of Richardis' brother, Archbishop Hartwig of Bremen, and much to Hildegard's displeasure, Richardis chose to accept the position of abbess at the convent of Bassum, to which she had been elected. But Richardis was forced in short order to rue this ambitious move. Before she was able to return to Hildegard, she died on 29 October 1152.

However, no matter how sharply Hildegard reproached herself, no matter how intensely she grieved, she did not allow herself to become embittered. In spite of a variety of maladies, some of which persisted for years, she summoned all her energies for new endeavors:

Between 1151 and 1158 she completed *Physica* and *Causae et curae,* two works which by reason of their focus on the study of nature and the art of healing deserve to be linked.

Between 1158 and 1171 she undertook four lengthy preaching tours: From 1158 to 1160 she travelled to the Main River area; in 1160 she was in Trier and Lorraine; in 1161 she went down the Rhine to Cologne; in 1170–71 she travelled to Suabia. Her sermons had a profound impact on her listeners and induced many to reform their lives.

Hildegard's second great book of visions, *Liber vitae meritorum,* was written during the years 1158 to 1163. As virtues and vices engage in poetic dialogue the reciprocal bonds linking God, human beings, and the universe are revealed.

On 18 April 1163 Hildegard was at the imperial court at Mainz to receive from the Emperor Frederick I an edict granting her as *abbatissa* and her monastery at Rupertsberg the protection of the realm. In the same year she began work on her third book of visions, *Liber divinorum operum,* a work, however, which she seems not to have completed until 1174. In the ten visions of this book the interaction of universe and humans and their relationship to the creator are portrayed.

In addition to expanding the cloister at Disibodenberg and planning and constructing the monastery at Rupertsberg, Hildegard established a daughter house in 1165 at Eibingen on the Rhine above

Rüdesheim. Worthy of special note is her courageous battle to preserve her rights during the interdict which ecclesiastical officials in Mainz had imposed in 1178. Hildegard of Bingen lived long enough to see the vindication of her position. Her appeal to Rome was successful, and the interdict was lifted before her death on 17 September 1179. The relics of St. Hildegard, who was never officially canonized, are found in the parish church of Eibingen near Rüdesheim.

In the midst of her demanding and multifarious projects, Hildegard of Bingen found time and energy to pursue her research and writings on nature, and she is often termed the first German female natural scientist and physician. The volumes attributed to her — *A Study of Nature,* also called *Physica* in its first printing in 1533, and *Holistic Healing* (universally cited with the short title *Causae et curae*) — are, obviously, no scientific or medical books in the modern sense. In the last analysis, they can only be understood in the context of Hildegard's oeuvre and her personal understanding of God and the world.

A Study of Nature is a book that deals with nature, plants, animals, and medicines. In its nine books the plant world, the elements, trees, stones, precious stones, fish, birds, mammals and other animals, reptiles, and metals are discussed. Of the total 513 chapters 293 have to do with botany. Fish too come in for a major share of attention. This is undoubtedly attributable to the fact that Hildegard was thoroughly acquainted with the operation of the monastery garden and was particularly conversant with all kinds of medicinal herbs. Furthermore, the immediate environs of the monastery at Disibodenberg at the confluence of the Glan and the Nahe rivers and the location of Rupertsberg at the point where the Nahe flows into the Rhine undoubtedly aroused her interest in aquatic life.

This reference book for the study of nature bears witness to Hildegard's deep love for nature and by that token to her love for God as creator. As such it can be seen as the logical and necessary complement to *Holistic Healing,* which binds theological, scientific, cosmological, anthropological, pathological, and therapeutic themes into an integrated whole.

The manuscript copy of *Liber compositae medicinae* (Book of Holistic Medicine), has been preserved in codex 90 b located in Copenhagen. A thirteenth-century scribe composed the title *Beate Hildegardis Cause et Cure* by shortening the subtitle which specified the contents: *de causis, signis atque curis aegritudinum* ("Concerning the Causes, Symptoms, and Treatment of Illness''). The same scribe is responsible for the division of the manuscript into five sections and for inventing the chapter headings, as well, which, it must be said, are of questionable value. Frequently they are found in the margin at the head of the individual units, but occasionally they are inserted within the text itself. Moreover, they do not always coincide with the content of the paragraph, at least not precisely; sometimes they are even misleading. It is clear that they are not part of the original text, for they are written in the style of the thirteenth century. Actually, entire chapters are of uncertain authenticity. For instance, both content and style suggest strongly that the sixth part, which deals with the influence that a particular phase of the moon at the time of conception has on the character or even the later fate of an individual, is not original. Matthew of Westminster cites this work in 1292 with the full Latin title: *Liber compositae medicinae de aegritudinum causis, signis atque curis.* John Trithemius (1462–1516), the famous humanist and abbot, was also familiar with the book. In 1859 it was rediscovered in the Copenhagen library by Carl Jessen. A portion of this manuscript was published by Cardinal Pitra in 1882. It was not until 1903 that the complete edition by Paul Kaiser appeared in print. Unfortunately, this edition is replete with errors and inaccuracies. Accordingly, a new critical edition, conforming to the strict canons of contemporary scholarship and taking into account the findings of previous research, remains an urgent requirement for continued scientific investigation of the works of Hildegard of Bingen.

Despite the precarious state of the text, there is a remarkably strong interest in Hildegard's teaching in *Holistic Healing,* an interest which is second only to that in her visionary writings. Even though the sources in individual particulars demand further research some conclusions can nonetheless safely be drawn: *Holistic Healing,* as a handbook providing information and suggestions in matters of sickness and healing, stands foursquare in the tradition of monastic and popular medicine which itself was based on the medical knowledge of antiquity. Added to this are oral traditions and Hildegard's own experience in medicine and care of the sick. The entire book bears the stamp of the author's faith and Christian culture.

It has been established that Hildegard of Bingen personally attended, treated, and healed the sick. Furthermore, throughout her whole life she was herself forced, as Wibert of Gembloux writes, to bear the cross of illness. She dedicated herself with all her energy to the care of the sick and infirm; she toiled incessantly to alleviate the physical and spiritual sufferings of all who sought her help; she offered advice to those who asked for it; she dealt with a whole range of health issues in her letters and books; her writings inevitably reveal a person who had learned from life-long experience what it means to be sick. In all these ways she sought to put into practice what St. Benedict says in chapter 36 of *The Rule* about those who are sick in the monastery: "The primary duty of monks is to take care of the sick. The sick are, indeed, to be served as Christ himself. . . . The abbot should exercise the greatest care that they not be neglected." As abbess, Hildegard of Bingen took very seriously the obligation to care for the sick. Not only was she a model in the way she provided for the infirm in her own monastery; she actually permitted men who were sick to come into the cloister to receive medical attention.

The numerous wars and plagues that occurred in the Middle Ages led to the fact that monasteries gradually came to be centers of medical practice. One fact militating against the continuing development of this kind of "monastic medicine" practiced by men and women religious was, of course, the traditional teaching of the Church that illness was generally to be seen as punishment for sin or as an affliction coming from the devil. Accordingly, standard therapy consisted of repentance, asceticism, prayer, and imploring the intercession of saints and martyrs.

Contrary to this view, Hildegard viewed sickness in general as well as her own afflictions in particular as a trial from God and not as a punishment for sin. She was convinced that "it is important to fortify the sick body so that it can offer resistance to the devil and his minions." Accordingly, taking her cue from the Benedictine motto, she believed that *ora et labora* ("prayer and purposeful action") belonged together. Thus, Hildegard took as her model Christ the physician *(medicus)* and Savior of the world *(salvator mundi).* She was attracted to Christ's dual role as healer and priest, the physician of both body and soul.

Hildegard of Bingen lived in a trying time of political, ecclesiastical, social, and spiritual upheaval. One need only recall, for example, the bitter conflict between emperor and pope, the impassioned summons to the Second Crusade proclaimed by St. Bernard of Clairvaux, and the glorification of human love and the life style of chivalry in the literature of the time. This was the time also of a fundamental change in the practice of medicine in the Middle Ages. In the year

1130 the Council of Clermont prohibited all members of religious orders from practicing medicine. The council argued that such activity was incompatible with the spirit of monastic life which implied withdrawal from the world. This prohibition marked the beginning of the transformation of so-called monastic medicine into a scientific discipline that was henceforth taught at the newly formed universities. Thus, scholastic medicine or the "medicine taught in the schools" *[Schulmedizin]* was born. In this way the twelfth century witnessed the shift from monastery to university as centers of education. As time went on this led to the demythologizing and secularization of science.

Holistic Healing is a book that ranges from matters of faith to data derived from empirical investigation. It deals with the creation of the world and the structure of the universe; it studies the healthy and diseased human body and its development, sexual activity, the principal illnesses from head to toe, nourishment, digestion and metabolic imbalances, mental illnesses, various kinds of medicine and treatment, and it offers prescriptions for a healthy life style. There are many errors and shortcomings in this book. Nonetheless, it would be wrong to judge it from the perspective of the nineteenth [sic] century and dismiss it out of hand as a naive compilation of absurdities. It must rather be approached in the framework of the cosmology of the period in which it was written as the author conceived it. In the Middle Ages one thought in interconnected polarities: God and humanity, angels and demons, good and evil, health and sickness, life and death.

Similarly, Hildegard of Bingen possessed a vision of a unified creation, a cosmic order, with man and woman in the center. As creatures and the handiwork of God *(opus dei),* they are commissioned to continue God's creative work. The effort to fulfill this call to creativity in the world does not lead, it is true, to an immediate understanding and experience of God; nonetheless, the created world does provide an indirect contact with God: "The heavenly harmony is a mirror of the divine, and human beings are a mirror of all of God's wonderful works." God created the world good, but humans succumbed to temptation and by sinning injected disorder into the world. Their primordial vitality *(viriditas)* thus radically weakened, they were subject to illness and in need of healing. Accordingly, they required divine grace as well as medical treatment. As a result, the question of the origin of disease raised the further question of the origin and essence of evil, of suffering, and of sin. Ultimately, it reached back to the primordial fall of Lucifer and the sin of Adam. It is for that reason that Hildegard's *Holistic Healing* begins with the story of creation and the establishment of the divine order *(cosmos).*

As the miniature on the front of the dust jacket of the second German edition illustrates, the human person, with hands extending to the very edge of the sphere *(rota)* bounding his or her world, appears as a rational being of body and soul, a microcosm standing in the center of the macrocosm, subject to the influence of the elements. All of creation is held in God's hands. Thus, human beings are engaged in an on-going dialogue with creation and creator. Body and soul constitute a unit like man and woman or heaven and earth. The body is seen no longer, as it was in antiquity, as the prison of the soul. Rather, it is perceived as the cloak of the soul, as the *imago dei,* as a creature formed in the image and likeness of God. This medieval conception of humans as a microcosm, that is to say, a being forming an image in miniature of the entire visible world, found expression already in Isidore of Seville (c. 560–636 c.e.), who described the relation of the world to human beings in the following words: "But in a transferred sense the world can appropriately be called 'man' (or 'woman'), for just as the world is composed of four elements, the human being is a product of the relative balance of four humors (temperaments). For that reason, the ancients saw the human being of a piece with the structure of the world. In Greek, after all, the word for 'world' is 'cosmos' while the word for 'human being' is 'microcosm,' which means little world. . . ."

If one wishes to trace the idea of the relationship of the four elements to the temperaments or archetypes one has to go back even further. In antiquity human beings were grouped into various categories depending on their intrinsic structure. Thus, they were viewed as a microcosm in close contact with the cosmos, receiving their energy from the macrocosm. Claudius Galenus, next to Hippocrates the most famous physician of antiquity (129–199 c.e.), distinguished four temperamental responses, namely the phlegmatic, the sanguine, the melancholic, and the choleric. According to the teaching on humors (fluids) it was widely believed that good health was determined by the proper composition and appropriate intermingling of these bodily fluids. Galenus accounted for these differing types by pointing to a particular mixture of the humors. This gave rise in each case to the various temperaments. Accordingly, a phlegmatic person is characterized and formed by the viscosity of the mucus (Greek: *phlegma* =

mucus), a sanguine person by the gushing quality of the flowing blood (Latin: *sanguis* = blood), a melancholic person by the depressed ill humor associated with the black bile (Greek: *melanos* = black), and the choleric person by the irascibility associated with the gall (Greek: *chole* = gall).

Actually, it was not until the beginning of the twentieth century that the classification according to temperamental response was replaced by categories based on types of readily observable physiognomic features. Thus, from about the year 1920 classification of individuals according to asthenic, pyknic, athletic, and dysplastic physiognomic features became common. These rather primitive and simplistic classifications were abandoned by Ernst Kretschmer, who hypothesized the existence of response patterns or response cycles based on certain predispositions. According to this view, for example, schizophrenia would occur overwhelmingly among those with asthenic characteristics, whereas a disposition to manic-depression would be linked almost exclusively to those with pyknic characteristics. Pioneering work was also done by Julius Baucher, who established a correlation between the classification by reaction type and the theory based on physiognomic characteristics.

This doctrine of classifications reached its culmination in homeopathic medicine which recognizes the grouping of pharmaceuticals into four main categories. Drugs of a specific type and patients of a particular type are then linked in accordance with their proper response patterns. Thus, it can be seen that from antiquity until well into the twentieth century the classification of individuals according to the four temperaments held sway. The interaction of the four elements with these four temperaments was recognized already in ancient times. According to this theory, the phlegmatic temperament betrayed the influence of water, the sanguine temperament was related to air, the melancholic temperament embodied the earth, and the choleric temperament corresponded to fire. It is, of course, worth mentioning in this connection that human beings can never be subject to rigid categorization. It is always a question merely of describing a general orientation which admits of endless transitional and dual types!

In any case, for Hildegard of Bingen a person is exposed to every kind of influence and force, whether earthly or cosmic. She viewed the four elements as the four fundamental principles which hold the universe together and by means of the bodily humors exert an influence on human beings. Accordingly, fire provides warmth and the sense of sight; air provides breath and the sense of hearing; water provides blood and mobility; earth provides tissue, bones, and upright stature. The warmth of fire produces a dry *(siccum)* phlegm; the moistness associated with air produces a phlegm that is moist *(humidum);* the aqueous blood produces frothy *(spumaticum)* phlegm; and the earthy tissue in humans produces tepid *(tepidum)* phlegm. A harmonious intermingling of these humors is responsible for health; an overabundance *(abundantia)* of any one of these components, on the contrary, disturbs the overall equilibrium and causes the humors to congeal *(coagulatio)*. This is expressed, then, in physical or mental or emotional illnesses. It is clear that Hildegard's teaching on health is not essentially different from the doctrine of the four humors current in antiquity; only the terminology is different.

Hildegard's ideas can be summarized and simplified as follows: The interaction and exchange of cosmic matter or energy makes life on this planet possible and gives it shape; this is particularly true of human life. With winds functioning as agents, cosmic forces are introduced into the human being's system of humors. These determine good and bad health as well as moral behavior. The human person is situated as a living being within the natural system with its forces and elements. The human person interacts with these forces and is influenced by them. To this extent, creation is a process, an endless dialogue.

In Hildegard's mind, the key concept, the fundamental symbolic color, is "viriditas," that life-determining force which allows everything to get green and to grow. This is the basis of life and well-being. Contrary to the situation in the later Middle Ages during the time of the persecution of witches, green as the color symbolizing life, goodness, and health has for Hildegard an exclusively positive connotation.

Disease as a condition influenced by the four elements and consequently viewed primarily as a disintegration of the proper balance of humors in the human organism is presented in the traditional manner, quite literally, from head to foot. The heart as the *situs* of the human soul is given the role of centerpiece of the entire organism. In view of the fact that an exact terminology is lacking and the various descriptions of illnesses are not infrequently sketchy, it is, obviously, often difficult to determine a precise meaning.

Probably the greatest surprise in store for the modern reader is the discovery of how openly a medieval nun discusses male and female anatomy and human sexual activity. However, sex for Hildegard of Bingen is something quite natural and a matter of divine design. As part of creation, sexuality belongs to the essential make-up of a man and a woman. It is clear, though, that a healthy sex life requires a long period of physical and spiritual maturation. (Hildegard alludes to this idea by her use of agricultural images.) In these matters too men and women are weak and in need of redemption. They are created for each other to provide opportunities for mutual self-fulfillment; they complete each other and form a unified whole, which is grounded in reason and responsibility. The female body, in particular, acquires an especially close relationship to nature. Hildegard's discussion of menstruation, however, reflects the ancient perception of it as a process of cleansing. In view of the high mortality rate in the Middle Ages, especially in childbirth, the latter is given extensive treatment. This, of course, does not yet constitute a medical-surgical treatise on obstetrics. It is rather a collection of practical experiences and reflections.

Thus, while conception and birth, complications in childbirth and gynecological diseases, menstruation and menopause are all extensively described, headaches, earaches, dental disease (the tooth worm, incidentally, was already recognized in Babylonian, Egyptian, and classical Graeco-Roman times as the cause of diseases of tooth and gum), eye disease, inflammation of the nasal passages, chest complaints, above all, pulmonary disease, and heart disease were all less comprehensively discussed and diagnosed. Stomach ailments, diseases of the liver, kidney, and bladder, gallstones or kidney stones, fever, and skin disease are mentioned, but it is often not easy to comprehend exactly what is meant.

The role of blood and the circulatory system in metabolic disorders and disease is expounded in great detail. Skin diseases are divided into leprosy, rashes, and abscesses. Not surprisingly, gout, a disease so prevalent in the Middle Ages, is described in rather more detail. Obviously, modern terminology should be avoided in referring to disease-producing microorganisms. Various fractures and trauma-related injuries, for example, knife and sword wounds requiring surgical intervention, are omitted, because, as has already been mentioned, clerics had been forbidden since 1130 from functioning as surgeons.

Nerve and mental disorders are distinguished on the basis of symptoms. Disturbances of mind and emotions, which are as unstable as the person and his or her system of humors, are ultimately attributed to original sin. Significantly enough, Hildegard considered the type of melancholy which Adam, the first human being, succumbed to after his sin to be a classic example of a condition likely to cause illness and disease. Accordingly, melancholy is given a particularly extensive treatment. The stabilizing effect of laughter and tears is documented by citing the example of Mary Magdalene. Just as her repentance awakened a yearning for salvation, similarly a turning from sin opened the door to physical healing. And healing, as Hildegard repeatedly emphasizes, is ultimately in the hands of God. Epilepsy is associated with the influence of the devil.

Cases of poison and the toxic effects of plants are described rather extensively. However, the analysis of the various illnesses caused by worms poses great difficulties. The topic of bathing is broadly discussed, befitting its great popularity and significance in the Middle Ages. Bloodletting and application of leeches were common practices in the Middle Ages following Galen's doctrine on the elimination of harmful humors. It is worth noting, however, that Hildegard adopts a strikingly critical stance with respect to this procedure and cautions against its excessive or indiscriminate use. Also not to be overlooked is her mention of the therapeutic value of precious stones, the place of cosmetics in contributing to the sexual attractiveness of women, music therapy, instructions for hygiene and diet, which clearly showed the influence of *The Rule of St. Benedict,* and efforts at diagnosis and prognosis. The latter can be noted, for example, in her discussion of skin color, the tone of the voice, the brightness or dullness of the eyes, pulse rate, breathing, various types of fever, degree of consciousness, or analysis of urine. Of considerable importance, in this connection, is pain. It is an indicator which, rightly understood and evaluated, makes healing possible.

The prescriptions, medications, and treatment which Hildegard of Bingen describes are in general an integral part of monastic medicine or of plain common sense, and they have in large measure stood the test of time. Only now and then do they appear grotesque or superstitious. For the most part, medicines have as their objective the removal from the body of noxious humors or decayed matter and the restoration of a proper balance. Hildegard follows Galen's doctrine of qualities and draws a distinction between the disease producing properties of the mostly hot, dry, moist, or cold qualities and the corresponding qualities of various medications. In the same way that *viriditas* symbolizes the life and procreative power which human beings possess, it characterizes the growth and healing power of plants.

Hildegard of Bingen offers concrete, exact directions for gathering, processing, storing, and using medicinal herbs. She points out places where these herbs can be located and the proper time of day and season to gather them. She explains how to prepare these herbs as soups, beverages, purgatives *(luterdranck)*, little cakes *(tortelli)*, powders and salves, and she describes how to use them as poultices, compresses, applications, and inhalants. Now and then, one runs across notions that are rooted in magic; sometimes one finds homeopathic remedies. For the most part, the medicines that are produced are intended for immediate or prompt use, but the book does contain instructions for proper storage to assure maximum effect for the longest possible time (for example, storage in new, earthenware vessels). References to measure and weight are practical, of course, but not very precise. Mostly, coins with specific weights are referred to along with single or multiple measures or partial measures.

The therapeutic possibilities of a healthy diet and proper nourishment are described in a way that has a modern ring to it; nonetheless, the basic philosophical principle undergirding the discussion of diagnosis and therapy is still the recognition that the human person is a unified being made up of body and soul. And when all is said and done, it is God who decrees health and disease, life and death. This conviction lies at the heart of Hildegard's life and work, as she wrote to Wibert of Gembloux: "I am greatly hampered by illnesses, and often I am so worn down with excruciating pain that I think I am going to die. Yet, to this point God has spared my life. Whether it is a question of my body or my soul I must admit that I don't understand myself very well, and I consider myself no better than a nonentity. I reach out toward the living God and I entrust myself to him, so that in all of this God, who is without beginning or end, may keep me safe from the evil one. I beg you too to pray for me that I may persevere in God's service!"

In spite of all the evidence in this work of systematic presentation, Hildegard's *Holistic Healing* has no organized conclusion. Structurally, linguistically, and stylistically the work lacks the finishing touch. The author's language is largely monotonous. Needless repetitions and awkward circumlocutions, cumbersome expressions, and the absence of rhetorical devices make it abundantly clear that this is no cultivated, elegant prose. She neither uses the typical technical medical vocabulary nor does she invent her own. Her syntax is marked by excessive use of long, involved sentences, which impedes easy comprehension. She employs many similes which are intended to add vividness and clarity but which frequently are confusing or incongruous. There are errors in orthography and grammar, especially regarding grammatical case and congruence. When Hildegard of Bingen humbly refers to herself as *humilis forma* and *simplex homo,* we can be sure that this is not merely meant as a conventional expression of modesty in the spirit of Christian humility. The linguistic deficiencies are traceable solely to the fact that she had not been the beneficiary of a thorough and systematic training in the technical language which physicians world wide had been using for medical works for more than 1,300 years, ever since Greek had been supplanted by Latin around 500 c.e. On one occasion she wrote to a schoolmaster in Paris as follows: ''Thus, I am not steeped in human knowledge nor have I any particular intellectual gifts. Neither am I bursting with physical health. Rather, I rely exclusively on the help of God.'' Many passages in the text remain obscure. Her collaborators undoubtedly polished her simple Latin, but they were careful not to alter the meaning of her words. Nevertheless, it is impossible to overlook the intellectual stature of her work, which is evident, if one may use Hildegard's own words, *quasi per speculum* (as it were in a mirror) or *fenestraliter* (as though through a window).

This [German] translation is faithful to the original text and is a complete edition intended for the interested non-specialist. Accordingly, the quotations interspersed throughout the text are not given in their Latin and Middle High German original. They can be consulted in the endnotes.

I.

The Creation of the World. God was and is without beginning before the creation of the world. He was and is the brilliant light, and he was Life. When God wanted to create the world, he made it out of nothing; the matter of the world existed in his Will alone.

Matter. Then as God's will to bring the work to completion revealed itself, matter, as a dark, as yet unformed clod, sprang immediately out of his Will, as God intended.

The Creation of the Angels. And the Word of the Father boomed through the heavens, "Let there be Light!" Light came into being and with it the light-bearing angels. For as soon as he said, "Let there be Light," at that moment, besides the lights in the heavens, the Father also made the light that the angels themselves are. When, however, he said, "Let there be lights!" that referred to the lights that we see in the heavens.

The Fall of Lucifer. To the North, Lucifer saw an empty waste that had yet to be included in the work of creation. There he wished to build his own home so that from there he might move out and erect still larger and grander things than God had done. He was not aware of God's further intention to add other things to creation. For he did not pay attention to the countenance of the Father, knew nothing of his might, and did not apprise himself of God's resources because he was bent on rebelling from him before he took the time to learn all these things. In fact, God had not revealed his intentions, but kept them concealed as a strong and powerful man sometimes does who hides his strength from other men so that he may learn what they are thinking and planning to do. As Lucifer attempted to rise up in his perverted will to nothingness — for it was precisely "nothing" that he wished to do — he was cast down directly into nothingness and could find nothing to arrest his fall, for there was no longer any ground beneath his feet. He no longer had any height above, nor any deep below him that could have arrested such a fall. As he tumbled toward nothingness, his first effort gave birth to evil which flamed out immediately as a consequence of his malice toward God and which did not know the brilliant Light in itself — falling like a wheel slowly spinning, concealing a glowing darkness at its center. In this way, evil became separated from good. The good did not disturb evil nor did evil disturb the good. Rather, God the Father remained complete in his goodness like a wheel because his paternity is full of goodness; so is his fatherhood entirely proper, just, strong, secure, and, when so perceived, comparable to a wheel. Now, however, a wheel must be filled with something. If a wheel has only its outermost rim, it would be empty, and it would not be possible for another craftsman to come up to it and place a hand upon it because two craftsmen cannot work on a wheel at the same time. O Men, look closely at yourself! For man has heaven and earth and everything in between stuffed within him; he is a shape that conceals everything within himself.

Fatherhood. Fatherhood is like the circumference of a circle; fatherhood is like a complete wheel. Divinity is in it, all comes from it, and without it there is no creator. However, Lucifer is not something complete and whole, but rather something partial and split since he wished to become something he should not have been. When God made the world, he planned the incarnation from the very beginning.

The Creation of the Soul. When God made light which had wings and could fly over everything, at the same time, he decided to bestow a material body on the spiritual life that is the breath of Life — specifically, an upright shape formed out of the clay of the earth that could neither fly nor hover and was not in a position to lift itself into the air. Thus, it should be earth-bound in order to perceive God all the more clearly. The old serpent hated this connection to the earth because thereby man, in spite of his bodily weight, could still raise his attention to God.

The Elements and the Firmament. God also made the elements of the world. These elements are also in human beings, and man works with them. They are fire, air, water, and earth. These four elements are connected so intimately one with another that one cannot be completely separated from the others. They maintain themselves so tightly together that man calls them the firmament.

The Sun and the Stars. Among these, the sun plays the highest role and spreads its light and its fire-glow over the others. Around it are various stars of such size and brilliance that they are like mountains of firmament compared to the earth. For this reason, they appear to be even brighter, the closer to the earth they are. Other stars of lesser size and brilliance are also around the sun so that when compared to the just-mentioned stars, they are like valleys. For this reason are they also less clearly visible.

The Weather. Whenever an excessively warm and glowing heat dominates the atmosphere, sometimes this ardor will unleash a sudden rainfall and send a dangerous drenching down to earth. Thence comes stormy weather and thunder claps. It is like what happens when a kettle is placed over a hot fire; it boils up and froths over the sides. Such storms are ordered according to God's judgment of previous sins or of men's evil deeds already begun. They also warn against future dangers such as wars, famine, or sudden death. For all of our deeds interact with the elements and are decisively influenced by them because they stand in relationship with the elements. Whenever the heat and glow that dominates the atmosphere lessens, the atmosphere releases less rainstorm and flood. The same thing happens when a kettle is placed over a weaker fire; it hardly boils at all or ever overflows its pot. However, whenever the air has the ideal proportion of fire and water, this brings good weather, and it is delightfully warm. Then it is like a kettle placed upon a mild fire. However, when the sun climbs high so that its heat burns strongly, then sometimes the air becomes very dry due to the sunshine, and the fire of the sun sometimes arouses the fire of the thunder.

Thunder. Thunder is the fire of judgment, cool and foul-smelling. As soon as the fire of the sun agitates the fire of thunder, the latter, thereby disturbed, emits bolts of lightening of great power.

Lightning. First it thunders for a while and then it stops — like a man who once in a while becomes angry but does not let the anger break out, rather suppressing and mastering it. However, once in a while the excessively great heat of the sun will tax the fire of thunder and set it into a great uproar until it sends out strong and dangerous lightnings and raises its voice to a great roar like a man who has fallen into a violent anger and is driven thereby to act violently. On the other hand, sometimes the fire of the sun disturbs the higher

3

fire of thunder, releases the cold that is concealed within thunder, and brings it together in one place, just as water gathers the ice into one place. This chill brings clouds and hail together where the clouds extract it, divide it, and send it down to earth.

Hail. Hail is like the eye of thunder. When the sun is declining, its heat rays no longer reach all the way to the height of heaven; rather, it then burns lower on the earth and no longer glows in the height of heaven.

Snow. As a consequence, the water that is located in the higher regions of the air becomes as though covered over with dust because of the cold, and releases snow to fall to the earth.

Rain. When the water is comfortably warm, it sends down rain. However, if the sun brings either too much heat or too much cold, then it sometimes also sends down a soft rain similar to a man, happy for the first time, who suddenly pours out tears of joy.

The Wind. The four major winds hold up the firmament above and below the sun; they keep it together and protect the entire circle, from the lowest to the highest part, like a cloak.

The east wind unleashes the lower wind and sends it gently downwards on what is dry. The west wind stays beneath the swiftly moving clouds so that they may hold their water, lest it fall down. The south wind has power over fire and keeps it from burning up everything. The north wind expels the darkness outside and keeps it from overstepping its border.

These four winds are the wings of God's power. If they were released all at the same time, they would mix all the other elements together, divide them, stir up the sea, and allow all the water to dry up.

Judgment Day. Up to now they have been closed up together with the key of the majesty of God. As a consequence, the various elements have remained in flexible harmony; they will bring no danger to men until the end of the world because then everything must be purified. At that moment, they will lift up their voices in beautiful harmony. There is no object of creation that possesses only one quality; rather, each rests on several.

Nothingness. Only "nothing" has no characteristic on which it rests; on that account is it nothing. In this manner, also, other objects of creation, who by their own will freely mix themselves with nothingness, lose their own characteristics and tend toward nothingness.

The Firmament and the Stars. The firmament embraces fire, sun, stars, and winds. Because of the firmament, everything has its permanence, and because of its characteristics everything has its firmness so that it cannot fall apart. Just as the soul holds the whole human body together, so do the winds hold the firmament together lest it break apart. They are invisible, just as the soul — which comes forth from the mystery of God — is equally invisible. Just as a house is not firmly grounded without a stone foundation, so neither would the firmament nor the earth, neither the abyss nor the whole world with all its different parts, stay together without these winds because they are all maintained in order thereby. Without these winds, the entire earth would burst and break apart. In the same way, a man would fall apart if he had no bones. The chief east wind holds the entire territory of the East together, the main west wind does the same with the western territory, the chief south wind with the southern area, and the main north wind the same with the North.

The Subordinate Winds. Each of these main winds has two other weaker winds like two poor people, one on either side. Once in a while, the main wind blows a part of its might into these weaker winds. These weaker winds have the same essence as the main wind has; you could say that each of these weaker winds has the chief wind as its head, except that they have much less power, and that they take the same direction as their main wind — just as two ears belong to the same head. As they are set in motion under God's command, they receive whatever power they have from their main winds. They can become stirred up and make much noise and dangerous clashing just as evil humors cause dangerous disturbances in human beings when they catch a sickness. Since the beginning of the world, the main winds have never been unleashed to their full power, and will not be until the Last Day. When they finally show their full strength and blow with their full power, then the clouds will be torn apart by their massive collisions and the highest heavenly bodies will be thrown down and dashed apart just as a man's body falls apart and all of his limbs decay when the soul leaves the body in death. The east wind has two wings with which it exercises its attractive power over the entire path of the sun, in such a way that one wing regulates the sun's trajectory from above to below and the other runs along with the sun and thereby keeps it from extending its path as it otherwise would. This wind allows all moistness to retain its moisturizing power, and it causes seeds to germinate. The west wind similarly has a mouth with which it divides the water and sends each stream into its proper course so that no river makes contact or interferes with another, but rather keeps to its own path. This wind dries out whatever it touches, especially all green things. The south wind has something like an iron staff that has three branches on top and a point on the bottom. It has an almost steel-like strength that holds the firmament and the abyss together. Just as steel excels and dominates all other metals and as the heart makes a man strong, so the power of this wind holds together the firmament and the abyss within its reach so that they do not fall apart. On top, it carries three powers like three branches. One of them regulates the heat of the sun at its rising in the East, one its heat at midday in the South, and the last allows the sun's heat to cool down at sunset, lest in this region it overstep its proper bounds. Below, the wind's staff has a point, since its power is also felt in the depths so that the moisture and cold from the depths cannot climb too high into the upper world. The same wind turns everything ripe and brings to fruition all the leaves in the forest, the grasses, the corn, fruit, wine, and all other fruits of the earth. The north wind has four columns with which it holds both the entire firmament and the abyss together. If these columns should be pulled down, the firmament would be torn from the depths. These four pillars contain the four elements which are both bound together and also divided from one another there in the Northern Kingdom; each one rests on a pillar so that it doesn't fall. However, when on the Last Day these four columns will be shaken by the wind's strength, then the firmament will snap together in the way we fold a writing table together. The wind itself is cold and brings coldness with it, causing things to freeze to death and at the same time holding them rigid so that they don't deteriorate.

The Sun. As was mentioned above, the sun stands at the highest point as though in the center of the firmament. It consists of fire and air and holds within that fire the support and foundation of the firmament, the air, the stars, and the clouds, lest they fall asunder or decay. In just such a way, the earth carries all created things located on it. The ether is also fastened by it. When the sun stands high in the sky, fire comes before it and offers it its services.

The sun brightens the entire firmament and spreads its light over all the earth, whereby it brings forth every kind of blossom and green thing. When the days are long because the sun moves high in the heavens, it is summer. However, when the sun comes down toward the earth, the cold in the earth rises up from the waters and meets it, causing all green things to wither. Because the sun has declined toward the earth, the days become short, and it is winter. In the winter, the heat of the sun is greater under the earth than it is on the surface. If the cold under the earth were to become as great as it is on the surface, or if, in summer, the heat under the earth became as great as it is on the surface, then the earth would be torn apart from the resulting imbalance. When winter is approaching, bad weather and storms come out of the water and obscure the light of the sun; hence the days become cloudy. When summer approaches, the bad weather retreats under the earth. Hence, the weather becomes clear and bright, and summer is here. The course of the sun is no longer shortened; rather, it is strong and undiminished and sends its light to the moon, when it comes near, like a man who sends his semen into his wife.

The Moon. The moon consists of fire and thin air. It is suspended in the air, has its proper place therein, and is held fast by it. When the moon wanes completely, it disappears behind the sun. From it, a sphere expands that draws the moon toward the sun as a magnet draws iron to itself. The sun causes the moon to be inflamed, as well as the other planets and stars; the air and the stars around the moon beam on it and help to ignite it. When it is inflamed, it gradually increases until it is full, just as a log on the fire or a whole house, once set aflame, burns slowly at first until finally it is engulfed in flames. While the moon is waxing and becoming full, the sun strengthens the upper region of the firmament and never ceases doing this. The sun brings the day with it, and they are together as long as the firmament above is bright. The moon leads the night forward because the earth is dark. When the moon is as round as a pregnant woman, it radiates its light and bestows more on the stars. Thus the stars become brighter.

The Dew. The stars warm up the air powerfully, and the heated air sends its sweat — that is, the dew — to earth and makes it fruitful. Thus the well-watered earth brings forth fruit. When the moon diminishes, because it has given its light to the stars and while, inflamed by the sun, it grows until it is full once again, the stars beam out light and warmth — which they have received from the moon — to the air to warm it powerfully, and the air causes their sweat to fall from heaven upon the earth to make it fruitful. Thus the stars are sometimes without light until the moon again becomes full, and they then replenish themselves with new light and warmth. When the moon has completely shrunk, the stars are full, and then they empower the air and the earth. When the stars have disappeared, the moon grows full again.

The Cleansing of the Air. When the stars light up the night so that fiery comets like blazing missiles stream across the firmament, it comes about that the stars impart their fire to the air to strengthen it so that it, in its turn, can make the earth fruitful with its warmth. Thus we often see and notice that the air is cleansed by the fire of the stars and that a kind of dirt falls down like soot.

The Air Threads. Similarly, when either summer or winter is coming to an end — either summer is going and winter is coming, or else winter is going and summer is coming — bindings, like white threads, fly in the air wherein the air is purified. They come down to earth at the meeting point of the two seasons, that is, whenever summer and winter come together.

The Darkness of the Moon. The fact that we occasionally observe darkness in the moon is to be explained by the fact that the elements and storms sometimes collide as if they were having an argument among themselves. The moon is not extinguished and does not disappear, but rather the storms darken it only for a time. For the power of the moon is so great that it overcomes the storms and sends forth its brilliance again because the power of the moon is greater than that of any storm.

The Five Planets. There are also the five planets. They have their light from fire and from the ether and are the actual strong points of the firmament. They have their proper paths through the high regions as well as through the lower realms of the firmament so that they may lighten these areas where the sun cannot reach and where one can scarcely see its glow. Whenever they are moving, they also assist the movement of the sun — braking the speed of the sun and causing its fire to go out — so that, because of their intervention, an excessive radiance does not stream out, which would happen if the planets did not prevent it. Just as the five senses keep the body together and are its ornament, so do the five planets hold the sun together and embellish it.

The Limits of the Heavens. The heavens spin around with great velocity. The sun runs slowly alongside it with the other planets and so retards its speed. If the sun did not slow the heavens down in this manner, or if the speed of the sun and the other planets equalled the heavens' speed, everything would run into everything else, and the entire firmament would break apart. If the heavens were stationary and did not turn, the sun would stand in place over the earth throughout the entire summer so that there would be no night, and spend the entire winter under the earth so that there would be no day. However, it now spins like this: as the heavens run next to the sun and the sun next to it, they become warmer; that is, as the sun traverses the heavens and penetrates and shines through with its radiance, it strengthens the heavens and holds them fast. Before the fall of Adam, the heavens were immovable and did not turn, but after the Fall, they gradually started to spin. On the Last Day they will again come to rest, as it was at the beginning before the Fall. Now, however, they turn upon themselves in such a fashion that they receive a strong foundation from the sun, the moon, and the stars. If they just stood still, they would quickly melt and dissolve. Because they turn so quickly, the elements are thereby cleansed. This cleansing occasionally manifests itself in the form of dark rain clouds, which we see. This is what happens when a pot of water is placed on the fire; it boils over, and so cleans itself.

The Harmony of the Heavens. When it turns, the firmament makes beautiful music which we, however, do not hear because of its great height and breadth. In the same fashion, a millstone or wagon wheel also generates a distinctive tone as it turns. But the firmament extends so far above and around the earth that men and animals on the earth are not killed by it. It is too far away from them. But if the firmament were nearer to them, then men as well as animals would be killed by the fire, wind, water, and clouds. Just as body and soul are one and mutually strengthen one another, so it is with the firmament and the planets. They warm and mutually strengthen one an-

9

other. As the soul enlivens and strengthens the body, so do the sun, the moon, and the other planets warm and strengthen the firmament with their fire. For the firmament is like a man's head; the sun, moon, and the stars are like his eyes. The air is like his ears, the wind like his sense of smell, the dew like taste, the sides of the world like his limbs and the sense of touch. The other creatures on the earth are like the stomach; the earth itself is like the heart. Just as the heart holds the upper and lower parts of the body together, so the earth is like a strong land for the waters that flow over it. On the other hand, the earth encloses the waters that flow under it, lest they break out improperly.

The Fall of Lucifer and the Creation of the Heavens. The abyss is to be compared with men's feet and carriage. As the devil fell from heaven where he wanted to sit and rule, yet could not make or create a single creature, God immediately made the firmament so that the devil might see and understand how great and marvelous a thing God could make and fashion. Then he placed the sun, the moon, and the stars in the firmament so that the devil might see them and realize what tremendous glory and lordship he had lost.

The Stars. The stars are not equal to each other either in size or in brilliance. Rather, some are larger, some smaller, some have greater brilliance, some lesser. The firmament is fixed above by the sun so that it cannot climb above a certain point; it is fixed below by the earth's atmosphere that holds the earth and the clouds together so that it doesn't transgress its lower border. In this way, the firmament is held together both above and below, as was shown above, in such a way that it cannot overstep its proper boundaries.

The Twelve Constellations and the Planets. As the firmament is guided in its path by the seven planets, so in the same way, these planets provide useful service to the twelve constellations. For example, when the sun approaches the constellation Capricorn, the two planets which have accompanied it to the constellation Sagittarius give a sign to the sun to return upward by the same path, and they encourage the sun to climb, just as they did earlier. This constellation is called Capricorn; it also has the inclination to climb higher. The names of the twelve constellations have no meaning other than that the five other planets, consistent with their tasks, cause the sun to climb in summer and sink in winter.

As the sun approaches the constellation Capricorn, the other three planets run under it and push it up gradually toward the constellation Aquarius. There, as it begins to climb again, it warms both the earth in the lower region and the waters that lie under the earth. That is why the waters under the earth are warmer in winter than in summer. There — in the constellation of Aquarius — this planet, which continually gets its fire from the sun — that is to say, the planet which stands under the sun in the constellation of Cancer — and the other planets which are joined with it, go back.

They accompany the sun up to the constellation Pisces, and when they have reached this constellation, the sun is as if it were in the middle of the waters. Pisces, the fish that up to now have hidden themselves because of the cold, now feel warmth and turn to spawning. The other planet, that was to the right of the sun in the constellation Cancer, approaches it and draws it upward toward the constellation Aries. As the sun approaches the constellation Aries, the two lower planets come close to it, grab it like a ram by its horns, climb slowly with it, and force it forward. When they have almost climbed over the constellation Taurus, the two planets stay there and two others come up to the sun. These last two planets are very rarely seen and only show themselves on those occasions when they bring some miracle with them. They propel the sun forward with great power — like a bull that charges powerfully with its horns — and bring it into the heights. There, when it has reached the constellation Gemini, one of them goes on one side of the sun, the other goes on the other side, and they thus split up until they reach their highest point.

In the constellation Cancer, when the sun must begin its downward movement, the planet to its right descends a little ahead of the sun and thereby meets the other planet that is below the sun. Immediately, the planet that has become aware of this other planet falls back, and the second planet follows it. The latter turns around again, and the first planet withdraws, and the other one follows it. So, like Cancer, for a while they go forward and backward until they cause the sun to descend. The planet that was on the left side of the sun stays there, and the two accompany it and stay near it in its descent so that it does not descend too fast. In this manner, they lead the sun toward the constellation Leo. There, the planets that were in the constellation Aries come up to the sun, lightly humming. Then the sun radiates a great heat as if it were angry at the difficulty of turning. At this point, lightning and thunder are noticeable because the sun's turn in order to descend is difficult. When it has reached the constellation Virgo, it encounters the two planets that met it in the constellation Taurus, and then it chooses a path that is gentler and more pleasant because its intense heat has been moderated. At this point, the earth brings forth no new fruit but rather stands rejoicing in its rich harvest.

Thus the planets accompany the sun as far as the constellation Libra where both growth and loss lie on the scales. At this point, the increase stops, and withering begins. Now one planet moves from one side of the sun to the other, and the other planet moves to the opposite side; they divide up in the same way as they did in the constellation Gemini. Thus arranged, they lead the sun to the constellation Scorpio. There, one of the two planets remains stationary. But then another planet approaches the sun — the one that had its course below Cancer. The planet that accompanied the sun and went back and forth, now remains by the sun, and both planets move along with it. In the constellation Scorpio, all the reptiles seek holes where they can pass the entire winter.

The two planets mentioned above accompany the sun to the constellation Sagittarius and remain there. In the constellation Sagittarius, the planets abandon the sun; they allow it to move forward alone, now slowly and gently, because it is already deep into its descent. By comparision, a man lets a ship drift with the tide, not needing the rudder which for a while is without use. Because the sun is setting, most of its warmth is under the earth and also in the waters that are deep below the earth's surface. The two planets that have accompanied the sun to the constellation Sagittarius then climb up to the clouds and heat the atmosphere with their own warmth more strongly than usual. Otherwise, all that is on earth would perish. In this way, they serve the sun on its way up to the constellation Capricorn where these same planets incite it to ascend to its previous path and are, as mentioned above, helpful to it.

The sun is like the hat of the firmament. It serves the entire heavens, the earth, and the waters and provides warmth to them, but not to all in the same degree. It is strongest in the middle of the earth. There, the earth is strongest because of the sun, and all things — both fruit and animals — are better developed there than anywhere else. As the sun shines in different degrees on different lands, the earth, the fruits of the earth, and the animals in those places where the lands are moving downward are more weakly developed than they are in the middle of the earth. For example, grapes require great heat and grow because of the heat; in a place where the sun's heat is great, the wine is strong. Grains need both warmth and cold, and where both the warmth of the sun and the cold are present, the grain harvest is superabundant.

The Different Kinds of Fruit. There are some lands that are hot, others that are cold, and some that are warm. Correspondingly, the men, animals, and fruits are marked by the characteristics of their country although they are all of the same species. Also, they have more or less strength, corresponding to the strength of the sun.

The Stability of the Heavens. The firmament is held in place by the stars so that it doesn't fall apart, just as a man is held together by his veins and arteries so that he doesn't dissolve and fall apart. Just as the arteries connect the human body from the heel of the foot to the top of the head, so do the stars bind the heavens. As the blood moves through the arteries and makes the pulse beat, so does the fire move the stars so that they send out sparks like pulse beats. These are the well-known stars that contain storms within themselves corresponding to their work which mankind then completes. In contrast, the planets are never aroused to such a commotion, apart, as has been said, from being influenced by the sun and the moon; also, certain immense constellations affect them. Each star leaves its starting position and runs through the entire heavens in a steadily climbing course just like an artery runs through the entire body from foot to head. Stars spread light and heat through the entire heavens like the blood vessels that crisscross the liver and provide blood and warmth to this organ. They are parceled out throughout the entire heavens, as much over the part that we see during the daytime as over that part which we see at night. The stars are for the most part hidden by the brilliant glare of the sun — which day brings — so that we cannot see them during daytime because the brilliance of the sun is far greater than the brilliance of the stars. It is similar to the situation where peasant folk quiet down when nobles come forth; however, the ordinary folk present themselves when the lords retire. It this were not so, we would see the stars as clearly in the daytime as we do at night.

What the Stars Indicate. The stars often give us signs as indications of what men are doing and how they are behaving. However, the stars neither reveal the future nor the thoughts of men, but only that which, either by word or in deed, a man has already indicated is his intention. For these intentions are picked up by the atmosphere which shares them with the stars, and these stars in their fashion, reflect the deeds of men. God made the stars to serve mankind; they are to provide light and be helpful. For that reason they also indicate his actions, just as a servant reports the will and the actions of his lord. Just as the soul at first enlightens a human body and then proceeds to its work, so do the stars at first light up the heavens, and then show a man's actions when the man is ready to proceed.

What the Planets Show. The sun, the moon, and the remaining planets only rarely reveal a man's deeds. When they indicate something, it must be something important concerning a public event. The highest planet, which is called the "eye," and the one that is directly above the moon and is called the "arm" are fixed like two pegs deep in the firmament. They cannot be seen by men, except once in a while when the clouds become dark and a bolt of lightening comes from them and is visible in the clouds. Then, these planets indicate the coming of some future event. The fact that signals are sometimes noticed on the sun comes from the fact that these two planets revolve around the sun, and for this reason, signals are visible from the sun when some marvelous event is in the offing. However, the planets themselves are not visible because man cannot see them completely before Judgment Day. Then they will suddenly send their brilliance from the heights down to earth, and thereby men of understanding will know that the Day of Judgment is at hand.

The planet known as the "Eye Star," which is next to the highest, accompanies floods and thus warns of their arrival. It doesn't look like an ordinary star, but rather sends out kinds of missiles. Sometimes, it has a rather pale look, and then it signals that something is coming. The next planet, known as "the kingdom," warned that Christ would fight against the devil. But now it no longer resembles a star, but looks rather like summer lightning in the heavens, and thereby it signals unusual future events. If the sun shows a darkening or an unusual change in color, that is a warning of important imminent events in the world.

The Dawn. The fact that the morning sun is red at its rising comes from the chill and moisture of the atmosphere. The moisture and chill which then predominate similarly redden people's eyes. Likewise, later in the day, toward evening, the sun again turns red. This is due to the chill in the atmosphere because the sun then sinks into the ocean.

The evening star, which is also called "the accompanier," is like a secret — though trusted — friend of the sun. It exercises an influence on both grain and grapes, sometimes more, sometimes less. After that comes the planet called "the poor one." It comes and shows its insignia as was described above; it causes a small harvest of farm produce.

What the Moon Indicates. If any sign appears on the moon, this is caused by the planets which are fixed deep in the firmament like two pegs, and which cause the sun to show its signs and influence the moon, either by inflaming or darkening it. The moon absorbs the contrary, unnecessary stuff from the atmosphere; the heat of the clean air; the stability of the useful air; the danger of storms; the powerful air that brings forth everything green; the air that causes the fruit in the orchard to ripen; and the air — that is, winter — that causes withering or stops growth. The moon gathers all this to itself like a man who pours wine into a wineskin, lifts it up, and drinks it all. So also, the moon gathers all this into itself when it waxes and drinks it to the dregs when it wanes. For that reason its days are sometimes good, sometimes bad; sometimes useful, sometimes useless; sometimes powerful, sometimes weak; sometimes disagreeable, sometimes beautiful; and sometimes dry. Sometimes these days have a lasting effect on the fruit.

As the moon has this changeable nature in itself, likewise human water retention shows a changeableness: in the course of suffering, from work, in a person's attitude toward life, and in happiness. People should not believe that human water retention is influenced by the sun because the sun remains in one and the same condition, in that it neither grows nor diminishes. Nor should it be connected with the stars because the stars are not independent, but rather depend upon the moon. The same is true for the seasons of the year since they are controlled by the moon; it is the same for the atmosphere — that is, for the rain or the harshness of winter or summer — because they are also dependent upon the moon. All is controlled by the influence of the moon since it is the mother of all time periods: just as the sons of a mother are counted after the mother, so are all time periods reckoned from the moon. Also, the atmosphere and the stars sometimes receive the deeds of men, spread themselves out on the basis of divine decisions, draw themselves back together, and expel their breath. When they rise to this purpose, the moon is set in motion. Corresponding to them, the days are either clear and bright or dark and stormy.

Just as a mother must undergo many dangers and pains during the birth of her children, so is the moon threatened with many dangerous storms. For that reason, the periods of the moon are healthy or unhealthy, ripe or unripe. If man were to behave as things really are, then every season and the weather in every season would be the same. That is, this springtime would be just the same as previous springs, this summer just like past summers, and so on.

However, since mankind because of its disobedience no longer has fear before God or love toward him, the elements and the seasons also overstep their authorization like the bowels of man. Thus, when man recognizes no measure or standard, his bowels behave in a corresponding manner. And when he disregards proper conduct and does evil deeds, he burdens and darkens the sun and the moon so that they, following his example, bring about storms, floods, and a harsh climate. Man's stomach and bladder remove everything that the body needs for nourishment. When these two organs extract too much food and drink, they bring severe burdens to the whole body in the form of bad humors. The elements behave in the same way toward mankind. Man sows seeds in the time when warmth and chill are properly balanced, and they then grow into fruit. Who would be so stupid as to sow seeds in the extreme heat of summer or the severe cold of winter? They would not grow, but perish immediately.

The Time of Begetting. So it happens with men who observe neither the immaturity of their age nor the time of the moon, but are ready to beget according to their mood and inclination. Because of that, their children have many injuries and bodily pains. However, God accepts these young buds even when they are physically defective. For that reason, a man should wait for his body to mature and observe the correct monthly period with great attention, as someone who brings forward pure prayer. That is, he should conceive children during a period when his children will not be ruined by injuries. Also he should not become like a man who consumes food like a glutton, who does not eat at the proper times; rather, he should be like someone who limits himself to the proper time and not be like a glutton. In the same way, a man should pay attention to the right time for begetting. The man should not come near his wife while she is still a maiden, but only when she has become a young woman because she is then mature. Further, he should not bother a woman before he can grow a beard, but only when he already has a beard because only then is he able to generate offspring. A man who only lives to eat and drink will often be sick and indisposed, whereas he who controls himself around food and drink will have good blood and a healthy body. It is the same with the man who, in his passion and bodily undiscipline, always satisfies his desires and then, when the desire to beget increases in him, spends his seed profligately. He is often disappointed with his offspring. The man, however, who husbands his seed in the right way produces healthy children.

The Elements. The elements absorb every human characteristic, just as a man appropriates the elements. For man is with them and they with mankind, and corresponding to this exchange, a person's blood flows. For that reason it stands written that heaven and earth complain about mankind. For the restless, warlike behavior of mankind often puts the very elements into powerful agitation, also, just as when a man holds a net in his hand and shakes it. In the same way, mankind also brings the elements into motion, so that they, correspondingly, exercise their influence over his works.

The Influence of the Moon. The time of the moon does not control man's nature as if it were God, as if man received any natural power from it, or as if the moon contributed something to human nature or excited it or defined it. However, the moon encounters mankind in everything that he does in this life when he breathes in air. Thus, a person's blood and humors are affected by the time of the moon's movement; specifically, the air moves to good or bad weather following the moon, and, corresponding to them, the blood and the humors flow within a person, and the water conservation affects human behavior. Also, when a person's blood vessels swell up, for example under the influence of anger and violent temper, fatigue, carousing, grief, bodily sickness, or a rapid change of behavior, the moisture in the person correspondingly takes on the natural taste, as when a particular cooked dish retains its taste corresponding to its sort. Moreover, the Holy Spirit penetrates the entire human nature, as was mentioned above, for example with the prophets, the sages, and good and holy people.

Since the Holy Spirit always chooses what is good and draws it to himself, he penetrates it as the sun does to storms and illuminates it; thus, this penetration with the fire of the Holy Spirit overcomes a person's changeable nature, as indeed it stands written that all that is born of God overcomes the world. As a consequence, this person does not sin. Just as ordinary dishes are changed into better-tasting dishes by the addition of seasonings and peppers so that they lose their usual taste, so is the ordinary nature of a person transformed through the fire of the Holy Spirit into a better sort, according to his receptivity and potentiality. In this way, a person becomes something different in his essence, in that the heavenly fully overcomes the earthly. Because of this, all rejoice in God because the Old Deceiver himself becomes deceived. But now, the remaining small stars, as was mentioned above, show various ordinary, unimportant deeds of mankind. For example, if cheerfulness reigns in the clouds so that there is no movement in the air, no wind, no storms, and no rainfall but rather the stars shine brightly, and then if a cloud hides all the stars, even though there is no air movement, so that they are invisible, and if it remains this way the entire night, or even a second and third night, then this truly is a portent.

However, if the clouds conceal the stars only in one place and then quickly withdraw again even though there is no air movement, this indicates nothing.

Why the Planets because of Their Essence, Do Not Warn. These omens do not come from a special power of the planet, star, or cloud, but rather from the permission, will, and decision of God, for God wished to show men his work, just as a coin shows the portrait of the ruler.

The Powers of Fire. When God made the world, he anchored it by the four elements — fire, air, water, and earth — as we have already said. Fire, the highest in the heavens and below the elements, possesses five powers; they are heat, cold, moisture, air, and motion, just as man has five senses. Fire is hot, but the cold opposes it so that its heat does not spread excessively. Water serves it because its steam can climb upward and escape. Fire is kindled by means of the air, and its flame lights because of the motion.

The Powers of the Air. The air has four powers: it sends down the dew, brings forth all green sprouts, causes the wind's breath to blow whereby it makes the flowers grow, and spreads out the heat whereby it makes all things ripen. The air itself is also spread out over the four corners of the earth. The air is the breath that bestows the moisture of dew on germinating plants so that they can turn green, brings up the flowers by its blowing, and by its heat brings all things to ripeness. The air, whose position is just below the moon and the stars, dampens the stars just like the earthly air does to the earth and that which is inanimate; indeed, it brings to life and moves each of the animals gifted with intelligence after its own fashion, and afterwards does not diminish. When these animals die, this air returns to its previous condition without increasing. Rather, it remains as it was before. The earthly air which moistens the earth causes the trees and plants to grow, turn green, and move themselves. As long as it is in them, the air does not diminish. It also does not increase, however, when the plants are cut or uprooted and it leaves them. Rather, it returns to the same condition as before.

The Powers of the Soul. The soul of man, which is sent down from heaven by God, gives him life and intelligence and does not die when it leaves a man. Rather, either it goes to its reward for a good life or to the eternal torments of the damned, there to live eternally.

The Powers of the Waters. Water possesses fifteen powers. They include warmth, air, moisture, flooding, rapidity, and motion. Water gives sap to the trees, taste to the fruit, their greenness to the plants; everything is full of its moisture. It carries the birds, nourishes the fish, allows animals to live in its warmth, returns reptiles to its waves, and keeps everything alive like the Ten Commandments and the Five Books of Moses of the Old Testament that God intended for spiritual knowledge. For water springs up out of living wells, and it washes away all dirt. Water is lightly moving in every animate creature, and it is also the igniting source of all growth in immobile creation. It flows because of the warmth of the moist air, and when it contains no warmth, it becomes hard from the coldness. It streams down because of the warmth and flows because of the moisture of the air. If water did not have air, it could not flow. By means of these three powers, namely the warmth, moisture, and the air, water is highly mobile so that nothing can withstand it when it gets the upper hand. It gives the trees their sap, puts them in motion by its airiness, and also, by its warm moisture, gives the fruits in the orchard their proper sort of taste. Plants also receive their growth and their greenness from the trickling moisture of water, and even the stones sweat as a consequence of their moisture. The power of water gathers everything so that nothing disappears, because its moisture permeates all things. Water, by its warmth, also keeps all water birds alive and nourishes the fish, for they arise within it and live by means of its breath. Animals that can stay in the water survive because of its warmth, and the reptiles, because of the wind that blows over the water, have air to breathe, so that in this way they can live. In this manner, water supports and maintains everything with its powers.

Matter and the Animation of Creation. In the beginning when the Word of God rang out, the deep was without fire and therefore cold. The Spirit of the Lord hovered over the waters. He was fire and life. This Spirit breathed life into each creature he had formed, each after its own fashion, and lit a flame by this inbreathing. Because of this, each creature now has fire and light in it, each after its own fashion. The work of the Word is growth. There would be no growth if it could not be received from fire and heat. Every creature would be without help and abandoned; it would fall apart and disintegrate were it not strengthened by its foundation in the fiery Spirit of Life.

The Principle of Motion in Water. Just as the Spirit of the Lord is both fire and life since it gives both being and life to every creature, so water is in itself a principle of motion because it gathers, receives, and strengthens the other objects of creation. It is slippery and unstable and it is the cause of both life and death for many. It also contains unusual creatures of strange shape that cannot raise themselves above the surface of the water because they would otherwise fall back in again. Sometimes they die and wash ashore. Yet there is both wind and fire in the path where the water flows.

The Sun and Its Waters. The waters — which are in the middle of the sun, so to speak, as the sun itself is in the middle of the firmament as if at its heart — possess much power and an enormous reach. As a consequence of the heat of the sun, the waters are dense and powerful because of the air. They are not beaten down by the effort of streaming because they do not stream; rather, they are moved by the wind. Once in a while the sun draws to itself the fire that lies in the waters. Occasionally, storm winds push these waters into a huge wave like a fire that sets something ablaze. Then the water rises up like fire that blazes up, the water follows the fire, and thus there arise things like hills and mountains. As they subside and calm themselves down, they drop their seed, that is salt, which arises out of fire and water just as plants expel their seed when they are ripe.

Salt. Because of fire, salt is dry; however, from the moisture of water it acquires its taste.

The Variety of Waters. The streams that flow out of these great waters — namely from the sea — and the springs that flow up from them are salty and have a greater fire and more power in them than the other waters. So also does the heart have greater powers than the other organs. Also, the larger rivers that flow out of them have greater powers than the other rivers because they flow over the first healthy sand laid out at the beginning, and not over what they have built up or released by their flow.

Water is like the water-body of the earth, and the earth is like the heart of the waters because the water embraces and flows through the earth exactly as the body encloses and hides the heart. The earth supports the water exactly as the the heart supports the body. The water of the large seas that surround the world is like the water that is located on top of the firmament because the water on the heights, that is located above the firmament, and the water of the depths, that is located under the firmament, stand in connection with one another. Between these waters stand many layers of the firmament that are laid together like the leaves of a writing table so that they can control the waters' various streams and floods. As the soul unites the reason, the understanding, knowledge, and the five senses, so the firmament receives into itself and upholds the four elements each according to its fashion. These waters always remain as they are. They water their roof, the earth, whereby water pours off and frequently spreads out on the earth and once in a while climbs back up. On other occasions, it pours down as rain; thereby, the water strengthens its roof by means of wind and air so that it will not wash away nor fall apart. The sand of the sea, that lay in the East from the very beginning, is often disturbed by the ceaseless air movement. On that account there are roots and other healing materials mixed in this sand. If man could obtain such things, he would not suffer any more sicknesses. If certain stones could be washed out of this sand and if mankind could obtain them in this manner, we would be able to get rid of all sicknesses, pestilence, and decay. But the water there is so large and deep that man could never obtain them.

The Outflow from the Sea. Because the sand and the beach are very deep in the East, the sea does not overflow its bank when it rises up and spreads out. In the West, the South, and the North, however, the sand and the beach are not so deep. Because of this, it often overflows there and causes great, wide floods if it is excited into a great frenzy by the fire of a storm. Because of this, it collects many unusable and dirty things and draws the waste of men, animals, birds, and worms into itself. For this reason, the rivers and springs that flow out of this sea region are not as healthy or as good as those which flow out of the sea in the East.

The Difference between the Waters. Salty springs and streams that arise from water of the eastern regions in the various lands are pure and, corresponding to the purity of the air, fairly green. They arise drop by drop in the sand where they flow, are healthy and useful, can be drunk, and are also well suited for the cooking of food. When a man who is sick drinks a lot of this water, he regains his health because it removes the foul air, the smell, and the decay of evil humors like a good anointing oil. However, if he is sound of body and drinks them, they seem to injure him and bring him inner distress because they find nothing in him which they can purify. The water of the river and of the lively spouting springs that spring up in this region of the East without a salty taste and flow in this direction from the East, are pure, and have an enjoyable warmth mixed with bracing freshness so that they have the right proportion of warmth and cold and are useful to men for eating, drinking, bathing, and washing. However, they are rather sharp and hard on the skin.

The salty waters that come from the West are somewhat cloudy like a whirlpool. Still, one can cook a meal with such water, for in boiling, they are somewhat purified by the fire. However, if they are drunk unboiled, they do damage, for in the Western sea they attract all kinds of dirty and decaying things to themselves and propel all kinds of corpses there. When one is in an emergency situation and cannot avoid drinking some of it because of a lack of other water, he should boil it first and then drink it after it has cooled down.

The fresh-water rivers and the lively, spouting, fresh-water springs that arise in the West and flow in this direction from the West where the sun sets and disappears, have a clear, thick water. They cannot become fully good either through heat or cold because both heat and cold are lacking. Because of this, neither of these waters should be used for human needs, that is, for drinking, washing, or bathing, for they have not been cooked by the sun. However, if necessity makes it urgent to prepare something with them, then one should boil these waters powerfully on the fire and afterward let them cool until they reach the right temperature. They can be used for eating because during cooking, they are boiled.

The salty waters that originate in the Southern regions of the sea, whether from springs or rivers, are rather clear, but they are still not really clean and so are not suitable either for eating or drinking because they are toxic. Tiny, poisonous worms and small life forms that are rather poisonous, that flee there because of the sun in order to escape the cold, are very much at home there because of its warmth, bathe in the water, and lie in it. They have the characteristic of salt and hence can endure the heat but not the cold. The waters of the rivers and lively spouting springs that have no salty taste spring up in the South and because of the dominating radiance there, they are hot and become easily dried out by the fire's glow when separated from the other water streams because they stand in connection with the drying fires and move out from them. They would be suitable for eating and for any other purpose because of their heat because they have been tested and boiled by the fire. However, once they have reached the cold rivers and have mixed with them so that they flow together, they easily churn up waves and throw up foam. They have a color like silver. They can be used for eating, drinking, bathing, and washing because they have been cleansed of their dirt and bitterness like water that is cleansed in a kettle by the heat of the fire. However, they make human flesh fat and darken the skin color.

The salty waters that spring up in the northeastern regions and flow from there in this direction are injurious to and easily bring disease both to man and beast. The power of salt is not healthy there, for in this region the heat is exchanged with the cold. For that reason, they are not suitable either for eating or drinking, so that one can hardly use them for any purpose. The other, fresh waters that also come from the Northeast are cold and useful because they have been lightly stirred by the air that blows here from the East. This air is healthy because it has the right temperature so that it is neither very warm nor very cold. This air blows between the mountains that have stood there from the beginning, and it is like a wing over the earth. Hence, for the living, it is more healthy and healing than any other air. Streams and springs that come from the waters that spring up here are mostly clean, but still somewhat cloudy. These waters have an aftertaste, in that they taste a bit like wine or something else. On occasion, this water suppresses the desire for water and keeps arthritis under control if men drink it who are plagued with these ailments. For the peculiarity of this water opposes the nature of other waters and also the nature of the usual waters. It restricts the ordinary water in whose proximity it flows and is superior to the others because of the peculiar efficacy it has. These waters should not be used for eating or drinking, for bathing or washing because they suppress the other waters.

The salty waters that rise up from approximately the middle of the northerly regions and flow elsewhere from there, are good and useful for man and animal, namely for eating, drinking, and the remaining needs of mankind because they are located in considerably warmer air that is neither too hot nor too cold. When these waters are drunk, they also cleanse men interiorly from bad humors. The rivers and the lively spouting, fresh springs that also arise in approximately the middle of these northerly regions and flow elsewhere from there, are clean and have the color of crystal mixed with iron colors. They are very cold and very useful since these waters are not dirty, smelly, or poisonous because the changing position of the sun does not affect them. These waters also have the correct taste. They are useful to mankind and to the other forms of life, and they are very suitable for eating, drinking, bathing, and washing. They can also be used for medicinal purposes.

The salty river and spring waters that come out of the northern corner of the western region, are somewhat dark or brownish. They are not very clean and also not suitable for eating or drinking because they cause death. For in the northeastern region there are large and very narrow worms that cannot either be seen or captured by men without the worms' dying. They take their food from these waters and then pour their waste into it. For that reason, these waters are also dangerous because they possess both heat and cold. The worms dwell there because they are cold and can endure the cold, but can't stand any heat. The waters that are not salty and come equally from the northwest, are clean and of a whitish or grey color. They cannot be used for livestock or humans, either for eating or drinking or for their other needs because one can only swallow them with difficulty and because people easily swell up because of them. For these waters are poisonous and afflict the bowels with ulcers. Sick people are substantially weakened by them, and the healthy can barely keep them down. In this northerly region, the nature of water is more various and multiform than the nature of water in the easterly, southerly, or westerly regions because the water in this area is penetrated and regulated by the warmth of the sun. This is not the case in the northerly region because the sun does not come into this region.

Stagnant waters, in whatever parts of the earth they might be, are almost pure poison because they carry within themselves both the worthless and harmful sewage from the earth and the poisonous foam of the worms. They are very poorly suited for drinking and the other needs of mankind except washing, if they are needed for that purpose. However, if someone must drink these waters in an emergency due to a lack of other water, he should cook it first, let it cool, and then drink it. The bread, food, and beer cooked in it can be enjoyed in large amounts, for the waters are purified by the fire. Any wells and spouting springs which rise out of stagnant water are considerably better than the other waters out of the swamps because they have been purified from certain contaminants. They can usually be consumed, but are not very good and not very useful. All waters that are injurious at their place of origin become healthier the further they flow from their origin because by their fast and long run they lose what is injurious and toxic within them; this is filtered and cleansed from them through their long flowing.

Water from wells that are dug rather deep in the earth, so that it stands still and has no overflow, is better and more useful for eating, drinking, and for the other needs of mankind than water that overflows from spouting wells. The situation with spouting and flowing spring water is like that with a mild anointing oil because the latter does not flow and most often is moderated by the mild air temperature. Water from spouting springs is hard and competes with food because of its hardness so that one can barely soften it over a fire. Because well water is clean and purified, it has little foam; for that reason it cleans food very little. Therefore, foods cleansed in this water are cleansed less than foods cleaned with regular water, although the foods prepared with this water are cleansed in the cooking. For the water that flows from spouting sources is finer and cleaner than river water because it is cleansed there where it springs up and flows forth through earth, sand, or stones. It is well suited to be used for drinking by humankind because it is fully purified. It is also hard and approximates wine in its unique characteristics, but because of its hardness it is unsuited for eating and washing the eyes.

The river waters that flow over the earth are thick because they are penetrated by the sun and the air, and they are somewhat foaming and not healthy to drink because the various conditions of the air and the elements are mixed in with them. They are also contaminated by the vapors, the so-called ''doume''; the fog that flows down from certain unhealthy mountains; and sometimes also by the air that is occasionally burdened with certain injurious things. For that reason they are not suited for drinking and do harm to men if they are not first boiled, whereby purifying them from the evil foam so that they may then be drunk in an emergency. They are rather well suited for cooking food in an emergency because they become purified through boiling and are then tastier and will go down more easily. It sometimes happens that evil vapors and dangerous fog from certain unhealthy mountains come down and that the air is occasionally contaminated by the presence of harmful elements. Thereby the elements are polluted and mixed with the waters of rivers, wells, and springs. Thereby an evil poison, like a deadly disease can be in them. If human beings and other life forms should drink these waters, they bring them death; the polluted waters call forth in them a disfigurement of the outer limbs or a disease. For that reason, it is necessary that such waters be drunk only after they have been boiled because, by boiling, the poison is driven out of them together with the foam. If desperation should drive a person to drink it because he has no other water to drink, he should boil it first, let it cool, and only then drink it because it seldom happens that there would still be any more dangerous contaminents in it from the air, from the birds that bathe in it, or from dead things that are contained in corpses. For that reason such waters should not be used for human purposes if they have not first been boiled. However, where there are small, clear, clean streams which come out of other waters like veins, they are cleaned thereby, in that they flow out of them. They are good and well suited for any intended need of man or beast.

Rain water is bitter and takes the smell, evil humors, and decay from sick people. However, it can do harm to the healthy because it finds nothing in them to clean. When it has stood a while in cisterns, it becomes milder; then, it is wholesome for both sick and healthy people. However, water from spouting, flowing springs is much better. When the sun pulls its warmth back into itself, then the waters take on a great coldness and send forth their foam, that is the snow, which covers the earth, makes it fertile, and sustains it. It does not harm the fruits of the earth. The snow's water, thin and dirty, is unsuited for human use. If someone drinks it, ulcers and abcesses often appear on them, and their intestines become full of mucus. Excluding rain water, if one tries to melt snow and drink it, it causes intestinal ulcers because of the sharpness of the stomach mucus.

If it is drunk, snow water does not sufficiently quench the thirst because it is thin and quickly digested. Both hail and water that falls suddenly during a thunder storm are as dangerous as boiling water in which hog bristles and hair from other animals have been cooked, in case anyone tries to use it for eating and drinking. That is, if people drink water from a cloudburst or from hail, they will become sick for a long time, their flesh will tear and break apart so that many will die from it.

The Powers of the Earth. The earth is naturally cold. It has seven powers; in part, it is cold in summer and warm in winter; it has the power in itself to cause growing and wilting; it brings seeds forth, keeps the life essences alive, and carries everything. God also labored for six days and rested on the seventh as he placed everything that he had created at the service of mankind. In summer, the earth is cold below because then the sun causes growth by the power of its beaming, but in winter it is mostly warm below. Otherwise it would fall apart as a result of the extreme cold. Hence the sun allows growth to be visible during the warm times and rigidity apparent when it is cold. In winter, the sun is infertile over the earth and directs its heat under the earth so that the earth can protect the various seeds. In this way, the sun brings forth all seeds by warmth and cold. The sun also protects all animals that move and run from sinking into the earth, for, because of the heat and cold, the earth becomes hard and hence can carry everything successfully. God has so arranged the earth that it causes germination at the appropriate time and ceases growth at the right season, similar to the way the moon waxes and wanes.

The Growth of Trees, Grains, and Grapevines. Trees that are in the easterly region and are watered by the easterly waters grow well and produce a good harvest of various fruits that have a good taste, but that cannot be kept a long time. The grain there is poor and does not do well because the earth is rather damp there. Earth that will bring forth a good harvest of grain must be rather dry because extreme cold does more harm to grain than does heat. For grain is itself rather dry. The vineyards in the East bring forth a bountiful harvest of grapes and produce a very good wine. The plants in the gardens and other plants that grow in this easterly region and are watered by the waters and are in proximity to water that comes out of the East are superior, have a good aroma, are good for medicine, and are also good for eating. Only rarely do worms grow in them and eat them because they are the result of a good mixture of heat and cold which the worms avoid because they themselves are nothing but stinking slime, as for example the caterpillar and similar creatures that come to be out of airy foam.

27

The trees that stand in the westerly region and are moistened by waters from the West grow well. However, the fruits of the various fruit trees — those that hang close to the earth and are affected by the moisture of the earth — are rather injurious. On the other hand, fruits that grow high on the trees are not so injurious because they are affected by the higher air. They taste good, and it does no harm when you eat your fill of them. They can be kept for a long time. The grain in the westerly region is powerful, but not abundant, and the wine is strong, but not excellent. It is tolerable, for the earth there has both heat and cold. The garden and wild plants that are affected and watered by the waters from the West in this westerly region stimulate the senses and excite fleshly desires, that is, lust, anger, a frivolous life style, and much loitering about. So the people who have eaten them are often happy, often sad, and often precipitous. The sap of these plants and the plants themselves grow and spread out, for the increasing warmth and the decreasing cold last much longer there. Hence their growth is strong, but injurious in light of their above mentioned uselessness. They are well suited for spells and other illusions, but they bring little health to the human body because in the place where they grow, day declines and night comes on. For the Evil-One revealed himself there when a king presented himself for his consideration, and he wished to darken the great king.

The trees in the southern region watered by waters that flow there flourish and bring forth much fruit that is edible, because it is penetrated by the heat. There is a surplus of grain there; it is abundant and tasty. There is also a surplus of wine; it is excellent and very strong and does not easily go bad. It can be preserved, for it is well regulated by the steady heat in that region. For grapes prosper better in the heat than in the cold, and cold hurts grapes more than heat does. In this region, garden and field crops that are watered from the waters from the South are weak, tasteless, and an insipid color; they easily perish because the air's correct humidity has been taken away from them. These crops are also not very useful for food or drink. They are not good enough as healing remedies because they easily dry out. Neither are they very well suited for livestock; hence, both man and beast derive little benefit from them.

The trees that are watered from the waters that have their origin in the northern region perish easily. Their produce, whether it be fruit or similar things, does not do very well because the cold hurts it. There, grain survives only with much work; it is overrun with darnel and weeds but is still fairly strong. Grapes also do poorly there; they are tart, acid, and not at all sweet because the sun does not really warm them. The garden and field crops that are watered by the northern waters are not abundant or very useful for medicines, either. They do not hurt healthy people; however, they do hurt sick people because they do not grow with the proper heat nor with the proper moisture, but rather in the cold. Therefore, they do not flourish and are not very productive.

The Rain. The rain that falls suddenly on the earth in a heavy downpour is harmful and damages the earth's foundation and the fruits of the earth because it contains various toxic substances. A more moderate rain is useful; it waters the earth and causes it to bring forth fruit because it softens. Also, it is clean and pure for all kinds of uses.

II.

Adam's Fall. God made man so that all the animals were subject to him and at his service. But since man disobeyed God's command, he changed as much in bodily as in spiritual form. The purity of his blood changed into something else so that instead of purity he expels the foam of his semen. Had man remained in paradise, he would have remained in a state of unchanging fulfillment and perfection. However, everything changed after his going astray, and that in a bitter way.

Semen. Man's blood, when it percolates in the glow and heat of passion, gives off a foam that we call semen; it is like a kettle that, set on the fire, as a consequence of the heat of the fire, throws off a foam from the water.

Conception. If a person is conceived from the semen of a sick man or from semen that is thin and, so to speak, undercooked, and if it is mixed with the germ of disease or decay, then often this person will be sick during his own life and as though full of decay like a piece of wood that is eaten through by worms and moulders. Hence, such a person is often full of ulcers and decay and easily gets a disease from food or a corruption of the decay that he already has. A person who is free of such an inheritance is healthier. However, if a superfluity of semen results from this condition, then the person who is conceived in this way is often untrustworthy, undisciplined, infirm, and prodigal.

Why Man Is not Hairy. The fact that man is hairless comes from his reason. For in place of hair and feathers he has reason with which he covers himself and flies wherever he wills. However, the fact that the male has a beard and more hair over his body than the woman comes from the fact that the male was fashioned from the earth, that he has great power and heat, and that he can generally do more things than the woman. In this way the earth, which is penetrated by rain and by the warmth of the sun, brings forth plants and grasses which nourish hairy and winged animals. The woman however is without a beard because she is fashioned from the flesh of the male, is subject to the male, and lives in greater peace. In the same way, reptiles that have arisen from the earth are also without hair, but they stay below the earth and feel the rain and the sun less than the other animals that live on the surface.

Reptiles. As animals were made to serve man, reptiles help to serve him in that they bore through the earth so that the rain can give the earth water to drink. For that reason, they always stay in moist places in the earth, warm them with their breath, and water them with their foam and sweat so that by means of such secretions and exhalations these places are solidified and held together a bit. The fact, however, that poisonous worms are present comes from the opposing decay of the earth. For rain and dew wash the earth's surface, and the sun warms it. Hence, it is clean on top and brings forth good fruit. The dirt and decay flow into the interior of the earth, and from them come poisonous worms, just as worms come out of the pus in a person's wound.

So the worms come to exist in the earth and are nourished by it. These worms have almost no bones, but a poison, so to speak, in place of bones and blood, and it gives them their strength. Some of them have no hair because they come to exist out of the moisture of the earth, are in the earth, and avoid the upper levels of the earth so as not to be reached by either the air or the dew from heaven, nor by the warmth of the sun wherewith the other animals are permeated and because of which they have hair. Since they have a nature that is opposed to mankind and to the more highly developed animals, reptiles are hostile to them, kill them with their poison, and hurt human beings as well as animals that are more highly developed than they are. Although they have poison in them, a few reptiles are suitable as a healing remedy for men and animals — not every part, but only a bit of their bodies — because they have something of the good humor of the earth. For the good humor of the earth brings forth good plants. Thus a stag can be rejuvenated by a snake that he swallows.

The Birds. Both the winged creatures and animals that can be of use to mankind live according to God's Law of the air and keep themselves above the earth. But the worms and the reptiles live from the humor of the earth and for that reason are content within and under the earth.

The Fish. The fish live from the water-air of the rivers. For that reason they also live in waters, and they cannot endure dryness. When they die, their entire life disappears with their flesh like snow in the heat, and what remains goes either into the air or into the humor of the earth or into the water-air of the river from which it came. What has so completely disappeared to that extent cannot bring any other form of life, that has already dried up, back to life. As the sap-filled green of the trees and plants dries and hardens in them when they are cut and, because it is dried out, brings no other plants to bloom, so the life of the unreasoning animals, after it is fully put out in them, animates no other being with life because it is no longer there, but has completely disappeared.

Differences in Conception. If a man pours out strong semen and comes close to a woman in proper love, and if the wife at the same hour has a proper love for the man, a male child will be conceived because it has been so arranged by God. There can be no other outcome except that a male child will be conceived since even Adam was fashioned from clay, which is a stronger material than flesh. This male child will be intelligent and talented because he is conceived out of strong semen and in the proper love that each one has for the other.

However, if the wife has no love for her husband so that at this time only the man has the proper love for his wife but the wife does not for the husband, and if the semen of the man is strong, then a male child will still be conceived because the love of the man is stronger. However, this male child will be weak and stupid because the love of the wife for the husband was lacking. If the semen of the man is weak, but he still has love for his wife and she has the same love for him, then a gifted girl will be made. However, if either the man loves the wife, but the wife does not love the man or the wife loves the man, but the man does not love the wife and if his semen at that hour is weak; then again a girl is fashioned because of the weakness of the semen. If the semen of the man is strong but either the man does not love the wife or the wife does not love the man, a male child will be conceived because the semen is still strong; but due to the bitterness of his parents, he will also be bitter in his character. If the man's semen is weak and neither of the two has a love for the other at the same hour, a girl with a tart personality will be born. The heat of women who are by nature fat overcomes the semen of the men so that the child often resembles the woman more. But women who are naturally thin usually bring a child into the world who more closely resembles the father.

The Diseases. The fact that many people suffer from various ailments comes from the phlegm that is currently in oversupply in them. If man had remained in paradise, he would not have this phlegm in his body from which many sufferings come; rather, his flesh would be healthy and without slime. However, because he chose evil and separated himself from the good, he became like the earth which brings forth both good and useful as well as bad and useless plants, and which has in itself both a good and a bad humor. Through the enjoyment of evil, the blood of the son of Adam changed into the poison of semen by which human children are generated. Because of that, his flesh is full of ulcers and sores. These ulcers and sores produce disturbances and vapors in people. Out of them comes the phlegm which brings various diseases to the human body. This stems from the first evil which man started at the beginning. If Adam had remained in paradise, he would have superb health and the best residence, just as the strongest salve alleviates the greatest dryness. Now, however, man has in him, on the contrary, poison, phlegm, and various ailments.

Temperance. There are certain men who can be abstemious when they want to be; however, if they do not wish to be temperate, they are strong in their will, they are eager and wish not to give up rich foods. Whence a dangerous, poisonous, thick, and dry phlegm builds up in them that is not moist, but bitter; it causes thick, dark, and sick flesh to grow on people. If these people do not wish to give up rich foods, they easily contract gout. The bitterness of this phlegm causes a secretion in the regions of the liver and lungs that is like the perspiration of melancholy; thereafter they are hot tempered and hard-hearted, and their sweat is not clean, but dirty. They are not very sick, but rather hearty and courageous, and because of this disposition to anger, they are tyrannical and greedy. The phlegm from this disposition weakens and kills some of them in a short time because its power is great. It leaves others alive for a while.

Intemperance. There are other people who are naturally excessive and intemperate so that they can barely hold themselves back, and because of this they are frequently sick. They have too much moist phlegm because a bad moisture builds itself up in them; because this harmful phlegm arises in them, it sends out an evil secretion into their chest and their brain. The moisture of this phlegm, which causes the secretion in the chest, builds a cold moisture in the stomach, and the moisture of the same phlegm in the brain decreases the hearing ability in the ears. For there is something like a harmful vapor in the stomach and the ears which harms good plants and fruits. This phlegm does not harm the lungs because the lungs are also moist, but it does harm the spleen because it is fat and repels moisture. In fact, it would immediately dissolve and wash away if it received moisture. It also weakens the heart, for the heart should always have its full power and always repels an excess of liquid. Men with this condition are soft and cheerful, but slow. Some of them live a long time because this phlegm does not kill them, but it prevents them from enjoying full health. There are other men who are hot tempered but who quickly get over their anger, are good-spirited and friendly, but passive. They have changing moods and are content with little food. From the three phlegms, namely the dry, the moist, and the lukewarm, they extract something like a watery foam that builds itself up from this phlegm and sends something like dangerous arrows into its veins, its marrow, and its flesh just as boiling water throws out boiling foam.

The Phlegmatic. If the various moist phlegms become inflamed in such people through excessive eating and drinking, inappropriate pleasures, sadness, anger, and unrestrained passion, these phlegms become disturbed, they gush forth like water in thermal springs placed on the fire, send out things like fiery droplets, shoot them like arrows into their flesh, into their blood, and into their veins, and they eat deeply into these men like biting smoke which stings the eyes. Whoever has such a constitution frequently breaks out in anger, but quickly forgets it because he prefers to be cheerful. It is like the sun shining again, soon after a storm breaks. Due to this distinctive phlegmatic disposition, such people tend to become angry easily, and then easily return to cheerfulness.

The Melancholic. There are other people who are dour, nervous, and changeable in their mood so that in their case there is no single constant disposition. They are like a strong wind that does harm to all plants and fruits. That is, a phlegm grows in them that is neither moist nor thick, but lukewarm. It is like a slime that is sticky and can be stretched to various lengths. It causes bile that came into being

34

at the very beginning out of Adam's semen through the breath of the serpent since Adam followed his advice about eating the apple.

Melancholy as a Disease. Bile is black, bitter, and releases every evil, sometimes even a brain sickness. It causes the veins in the heart to overflow; it causes depression and doubt in every consolation so that the person can find no joy in heavenly life and no consolation in his earthly existence. This melancholy is due to the first attack by the devil on the nature of man since man disobeyed God's command by eating the apple.

From this meal, this melancholy developed in Adam and in all his posterity; and it is the cause of all serious disease in humans. Because the above-mentioned phlegm is lukewarm, it cannot overcome the power of the melancholy as the other two above-mentioned phlegms can do. These two — the one on the basis of its moisture and the other on the basis of its thickness and bitterness — have so great a power that they can withstand the melancholy like a kettle that hangs over the fire and holds the fire down so that it does not blaze up. People with such a disposition are often angry and — which is a good thing — show reverence before God and men. Some of them live a long time because the strong influence of the above-mentioned phlegm is such that it neither completely kills nor fully empowers, just as happens to a prisoner who is neither killed nor set free. So man lives, as we said above, from the four humors just as the world rests on the four elements.

The Confusion of the Elements. God has so fashioned the world out of the four elements that they cannot be separated from each other. For the world could not last if one of them could be separated from the others. They are definitively fused to one another. Fire dominates, controls, and ignites the air, and is stronger than it. Air is next in line after fire; it lets it blaze up like a bellows, and dominates it. For fire is like the body of the air, and air is like the bowels and wings and feathers of fire. Just as the body is not without the bowels, so also fire is not without air because air makes possible the movement of fire. Fire could not burn or ignite if it had no air. Fire also causes the heat and warmth of water and causes it to flow. Water would not be liquid and flow, but rather it would be hard and rigid as ice or steel if it did not conceal the warmth of fire within itself. One can see this with ice.

Water constitutes the chill of fire, and it is stronger since it puts out fire. At the beginning of creation, the water was cold, and it did not flow since the earth was still empty and dry. However, the Spirit of the Lord hovered over the waters and warmed them so that they had fire in them, and they became liquid and began to melt. This same cold of the waters naturally drives the fire out of it, and hence it boils. For the water contains fire, and fire naturally contains the cold of water because water would not flow if it did not contain fire, and fire would never go out, but would always burn if there was no chill in it from the water. Fire also governs the proportions of the mixture for the earth since it fortifies and dries its fruit and brings it to ripeness. However, earth is an obstacle for fire, to keep it from exceeding its size and limit. The air is also the wind and a help for water just as it is both a help and a break to fire so that it keeps its flowing in moderation. If air did not hold water to the right amount and on the right path, it would flow to excess and flood every place it reached. Water gives the air movement, fast when it blows and fruitful by its sweat since it makes the earth fertile when it sends the dew down to cover it. The air is also like a cover to the earth. It protects the earth from both heat and cold since the air both heats it and sends it the dew which it drinks. The earth is like a sponge, a material that attracts and extracts fertility from the air. If there were no earth, the air would not have the duty to make the earth fruitful. Water is also a binding agent for the earth; it holds it together and binds it so that it does not flow apart. The earth carries the water and holds it together, creates for it the right path, and guides it on its surface so that it takes the right way and does not well up inappropriately under the earth. Under the earth, it keeps the water in the dark and controls it on its surface. The dew that makes the earth fruitful comes from the correct mixture of fire and air, as mentioned above.

The Dew. In the summertime as a result of the heat, when fire and air complete their mutual duties in an appropriate mixing behavior, they sweat the dew out into the mild and clear air, if there is not stormy weather. The dew pours out fertility and productivity like a semen full of blessings for the fruitful use of the earth.

Ripeness. In winter, as the air bends down to the cold of the earth, both the air and the cold bring forth ripeness as a consequence of their juncture. This interaction harms the plants and new blooms and causes the earth to freeze and dry out. However, the elements out of which the earth is made are, as mentioned above, so bound up and connected to one another that they can never be separated. Thus, there is no fire without air, no air without water, and no water without earth although fire posseses greater powers than the air, water greater ones than fire, and the earth is more fruitful and enduring than all three. The roughness of one of these elements elicits the mildness of the other, for the mildness of one mitigates the roughness of the other so that they naturally harmonize with one another. Normally, one does not disturb the other, but once in a while by a divine injunction against evil, the elements are called into action and produce fires, storms, floods, and droughts.

Fog. By God's command, there appears a kind of fog on many mountains, in many valleys, and in many other places. First it is dark, but as it spreads out it moves in a stormy fashion and has a somewhat threatening, dangerous noise. As fog spreads itself wider over the world, it brings diseases, pestilence, and death to human beings and beast alike. Sometimes, fog rises from the moisture of water, somewhat disturbs things on the ground, and then spreads across the world. It brings only slight sickness and disease to man and beast, and does not kill them. Frost, one kind of fog, destroys the first spring blooms on the fruit trees and damages the fruits so that the trees and plants draw their leaves together and dry out as if they had had hot water poured over them. Another type of fog rises as a result of extreme heat, overfullness in the air and clouds, and as a result of their moisture, but it is not dangerous. A fog also arises out of the cold and moisture of the earth, and from the various waters; however, they bring no danger to men or beasts or the fruits of the earth because it lies in their nature to disperse at the proper time. At its rising in the morning, the sun appears red because of the cold and moisture in the air since the moisture and the cold that predominate there also turn men's eyes red. It is similar in the evening when the sun again turns red; that comes from the cold in the air because the sun is then declining and ready to set.

Why There Are Only Four Elements. There cannot be more or less than four elements. They exist in two ways, the higher and the lower. The higher elements are the heavenly, the lower ones are the earthly. What exists in the higher group is not accessible and consists of fire and air; however, what exists in the lower one can be obtained, has bodies fashioned, and consists of water and earth.

Souls and Ghosts. The spirits consist of fire and air; however, man consists of water and earth.

The Creation of Adam. When God made man, the earth out of which man was formed was glued together by water; God sent the breath of life — fire and air — into this form made from earth and water. Because the human form was made from earth and water, the earth became flesh through the fire of this breath of life and through the air, the water, through which the earth was held together, became blood. When God made Adam, his glance embraced the entire earth out of which Adam was made. This earth showed itself outwardly in Adam's fashioning — in the shape of his limbs — but Adam was hollow within. Then from the same earth God created on the inside the heart, liver, lungs, stomach, bowels, brain, eyes, tongue, and the other inner organs. As God breathed life within, the material that consisted of bones, marrow, and blood vessels was held together; the breath of life entered this mass the way a worm crawls into its house, the way green embraces a tree. The limbs were fastened in the same way that silver is changed when the smith places it into the fire. Thus, the breath of life has its seat in the heart. Further, in the same mass, the flesh and the blood were fashioned out of the fire of the soul.

The Hair. The growth-producing power of the soul sent foam and moisture toward the head, that is, into the brain. Because of this, the brain is moist. As a consequence of this moisture, the head causes hair to grow.

The Inner Organs of Human Beings. The soul is fiery like air and moist, and it fills the entire human heart. The liver heats the heart, the lungs cover it, and the stomach is a place within the human body for the reception of food. The heart is the seat of all knowledge, the liver is the seat of the feelings, the lungs are like veins in the leaf of understanding. The mouth is the mouthpiece for what the person expresses, and it receives that which keeps the body alive. It brings forth the voice; however, it does not hear the voice. Rather, the ear hears the voice but does not bring forth the voice.

The Ears. The two ears are like two wings that guide all the tones and noises in and out just as its wings carry a bird in the air.

The Eyes and the Nose. The eyes are paths for mankind, and the nose is mankind's guide for tasting. Man is fashioned in the same way in his other members.

The Elements Are in Human Beings. The elements, namely fire, air, earth, and water, are in human beings, as was mentioned above, and they exercise their powers in man and surround him in everything that he does, as quick as a wheel in its turnings. Fire has the five above-mentioned powers in the brain and in the marrow of men. When the first man was set upon the earth, a red fire was burned into his blood by the power of God. That is why the blood is red. This fire expresses itself as heat by seeing, as cold by smelling, as moisture by tasting, as air by hearing, and as movement by feeling.

Air exists with its four powers, in human breath and in man's reason, as mentioned above. It carries out its service to human beings through its living breath which is nothing else than the soul because it carries the soul. It is the wing of his flight, as man draws breath into himself and breathes out so that he may live. The soul is the fire that courses through the entire body and enlivens man. Air ignites this fire, and through air, fire burns in everything. The air expresses itself by sending out the dew, calling forth growth, moving the wind, and helping man to prosper through its production of heat. Water with its fifteen above-mentioned powers is contained in moisture and in the blood.

The Blood. Water is contained in human beings because they have blood. Blood maintains moisture in humans so that the life power in them remains fresh and their bones stay hard. Through its cold the blood vessels are also strengthened because the blood flows through them, consists of droplets, and moves the entire body. Water washes the flesh with blood so that it may stay strong, just as it holds the earth together. Fire overcomes the cold of the water, so that it flows; water penetrates the earth with fire and cold so that it may become hard. Frost, which covers the waters with a hard cover of ice, comes from the rocks. That is why they cannot be softened, just as the bones in human flesh are hard. So water manifests its heat in the blood of men, its air in his breath, its moisture in his entire body construction, his ability to release a flood in the elimination that purifies the body, his speed in growth, its power in his strengthening, enjoyment in his fertility, his manliness in his generativeness, in his strength its wetness, and its moisture in every human joint. Earth too is contained in the flesh and bones of men with its seven above-mentioned powers. Because of the water in blood, the flesh stays wet and grows.

The Flesh. As the earth was formed with fire and water, so is human flesh put together out of blood vessels and moisture. The construction of secure bones comes about through its coldness. Fire overcomes all this, so it is the power of man. Human flesh comes from the earth and possesses a cold moisture, but blood warms it. If it were not warmed by blood, it would turn back into clay, as it once was. Thus human flesh is secured by the heat of the blood, just as the earth is by the heat of the sun. However, because of its softness, human flesh is bloody and has the powers of the earth in it. It sweats due to the cold moisture, is warmed as a consequence of the heat, and, like the earth, cannot endure without the cold.

Begetting. Man is made fruitful by the cold and the warm and like other creatures he has joy in living. From himself, he begets the next generation. The heat determines his growth and the cold his decline and death. By both of these means, he spreads and procreates himself. As old age draws near to a man, however, all external warmth turns inward, otherwise he could not live. So his outer flesh becomes cold while he is still warm on the inside. For that reason an old man is soon made weary by everything that he does. There are many animals around him since he feeds himself from them and also feeds them. In this sense, man carries everything since all of creation is in him. In human flesh, the earth manifests its chill in man's warmth, its warmth in man's chill, its living power in his growth, death in his decline, its power to spread life in his propagation, its support in his increase, its interconnectedness in his support for all his members. Man derives his feelings and his desire from fire, his thinking and instability from the air, and his knowledge and movement from water.

Bringing Adam to Life. When Adam was nothing but earth, fire aroused him, air woke him, and water poured through him so that he began to move. Then God caused him to fall into a deep sleep. He was cooked by these powers so that his flesh became hot because of fire and he breathed because of air and the water flowed over him as in a mill. When he woke up, he was a prophet of heavenly realities and understood every power of creation and how to do everything.

Adam's Prospect. God put the entire creation under man so that he might master it with virile power since he already understood and had the power. Man contains the entire creation within himself, and the breath of life that never dies is in him.

The Infusion of the Soul. What is sent into the body as a soul is breath. Breath is sent from God and receives its reward on the basis of its physical deeds, according to whether they are good or bad. These deeds bind all moral development together. Just as a small child knows nothing at first of what he will later understand because he receives, with growing maturity, the insight into everything, and just as he later grows weary as a result of age, so the soul develops within him and makes progress by means of his works. The soul is wrapped around by good works as with a king's mantle, but it becomes darkened by evil deeds as the earth also is penetrated by water. As waters flow over certain places, so the soul penetrates the body and is more noble than it. Even when our external eyes are closed, the soul often sees the future by means of its prophetic powers because it already knows that it can live without the body.

Adam's Sleep. After Adam's first sleep his visionary powers were undiminished because he had not yet sinned, but later they were mixed with the lie. Then Adam, who was fashioned from the earth and was awakened to life with the help of the elements, changed, but Eve, who came from one of Adam's ribs, did not change.

Eve's Sin. From the power of the earth Adam was manly, and from the elements he was strong. Eve, however, was soft in her marrow. She had a light, sharp awareness and a comfortable life since she did not yet have to carry the burden of the earth. As she came forth from the man, so did the entire race of men come forth from her. Man's life is divided in two — into waking and sleeping. The body of man is also nourished in two ways, in that he both consumes food and also restores himself through sleep. However, if the soul leaves the body, then it will stay with him in a different way, a way that it can hardly endure because it is good. Thus it cries to God and says: "When will I put on my flesh, with which I daily lived?" For when God created the world, the day was pure light, which night had not yet divided.

Adam's Expulsion. When Adam sinned, night came into being. All the elements were wrapped in a great darkness in which Adam was sent into exile. When he saw the light of the world, he rejoiced because he himself belonged to the darkness, and said between his tears, "Now I must begin to live in a different way than God allowed me to live before." So he began to work and to sweat. Before Adam and Eve had broken God's commandment, their splendor sparkled like the sun, and this brilliance was like clothing to them. However, when they broke God's commandment, they did not shine as before, but became dark and remained in this darkness. When they saw that they did not glow as before, they recognized that they were naked and covered themselves with the leaves of a tree, as stands written.

Before the fall, Adam shone like the sun and did not need to work because he had also not yet performed any work. At the end of the world, the just will also shine like the sun; it stands written that the just will shine like the sun in the kingdom of their father. They will shine because of their good works. For in the splendor that the Holy ones will then have, their holy deeds will shine and sparkle like precious gems set in gold.

Why Eve Fell First. If Adam had been the first to disobey God's command, this violation would have been so serious and difficult to undo that man would have fallen into such an impossible obduracy, that he neither could have desired nor been able to be rescued. Because Eve was the first to disobey God's command, the offense could more easily be made up because she was weaker than the man. The skin and flesh of Adam was harder and stronger, as is still the case with men since the day Adam was made from the earth and Eve was made from him. But because she gave birth to sons, her flesh became weak and decrepit; so it will remain until the last day.

The Flood. When Adam was driven out of paradise — that is, before the flood — the water did not flow as fast and was not yet as liquid as thereafter. It had a kind of skin on its surface that slowed down its streaming, so that it only flowed gradually. In those days the earth was not yet as muddy, but rather dry and ribbed because it was not yet penetrated by water. But corresponding to this first condition, it gave abundant fruit. In those days, human beings had forgotten God so that they comported themselves more like animals than according to the will of God. Thence many people loved animals more than men. Women as well as men were familiar with animals and even united with them, so that the image of God was almost distorted by them. The entire human race transformed itself into a monster, so that some men began to behave and to act like wild animals as they ran around, yelled, and lived in this way. Before the fall, the wild animals and the cattle were not yet as wild as they became afterward. Men did not flee before them, nor they before mankind, and they were not afraid of one another. The wild animals and the house pets were comfortable in man's company and man in their company, for at the very beginning they had arisen at practically the same time. The wild animals and house pets caressed man, and man the animals. Hence they loved one another ever more in an unnatural way and hung on one another. However, Adam had begotten several sons who were so filled with the Spirit of God that they desired no shameful union, but rather wanted to remain in holiness. For that reason, also, they were named the sons of God.

Why Sons of God? They looked around themselves and began searching to see if there were any men who had not trafficked with beasts nor degenerated through such comportment although, as was mentioned above, it was sons of men who had violated God's command. They were also sons of men for the reason specified, because they had not been disfigured either in their outer form nor by traffic with the animals. They took wives from among their daughters and begot sons. It stands written that the sons of God saw that the daughters of men were beautiful. Even today there are still certain wild and domesticated animals which have taken over from men quite a bit of human nature in the way referred to above. Then a cry went up over this crime even to the seat of God because the image of God had been distorted and destroyed and the rational order had spun into disarray. At this, the Spirit of God, that had hovered over the waters at the creation, released the waters. The skin by which the water had been held back before so that it did not flow as fast as it now does, was ripped open. The water became a roaring cascade and drowned mankind. On that occasion the water so flooded the earth that the earth became almost like iron. It gave a new and stronger sap to all its fruits than before, and it caused grapes to grow where before there were none. Also, the rocks that were created with the earth but had been covered by the earth, were now exposed for the first time, and some of them that were whole before were now split.

The Creation of Stones. Stones came to be, neither earlier nor later, with the exception of those that appear as clear nuggets in the rivers. They were made together with the earth, and only came to be seen for the first time because of the flood.

The Rainbow. Then God set his bow in the firmament to strengthen the firmament and to set limits to the waters. This bow flamed like fire and had the colors of water. These colors are as powerful in regard to the waters as to the clouds, so that the rainbow withheld the waters with its fire and its colors as a net holds the fish so that they cannot swim out. After the flood the wisdom and talents of men became greater than they had appeared up to then. Before the flood, the entire earth was full of people and animals. They were not separated from each other either by water or forests because there were not yet great rivers or forests. There were only springs and small streams that one could easily wade through, and only a few groves of trees that one could easily traverse. However, after the flood, several springs and streams were changed into great and dangerous rivers. Great woods grew up, by which people and animals became separated so that after that people tended to avoid animals and animals tended to avoid people. Also, it never rained before the flood, but only a dew fell upon the earth. Now, however, since the earth was inundated and consolidated by the waters of the flood, it naturally seeks rain water.

The Position of the Earth. The earth is of moderate size and is located near the bottom of the firmament. If it were in the middle of the firmament, it would have to be larger, and then it could easily fall down and break apart if it had as large an amount of air under it as it has above it. To the south, it slopes like a mountain; hence it receives greater heat from the sun because the sun and the firmament are closer to it there. To the north, it is high as a protection against attack, and a terrible cold reigns there because neither the sun nor the firmament is close to the earth. In fact, the firmament spreads itself out there.

Man is Made from the Elements. As the above-mentioned elements hold the world together, so in the same way are the elements responsible for the well-being of the human body. They are spread through his body and divide their tasks so that man is maintained by them. In the same way, they are distributed throughout the world and operate in a similar way there. Fire, air, water, and earth are in every human being who consists of these four elements. From fire he derives his warmth, from the air his breath, from water his blood, and from the earth his flesh. Similarly, he derives his power to see from fire, from air his hearing, from water his movement, and from the earth his pace. The earth prospers when the elements fulfill their duties in a good and orderly fashion so that the heat, the dew, and the rain divide and come down moderately at the right time to give the earth and the fruits the best weather conditions and bring much fruit and health. If they all suddenly fell on the earth at the same time and not at the correct intervals, the earth would burst, and its fruit and health would be lost. If the elements work properly in a human being, they sustain him and keep him healthy. However, if they do not live harmoniously in him they disturb him and make him sick. If the connections of the humors — that come from heat, moisture, blood, and flesh and which are all present in a person, — work in peace and maintain their correct proportion in him, they bring health with them. However, if they encounter each other simultaneously and in an unmeasured fashion, and invade him in excess amounts, they make him weak and undo him. For as a consequence of Adam's sin, man's heat and moisture, blood and flesh have been transformed into opposed phlegms.

The Variety of Phlegms. From the heat of the fire a dry phlegm is secreted and separated off, from the moisture of the air a moist phlegm, from the watery blood a foamy phlegm, and from the earthly flesh a lukewarm one. Whenever any one of these phlegms increases in someone beyond normal so that it cannot be complemented and kept in balance it puts that person down and makes him sick. However, if each phlegm maintains its proper amount so that it is so balanced with the others that it can be kept to its proper size, it makes that person well and keeps him healthy. For if one phlegm wins outright supremacy and dominates the others, its opposite is thrown into servitude to it, and the other two follow slowly after with the slime so that the person finds himself in bodily peace.

The Humors. There are four humors. The two dominating ones are named phlegm, and the two that come after them are named slime. Each of the dominating humors is covered with a quarter of the one coming after and a half of the third. The weaker humor regulates the two parts and the remaining part of the third, to make sure it doesn't exceed its limits. In this manner, the first humor dominates the second. These two are called phlegm. The second humor dominates the third, and the third the fourth. These last two, that is the third and the fourth humors, are called slime. The stronger humors surpass the weaker because of their excess, and the weaker humors have a moderating influence on this excess by their weakness. A person in such a state finds himself in peace. However, whenever any humor increases beyond its proper amount, the person is in danger. Whenever either of the above-mentioned slimes exceeds its proper amount, it does not have enough power to take control of the humors lying on top of it, whether it be aroused by an inferior slime to be the preeminent humor, or whether it is an inferior humor supported by a superior one. If such a slime spreads out excessively in a person, his remaining humors cannot remain in peace unless we are dealing with people in whom the grace of God has been poured out — either as strength as with Samson, wisdom as with Solomon, prophecy as with Jeremias, or as with certain pagans, for example Plato and people like him. When the above-mentioned people are not healthy, the grace of God sometimes moves them to change so that they are first sick, then healthy; now anxious, then strong; sometimes sad, then happy. God brings them back to order; that is, he makes them healthy when they are sick, strong when they are anxious, and happy when they are sad. If the dry humor is stronger in a certain person than the moist, or the moist humor than the foamy and the lukewarm, then the dry phlegm is like a lady and the moist like a servant, and the foamy and the lukewarm ones are like two smaller slimy servants standing in the background. For these last two are, corresponding to their powers, the slime of the first two. Such a person is naturally clever, angry, and stormy in everything that he does. He does not have patience, for the dryness consumes these humors and then easily lifts itself again like a flame that quickly falls back and then quickly raises itself again. He is healthy and lives a long time although he will not reach advanced age because he does not receive adequate support from the moist phlegm, and as a result his flesh becomes dried out by the fire.

Madness. If ever the foamy or the lukewarm humors that were drawn together as slime behind the before-mentioned phlegm — that is, of the dry and the moist, which should maintain themselves peacefully — have exceeded their proper amount, like a wave in the water that becomes too big, they change themselves into a poison. A tempest arises out of them in such a way that no humor can be balanced with any other, and they no longer carry out their tasks. These above-mentioned humors fight so strongly against the two harmonizing ones that all four fall into conflict.

Any person who suffers this opposition and contradiction in his body will become mad. For when the inner humors rebel against one another, the person turns violent and fights himself if he is not bound with ropes. This lasts until the above-mentioned foamy and lukewarm humors have weakened and returned to their proper order. Such a person will not live long. However, if the moist humor is stronger than the dry and the dry stronger than the foamy and the lukewarm, which then constitute the slime following after them, such a person is naturally clever and constant, remains so, is sound of body, and will live a long time.

Arthritis. If the foamy and the lukewarm humors which now constitute the slime of the moist and the dry, exceed their proper amount so that the foamy climbs up and becomes like a hot-water steam and the lukewarm pours itself out in drops, then these humors, because they are causing confusion by their disunity, bend a person's neck, curve his back, and make him entirely stiff until he is released from this suffering; however, he can live that way for a long time.

Idiocy. A person in whom the dry humor exceeds the foamy and the foamy exceeds both the moist and the lukewarm, is easily enraged and then again easily quieted. He is not weak but powerful, and can live a long time if it is the will of God.

Paralysis. If the moist and the lukewarm humors — which constitute the slime of the dry and the foamy — have belched out their amount like a dangerous wind, they are then thrown into a strong wind movement and cause a dangerous noise like the crash of thunder. This sound reverberates even into the blood vessels, into the marrow, and into people's sleep. Whoever suffers from such a condition will be paralyzed and his entire body will no longer be powerful. This lasts until the mentioned slimes have decreased and have returned to their proper paths. However, he can live a long time if God allows it.

Good Character. If the foam exceeds the dry and the dry exceeds the moist and the lukewarm, then the person has a good character, is well-intentioned and frail of body, but does not live a long time.

47

Insanity. If the moist and the lukewarm humors, which constitute the slime of the foamy and the dry, exceed their proper amount,
then the moist humor soon becomes like a wheel that has spun off,
throws the person now into the water and then into the fire, and the
lukewarm throws him into craziness. Such a person is then in such
a condition that he loses his intelligence. He becomes crazy. He is
neither completely healthy nor completely sick.

Delirium. If, in someone, the dry humor exceeds the lukewarm
and the lukewarm exceeds the moist and the foamy, the two following immediately after, then this person is sick in both body and spirit;
he is fearsome in his behavior both to himself and to his neighbors,
is useful for nothing, unreflective in every situation, and only mini-
mally healthy; however, he can live a long time.

Despair. If either the moist or the foamy humors, which then constitute the slime of the dry and the lukewarm, exceed their proper
size so that the moist sends an acid haze into the person and the foamy
humor makes it slimy and slippery like a toad, then they arouse in
him a sound like the sound of the howling north wind and attack the
heart and the senses of the person so that he can no longer place his
hope or trust either in God or in any man or in any part of creation.
This condition lasts until the above-mentioned slime leaves off in its
fearful effect. It would be better for such a person to die rather than
live. However, he can live a long time.

The Anxious. If the lukewarm humor exceeds the dry and the
dry exceeds the moist and the foamy, this brings many psychological
sufferings with it — anger and madness and occasionally happiness
— but he does not stay with this last one because he is anxious about
everything like a wave on the ocean since he is afraid of everything.
Some of these persons live a long time, but the majority die soon.

The Dumb. If the moist or the foamy humor — which in this case
constitutes the contracted slime from the above-mentioned phlegms,
that is, from the lukewarm and the dry phlegms — which actually
should behave themselves peacefully, exceed their proper amount,
then the moisture begets something like a hot-water vapor, and the
foam chains and chokes a person's reason so that he cannot speak,
but rather is dumb. Although he cannot express himself exteriorly,

inwardly he is much wiser. Also, because his reason is oriented externally, he has a clear understanding in himself and also feels such. Such a person is not at all inferior; he is sound of body and will have a long life.

Good Natural Conditions. If the moist humor exceeds the foamy in a person, and the foamy exceeds the dry and the lukewarm that follow, then these two phlegms that come after them constitute — according to their powers — the slime of the two superior ones, that is, the dry and the foamy. Such a person naturally has a very good character and a cheerful disposition; his flesh grows, he does not easily become angry, and he does not become bitter. However, he is weak and will not live long because the dry humor is present in him only in small amounts.

Cancer. If the dry or the lukewarm humors that in this case build up the slime of the moist and the foamy exceed their proper amount, they cause noisy belches and hiccups in people and cause cancers to break out. They also bring it about that the worms eat him and the flesh on his body swells up into ugly boils so that because of the growing malignancy one of his arms or feet becomes larger than the other. They do this until they have let go of this disagreeable disease. For that reason he cannot live a long time.

Gout. If the foamy humor exceeds the moist and the moist exceeds the dry and the lukewarm, then such a person has a good knowledge of things but he is in a hurry and goes around blustering with his knowledge so that he sprays his knowledge around in different directions like water that is dispersed by the wind. Thereafter he strives to dominate others. He is sound of body, except that he easily becomes weak on his feet and easily contracts gout. However, he can live a long time if it pleases God.

Suicide. If the dry or the lukewarm humors, that in this case constitute the slime of the foamy and the moist, have worked their way out of their proper paths, then the dry humor exceeds the foamy and the moist and brings them into confusion. In human beings, the lukewarm humor causes a hot-water vapor to the point where such a person takes his own life if he is not prevented from doing so either by God or by other people. Such a person is neither entirely healthy

49

nor entirely sick, but between the two. He can live a long time if he is closely watched.

Arthritis. A person in whom the moist humor exceeds the dry and the lukewarm exceeds the dry and the foamy that is still remaining here, can endure vexations in himself and in other people. Such a person is dour in outlook but knows no strong anger, and, as far as his character goes, is useful. He is usually healthy except that he occasionally suffers from the ailment that men call arthritis. He will live a long time.

Instability. If the dry or foamy humors, which in this case constitute the slime of the moist and the lukewarm, exceed their proper amount, then in such a person the dry strives upward as in those plants that are called "bindweed." The foam causes a disagreeable eruption in these persons. They also cause an irregular hurrying in the person so that he would like to run all over the place. He would completely unsettle himself if people let him. This reaction lasts until the slime has disappeared. But he can live a long time if God and people watch over him.

The Angry. If the lukewarm humor exceeds the moist and the moist exceeds the dry and the foamy, such a person is cunning, avoids peace, and loves opposition and fights. He is thin of body but enjoys eating. He is not healthy; however, he does not stay in bed on that account but is constantly active. He can live a long time, but usually does not reach an advanced age because he dies before he reaches it.

Fainting. If the dry or the foamy humor that in this case constitutes the slime of the lukewarm and the moist exceeds its proper amount, then the dry blazes up so that such a man becomes a glutton in his intemperance. The foam makes him desire to eat. He sometimes runs around like a wheel, and then occasionally he falls over like a dead person. This disease holds his life spirit to itself since he need not die until it gives out. Such a man is sick and will not reach a great age.

Instability. If the foam exceeds the lukewarm humor in someone and the lukewarm exceeds the dry and the moist, which in this case follow like a slime that stays close by, as it was described above with regard to the others, such a person shows both an inappropriate cheerfulness and also a malancholy that is out of place, and, on occasion, horrible anger. However, he actually has a good disposition. Inwardly, he suffers from a dirty, foul-smelling phlegm and from an unattractive smell and taste. He is not very intelligent, and he seldom becomes old.

The Possessed. If the dry or the moist humors, that in this case constitute the approaching slime of the above-mentioned phlegm — that is, of the foamy and the lukewarm which ought to comport themselves peacefully — exceed their proper amount, the spiritual consciousness of that person shrinks and perishes, and also his sense of taste and his senses. Then the spirits of the air threaten him, incite him to heresy, and surround him with a wall since his spiritual consciousness has fallen asleep. Such a person finds himself in great danger if God does not drive away these spirits. For this reason, such a person withers within and cannot live a long time in this condition.

Unfriendliness. If the lukewarm humor exceeds the foamy and the foamy exceeds the remaining two phlegms, that is, the dry and the moist, which then, as a slime, oppose the foamy corresponding to their powers, then such a person is hard; he spares no one, seeks out evil, is unfriendly in his behavior, and is satisfied with nothing. Although healthy and strong, he cannot live a long time.

Hallucination. If on occasion the dry or the moist humor that in this case constitutes the approaching slime of the above-mentioned phlegms — that is, the lukewarm and the foamy, that actually should behave itself peacefully — exceeds its proper amount, then the dry slime grows without limit, penetrates the person, and drives out his spirit in an instant. Also, the moist slime calls up bizarre representations in his imagination so that he becomes deranged and hurls out evil as well as crazy words. He also has a quick temper and is malicious, crazy in his brain, and disruptive. Only seldom does he reach old age.

Good Health. Should the above-mentioned humors maintain their correct balance and proper proportion in a person, as was said above, he finds himself in a condition of peace and health. However, when they conflict with each other, the humors make him weak and sick, as was already said above.

Why There are Only Four Humors. Man cannot maintain himself using one, two, or even three humors; he requires four so that they can regulate one another. In the same way, the earth consists of four elements that harmonize with one another.

Divine Punishment. Whenever these elements, by God's decree, release their terror in a chaotic way, they bring many dangers to the world and to men. Then, fire like a lance, air like a sword, water like a shield, and earth like a javelin are summoned as a judgment on men. That is, the elements are subject to mankind, and when they are disturbed by the deeds of men, they then complete their tasks. For when men degenerate into fighting, terrible deeds, hate, envy, and sinful exchanges, then the elements transform themselves into an opposing and corrective force such as heat or cold or great deluges and floods. That derives from God's first directive, for it was decreed by God that the elements should affect the deeds of mankind since the elements are affected by the deeds of man as human beings carry on with them and in them. When mankind is on the proper path and does good and evil in due proportion, then human beings carry out their tasks by the grace of God, which is necessary for mankind.

Evil. If the elements inflict their terrible punishments on mankind, as described above, then men should wail and cry out between sobs and tears, that the elements stop punishing them. They should refer their problems to the blood of the unblemished Lamb, and the grace of God will come to their aid.

The Fall of Lucifer. Lucifer was thrown out of heaven with so much force that he may never again raise himself from hell. If he could, he would change all the elements by his power so that he would even cause the firmament to turn backwards; he would darken the sun, the moon, and the stars; he would block the flow of water and set loose much evil amidst creation. The entire troop of demons depends upon him, among whom some have great, others a lesser power. There are also some demons who frequently traffic with human beings, who do not avoid holy places, and who are not terrified before the cross of the Lord and the Holy Liturgy. They all collaborate with Lucifer against the world. Compared with Lucifer's power, the devil is almost as strong, powerful, and evil, as though he were both Lucifer's desire and his will. Because Lucifer cannot move himself, the devil was sent into the world as the serpent of the demons. He has the power to deceive through appearances and has many other evil characteristics. Thus he seduced Adam in paradise and pronounced him lord of the earth. Later, by his own power, the devil will bring Lucifer's breath to the AntiChrist so that he might lead this one astray. His might will increase up to the point from which the devil was thrown down and fell into the depths. There, the anger of God became a fire in the black mass of storms, with such a bitter power that he often flames out in the elements, tears them up, and spreads terror with his voice. The devil does not dare to show his power openly for fear before God, but rather is like a thief; thus he is also a liar. This anger will also burn up and destroy the elements on the Last Day. That is God's judgment. God commanded the holy evangelist John to write down the voices that spoke out of the thunder because, at that time, they revealed all the fears and terrors that have faced mankind before and since. If man had known about them ahead of time, he could not have endured them because of the weakness of his flesh and the excessive terrors. For man withstands troubles better if they occur in the course of time and in occasional events, rather than when he knows them all at once in advance. It also happened that way because thunder is so frightening, so powerful, and terrifying; and if man knew what kind of condition thunder was, he would fear it. He would neglect the true God out of fear of thunder whenever he heard its voice. (The winds blow above and below the sun and around it. Their strength divides and spreads its fire. If the winds did not do this, the sun would emit such a powerful glow that neither the earth nor the other elements nor the other objects of creation could endure it.)

Raving. If one humor overcomes the others in a person and does not observe its proper limits, that man becomes sick and weak. However, if two such humors arise simultaneously against the order in a person, he cannot endure it; he will then be destroyed either physically or mentally, now that the proper proportion is missing. If three such humors spread out simultaneously and excessively, the person will become sick and soon die. If all four humors rise up against the proper order, that person will quickly, in an instant, be killed by them on that very spot. At no time can he endure such a conflict, but will experience a complete breakdown. In such a manner all things will be smashed on the Last Day as the four elements fight among themselves.

The Creation of Adam. God made men out of clay. The man was transformed from clay into flesh. For that reason, he is the actual ground and the lord of creation. He works the earth so that it brings forth fruit. There is strength in his bones, his veins, and his flesh; he has a fully able head and a firm skin. He has his procreative power in himself and generates his seed as the sun generates light. Woman was not transformed in a like manner because, taken from flesh, she remains flesh. Hence, she is given the artistic work with the hands. Woman has a kind of airy essence. She carries the child in her womb and brings it into the world. Her skull is cleft and her skin is soft so that the child that she carries in her body can receive air.

Conception. The conception and origin of such a person comes about in the following way. In man, there is will, reflection, power, and understanding. First comes the will, for every man has the determination to do this or that. Reflection follows; it tests to see whether the thing to be done is suitable or unsuitable, becoming or shameful. Then comes power which has the duty of bringing the work to completion. Understanding comes last, for a work cannot be brought to completion if it does not agree with understanding. These four powers are present at the formation of a person. Then the four elements, which the four humors in mankind arouse, become excessive and unruly in such a manner that fire through the dry enflames the will excessively, air through the moist excessively disturbs the reflection, water through the foam causes the generative faculties to produce excessively, and also earth through the lukewarm throws the understanding into confusion. As a consequence of their surplus, these all unleash a kind of storm and a poisonous foam from the blood. This is semen. When it reaches its proper place, the woman's blood joins with it, and then it becomes bloody. The desire which the serpent gave to man with the apple comes from the earliest beginnings of mankind. Thereby, man's blood is aroused by desire. From thence, the blood causes the cold foam to flow in the woman, which, as a consequence of the warmth of the motherly flesh, develops into a bloody creature. This foam stays warm at a constant temperature then grows — by the separation of the dry from the nourishment of the mother into a small human shape — until the finger of the creator, which fashioned humanity, entirely penetrates this human shape just as an artisan forms his most noble work. For the manly power in the generative member transformed itself into a poisonous foam at the fall of Adam, and the woman's blood transformed itself into an unattractive discharge. His blood produces semen because of the strong and upright essence of the male since his flesh was taken from the earth. As is proper to her nature, a woman's blood produces no semen, for her blood is weak and soft. Rather, it produces only a thin, scanty foam because the woman — unlike the man who consists of the two forms, earth and flesh — was only taken from the man's flesh. For that reason, she is weak and easily broken and a vessel for the male. The blood of the woman is aroused by the male's love passion, and it produces a kind of foam for the seed of the man, but one that is more bloody than white. This binds with the seed, warms it, makes it bloody, and strengthens it. After the semen is placed in the proper place, it becomes cold. It remains only a poisonous foam until the fire, that is the warmth, warms it; until the air, that is breath, dries it; until the water, that is the flow, causes a pure moisture to reach it; and until the earth, that is a little skin, draws it together. Then it becomes bloody — that is, not entirely blood, but only mixed a bit with blood. The four humors that preserve mankind from the four elements remain now in a proportionate mixture around the seed until it thickens into flesh and becomes firm so that a human shape can be formed out of it. The marrow and the veins fuse themselves like feathers into the whole form, divide it among themselves, and build the network of the body's construction within. They also surround the marrow with something like an egg shell; later, the bones will develop from this. Then the entire thing will be as clearly and completely fashioned as the shape a painter develops out of a particular form. All over, there are cuts and indentations made in the skin that holds all this together where later the limbs will be. It is the same with clay that develops cracks in the glow of the sun. The dried flesh is then freed from the poison by being dried out, and healthy flesh is enlivened by being pumped with proper blood. Through the warmth of the mother this develops into a thick mass that is not yet alive, but remains in the above-mentioned warmth. This work takes place in the first month, that is, in the time it takes the moon to wax and wane one time. In this manner, the above-mentioned mass grows and becomes fat because it would fully dry out if it did not have this fat. In case of such a drying out, the mother becomes injured and suffers much.

The Inflowing of the Soul. Then, as God so wills it and as he arranged it, the breath of life comes which enlivens this form. Without the mother knowing it, the breath of life comes like a strong warm wind, like a wind that blows loudly against a wall and streams within and fastens itself to every joint and limb of this shape. In this way, the various limbs of this form are gently separated from one another, just as the flowers unfold themselves in the warmth of the sun. But there is still such weakness in this form that it cannot move itself, but only lies there, sleeps, and barely breathes. The spirit of life penetrates the entire form, fills and strengthens it in its marrow and in its veins so that they grow more than before, until the bones are spread out over the marrow and the veins become so strong that they can contain the blood. Now the child begins to move, and the mother feels it as though she received a sudden kick; from then on it remains continually in motion. For the living wind, that is the soul, enters into this form, as was mentioned above, according to the will of almighty God, strengthens it, makes it capable of life, and wanders around within it like a caterpillar that spins silk from which it becomes covered and closed in as with a house. In this form, the spirit of life discerns where the soul can divide itself, bend, and turn about; it also pays attention to all the places where there are veins, dries them out like the inner walls of a reed, and joins itself with the flesh so that by the heat of its fire it becomes red like the blood because the soul is fire. Thus it penetrates the entire form of the child with its breath, just as an entire house will be illuminated by a fire at its center. All the veins maintain their positions where they are held together as the earth also is held together by its waters. The soul causes the blood to flow like living air through all the above-mentioned parts of the body, and it holds the flesh together with a bloody slime and a constant moisture just as food is cooked in a pot by the fire. The soul strengthens the bones and introduces them into the flesh so that the flesh will thereby be supported and not give way. In the same way, a man will build his house with rafters so that it will not fall in and be destroyed. This all happens during the second month when the above-mentioned form is strengthened by the soul while the moon wanes and again waxes. Because the soul is located in the blood vessels, it fills the flesh and the bones with blood, which is what the increase of the moon signifies. However, the decrease of the moon means that the form cannot yet move itself. The soul remains in this form and inspects all the places in the body with which it will eventually complete its work because it realizes that eventually it will move this form as a whole, just as the wheel causes the entire mill to turn. Corresponding to the course of the sun, it begins its path. As the sun comes up in the morning and moves along its course from morning until terce, from terce until sext, from sext until none, and from none until vespers, so the soul has its seat in the eyes, to prepare them, so that the soul can see light through the windows of the eyes. The soul is also in the breast, to cause it to follow its thoughts; and further in the heart, so as to show that knowledge gives it wings. The soul keeps all the bowels together like a net in the stomach and strengthens them in a shape with hollow places for the reception of food, through which the above-mentioned body nourishes itself. The teeth, which have no marrow, chew this food; the teeth are planted without water by the moist fire of the soul. Thus food reaches the stomach in which it remains a suitable time. The soul also separates the humors for the nourishment of the brain, the heart, the lungs, the liver, and all blood vessels. With the strength of its warmth, it empowers the stomach and the intestines, which transport the nourishment so that it doesn't flow away but remains at that place. Then the soul descends to the loins, strengthens them through its fiery warmth, and supports all the organs lying in the region of the loins just as a house is strengthened and supported by pillars. Then the soul brings life also into the feet and the toes, just as God planned and fashioned it, since man's feet carry his loins just as the base of pillars carry the pillars themselves. The soul itself establishes the bodily form and enlightens it because it is a flaming fire in the body, just like a fire that brings light to the entire house and to every corner, so that the entire house becomes bright.

For this reason man is like the sun and the moon. For as the first hour announces the day, the soul sees and looks out at the light through the windows of the eyes. As the third hour spreads out the light of day, so also the soul multiplies and varies the thoughts in the breast. As the sun burns strong at the sixth hour and has everything under its influence, so also the soul knows much in the heart and lets much of this become visible in its work. Just as the sun brings a certain cooling at the ninth hour since it has already accomplished its daily chore, so it is with the soul when it works in the stomach with the food by which the person is nourished, that food which the sun helped to send out roots, grow, and become ripe. As evening falls, the sun dips beneath the earth and night comes on. The soul sinks to the legs which carry the entire person. During this time the man sleeps, weary from work and empty of food, until the sun rises again. The soul directs the nourishment from the food along the proper paths throughout the entire body and expels what remains, just as wine is separated from its dregs. The body cannot operate without the soul which penetrates the entire body with its own warmth.

Man is formed from the four elements and has his foundation in them. Of these, two of the elements are of a spiritual nature and two of a fleshly nature. Fire and air are spiritual; water and earth are corporeal. All four join together in unity in a person, and they also heat him in such a way that he and all his appendages become bloody and fleshy. However, fire and water remain in opposition to one another and cannot come into close proximity. Therefore, it is essential that each of the two be guided by a master. Specifically, water opposes fire in order to keep it from burning more than is set for it and from spreading. Similarly, fire hems in the water so that it does not flow over the dry hot land beyond its allotted measure. These two powers of fire and water regulate the entire earth, together with the air in the clouds, so that it has a secure foundation and does not perish. It is similar with human blood. It takes its red color from the fire's heat, and it is fluid because of water's presence. For if the warm blood were not fluid, it would not flow at all, but rather dry up and fall to the ground like a scale. If the earth also were not fluid, it would scatter like straw, and no creature would remain unharmed. For that reason, the rest of creation depends upon these two powers. Without them, no form could maintain itself. If these two elements had not been fused into a unity, the remaining forms could not have developed. For God made man out of the clay of the earth so that he consists, with the breath of the soul, of fluid, fiery, and airy elements. Similarly, the soul moves mankind by means of the four elements: his form, fashioned from the earth, endures by the finger of God and is mixed with water, moved by the air, and heated by fire. The body possesses the sense of taste, and taste leads to enjoyment. The soul, however, develops desire, and desire leads the will. The soul is like the fire, the body like the water, and the two build the whole. In this way, man is the work of God. For that reason, the soul must also repair every need that the body asks of it, and hence the soul is the fulfiller and the body the petitioner. The soul is more powerful than the body because the one satisfies the other's demands. The soul would not have the power to do this without the human body, this power that penetrates and moves man who is himself the work of God. The soul itself would not exist without the body; similarly, the body with its flesh and blood could not move itself if there were no soul. The soul can live without the body, but the body can in no way live without the soul. After the Last Judgment, the soul will demand its covering back and direct it then according to its own commands. Thus, man consists of two natures, body and soul, just as flesh cannot exist without blood nor blood without flesh. Although each one's nature is different from the other, the soul can exist without a body, but God can not exist without work. For his work was before eternity and is eternally concealed in him just as the soul is concealed invisibly within the body. However, the soul lives without the body and after the Last Judgment reclaims its covering from God in order to put it on again. In the same way, God, who was Life before eternity and in eternity without beginning, put on his covering at the proper time, a covering that eternally was hidden in him. In the same way, God and man are one like the soul and body, for God created mankind after his own image and likeness. Just as everything casts its shadow, in the same way man is the shadow of God, and the shadow is the visible sign of his creation. Man is the clear pointer toward almighty God in all of his wonders. He himself is a shadow because he has a beginning; God, however, has neither beginning nor end. For that reason, the harmony of the heavens is a mirror of the divinity, and man reflects all the wonders of God.

Begetting. In mankind, phlegms and humors develop according to the nature of man's seed, just as seeds bring forth different grains depending on whether summer or winter wheat or barley seeds are sown. Just as excessive humors in mankind often lead to various forms of craziness and many dangerous illnesses until they calm down again and return to their proper proportion, so also from the first implantation of the seed, the child is pushed back and forth by many changes before the spirit of life quickens in it and directs it along the correct path.

The Placenta. After the man's seed has reached its proper place so that it can take on human form, out of the woman's monthly blood, a small skin grows around this form, surrounding it and holding it together so that it cannot be moved back and forth or fall away. The flowing blood concentrates there to let this form rest in the midst of it like a man in the living room of his house. It finds warmth and support there, and there, until its birth, it will be nourished by the dark blood from the liver of the mother.

Reason. The child remains shut up in this vessel until reason is fully implanted within it and seeks to break out. After that, it cannot and should not remain shut up and silent, for the child cannot cry in its mother's womb.

Birth. When the birth is imminent, the vessel — in which the child was confined — tears. The eternal power that took Eve from the side of Adam comes and is present, and every corner of the mother's body is wrenched out of place. All the parts within the woman's body rush to meet this power, take it up, and open themselves. They behave in this way until the child comes out. Then, they close themselves up again as they were before. While the child is coming out, the soul of the child also feels the eternal might that has sent it and rejoices.

Consciousness. When the child has come out, it immediately breaks out crying because it perceives the darkness of the world. As God sends the soul into the human body, it takes on consciousness, but as if it were asleep. But when the soul actually enters the body, consciousness is thereby awakened when it rushes into the flesh and the blood vessels.

Knowledge. When the birth of a child is imminent so that the divine power opens the womb of the mother, then the child experiences the power of God. The awareness arises in his soul to learn and grasp all things, and it is aroused to this awareness by its own wish and desire. For if a person desires to understand some work or art or something else it is curious about, then the Holy Spirit showers down his dew on this interest. From that, the person grasps and learns what he desires to learn. Just as the father and the mother answer the child when it seeks to learn something from them, so also the Holy Spirit aids human knowing in any and all knowledge if a person seeks to learn it by his own wish, desire, and effort. However, if a person seeks to acquire something bad or to know an evil science, then the devil sees this and influences the man's knowledge with cunning malice so that he might quickly learn the evil that he wishes to acquire. For man has knowledge of both good and evil. However, when the child has left the mother's womb, it is moving, active, and capable. It sweats and has the various phlegms and humors from its very beginning according to the nature of its bodily constitution. Corresponding to them, it can grow or diminish according to its food and drink.

Milk. When the woman receives the semen from the man so that it begins to grow in her, then the blood of the woman will also be drawn up toward the breasts by this same natural power, and what normally would become blood from food and drink is changed instead into milk so that the child that grows in the mother's womb can be nourished by it. As the child grows in the womb of its mother, the milk in her breasts also increases so that the child can be fed from it.

The Subjugation of Woman. As the woman serves the man until they are one, so also the woman joins the male's seed with the female blood so that they become one flesh.

Conception. If the male's seed comes to the right place, then it takes in the woman' blood with lively desire and draws it to itself just as the breath draws something into itself. In the same way, the blood of the woman mixes itself with the man's seed, and they become one blood so that the woman's flesh is also heated from this blood mixture, grows, and increases. And so, through the man, the woman is one flesh with the man. However, the man's flesh becomes heated — both on the inside and the outside — by the woman's warmth and sweat, and it draws something into itself from the foam and sweat of the woman. For when the man's desire is at its strongest, his blood becomes thin and watery, and it flows and circulates as in a mill. It takes something into itself from the foam and the sweat of the woman so that his flesh becomes mixed with the woman's whereby he becomes one flesh with and through the woman. Because the man and the woman become one flesh in this fashion, the woman easily conceives a child from the man, always presupposing that she is fertile. However, the fact that the man and the woman become one flesh in this fashion goes back to the side of the man, for the woman was taken from the side of the man and became his flesh. For that reason, in their blood and their sweat, the man and the woman fuse together much more easily in conception. In this way, the power of eternity, which draws the child out of the womb of its mother, makes the man and woman one flesh.

Divorce. If a man and his wife lose sight of their proper connection and, with burning passion, turn to another liason so that they enter into relation with another person in an improper manner, then the man mixes his blood, which is due to his proper wife, with another woman, and in a similar way the woman mixes her blood, which is now the blood of her proper husband, with a strange man. For that reason, the children that result from such proper as well as improper husbands, or from proper as well as improper wives, often do not prosper because they are the result of a conception where, either on the father's or the mother's side, the morals and the blood were separated. For that reason, before God, such parents are called Breakers of the Proper Order that God founded in Adam and Eve. As Adam and Eve violated the command of God and delivered themselves and all their posterity over to death, so also those who evade the divine ordinance in this fashion, blemish themselves and also those who result from them. They condemn them to unhappiness because their reason is blemished and because they have made themselves base in their trafficking with animals.

Weak Semen. If a woman conceives and shortly thereafter, if the semen is still thin, lets another man approach her, then often the sweat and the heat of this man binds a bit with the seed so that it will thereby be polluted as if by a foul-smelling wind. Milk is polluted in this fashion if someone adds another liquid to it as it flows.

The Different Kinds of Seed. A man in whom the dry element — that is, the fire — is dominant, is not well-equipped to master the sciences. However, once he has grasped them, he holds onto them tightly and for a long time. In those in whom the moist element — that is, the air — is in command, that person has a quick power of understanding and an ability to master the sciences, but his knowledge does not endure. Once he has learned something, he quickly forgets it again. The person in whom the foamy element — that is, water — is dominant has a swift power to grasp something he is trying to learn; however, he believes he understands it before he really does or before he has firmly grasped it. For that reason, he fails if he tries to go forward in the sciences, for he has not yet fully appropriated them. One in whom the lukewarm element — that is the earth — rules is so disposed that he takes on the sciences slowly and with great difficulty. Even when, with great difficulty, he has learned something about a certain area he cannot retain it because of his clumsy disposition. For that reason, he often gives up trying to learn since he cannot retain anything and loses what he has already learned. However, in certain areas he is clever — areas that concern the earth and practical considerations.

Carnal Desire. The blood vessels that are in the liver and the stomach of the male meet in his sexual organs. As the storm of desire leaves man's marrow, it descends into his loins and arouses a foretaste of desire in the blood. Because the area of the loins is rather narrow, tight, and self-contained, such a storm cannot spread very far there. Then the man burns forth in so strong a feeling of desire that in the heat of this passion he forgets himself and can no longer hold back the spilling of his foamy seed. Because of the narrowness of the loins, the fire of desire breaks out all the stronger in a man, but also less often than with a woman. Like a ship in high seas that ascends the rivers as a result of strong storm winds, and becomes so endangered that occasionally it can scarcely maintain itself, so also, only with difficulty, can man's nature be restrained and mastered in the storm of desire. But a small boat can still stop in waves that arise as the result of soft winds and in whirlpools that arise as a result of light gusts, although only with effort. So is it with the nature of the woman in the condition of desire because her desire can more easily be curbed than the male's desire. For desire in a man is like a fire that quickly goes out and quickly flames up again. A fire that would burn for a long time, would destroy many things. In this way, desire flares up in a man now and again, and then dies down again. For if it would burn continually in him, he could not stand it.

Male Cholic. There are some men with special manly strength. They have a powerful, solid brain. Their exterior small blood vessels, which hold the skin together, are rather red colored. The color of their face is also somewhat reddish, as it seems in certain pictures that are painted a red color. They have strong and firm veins that carry hot, wax-colored blood. They are thick-set in the chest, and they have strong arms. They are not very fat because the powerful vessels, the powerful blood, and the strong limbs do not permit their flesh to take on much fat.

The Loins. The wind in their loins is more moist than windy. This wind has two receptacles under it into which it blows as into a pair of bellows. These receptacles contain the trunk of all manly power and support and defend it like small buildings next to a tower. There are two of them so that they may the more strongly surround, establish, and maintain the mentioned trunk and absorb all the more effectively the above mentioned wind, store it, and equally let it go like two bellows which both blow into a fire. If they erect this trunk in its power, they hold it fast, and in this fashion bestow this stem with posterity.

Once Again, Regarding the Expulsion of Adam. When Adam was made blind and deaf at his disobedience, this power was also expelled with him and moved to a foreign site; it flowed secretly into the above-mentioned loins of the man and stayed there. The men about whom we spoke before are clever, they are feared by others, they have a strong attraction to women and are disposed to go out of their way to avoid other men because they prefer women to men. They love the female form in intercourse so much that they cannot master themselves. Their blood is inflamed in even greater passion if they see or hear a woman or remember her in their thoughts. For their eyes are like arrows aimed at the love of women when they see them, their hearing is like a very strong wind when they hear them, and their thoughts are like hurricanes that no one can stop from moving over the earth. They are really manly men, and people call them master builders in their fertility because, in their passion, they are always fruitful and can produce many offspring like a tree that spreads itself out in many branches. For that reason, because of the great fire of their embrace, they are like arrows. When they have relations with women they are healthy and happy; however, when they must forego them, then they dry up in themselves and go about like dying persons. Then it happens that, as a consequence of wayward dreams or thoughts or because of some other perversity, they spray out the foam of their seed. They find themselves is such a glow of passion that sometimes they even turn to inanimate, insensate objects and so roll around with them that — to combat this glow and to relieve this desire and pulsating passion that is in them — finally exhausted, they spray out the foam of their seed. For them, continence is very difficult.

If such men wish to avoid women for some reason — whether it be shame, fear, or the love of God — then they should avoid them like poison and flee before them because the temptation is too great. When they spy women, their feelings of shame and their efforts at self-mastery will hardly be able to restrain them from embracing them. Frequently their offspring have a repellent nature; these offspring are undisciplined in their passion and as different from the usual male behavior as an unshaped block made from a shapeless, charred piece of wood is from a beautiful and handsome shape that arises from a normal piece of wood. For the temptation of the devil is very near by means of intercourse in which excessive seed is wasted. However, if such men love with a passion that is mastered in a good and proper fashion, then their children will be bright, useful, and adroit, and they will appear manly and attractive.

The Sanguine. Other men have a warm brain, lively facial color of mixed white and red, thick veins full of blood, and thick blood of the proper red color. They have a humor within them that makes one happy; it is not suppressed by dark sadness and is undisturbed by the dark nature of melancholy. Because they have a warm brain and the proper blood and because their humor cannot be suppressed, they have fat flesh on their body. Their sexuality, which has its seat in their thighs, has a nature more like wind than like fire. For this reason they can maintain continency, for the very strong wind that is in their thighs keeps the fire within and masters it. When occasionally this wind and fire descend into the two receptacles, they carry out all their tasks properly and with rational love so that the stem also blossoms and performs properly. In a proper embrace, they are called the golden house because reason sees in them where it comes from. Such men develop self-mastery and a manly manner of behavior. For them it is necessary to get properly married, for the female nature is softer and gentler than the male nature. They can live in propriety and fruitfulness with women. They can also renounce them and then look at them with admiring, discrete glances. Where other men's glances are directed at women like arrows, their looks establish an upright, harmonious relationship. Where the words of other men come at women like a powerful wind, their words sound like a harp. And where the thoughts of other men are like a hurricane, these men, by contrast, are esteemed as prudent admirers in good repute. However, they often suffer from many pangs when they attempt to master themselves as far as possible; however, a clever dominance reigns in them, an art over which woman rules, and she may induce a proper continance. Such men also have insight and understanding. Their offspring are disciplined, happy, useful, and successful in all their enterprises and remain free from envy because the wind and the fire in the thighs of their parents endowed them with the proper mixture. Whoever comes from such a union will become a useful person. However, if the above-mentioned men are without women, they are as listless as a day without sunshine. However, just as the fruit can be protected from drying out on a day without sunshine, so can these men maintain a properly balanced outlook without women. However, they are more cheerful when they can interact with women, just as a day is brighter when the sun shines. Because they are more worthy than other men in appearance, in their language, and in their ideas, they emit watery semen more often than other men, not heated sperm. This happens to them when they are awake as well as when they are asleep. They will more easily be released from the heat of their passion by themselves and with the help of other circumstances.

The Melancholic. There are other men whose brain is fat. Their scalp and blood vessels are entangled. They have a pale facial color. Even their eyes have something fiery and snake-like about them. These man have hard, strong veins that conduct dark, thick blood; large, firm flesh; and large bones that contain but little marrow. However, this burns so strongly that their behavior with women is as improper and undisciplined as animals and snakes. The wind in their loins comes out in three forms: fiery, windy, and mixed with the smoke of bile. For that reason they really love no one; rather they are embittered, suspicious, resentful, dissolute in their passion, and as unregulated in their interaction with women as a donkey. If they ever refrain from their desire, they easily become sick in the head so that they become crazy. If they satisfy their desire for women, they suffer no spiritual sickness. However, their cohabitation with women which they should maintain in a proper way, is difficult, contradictory, and as deadly as with vicious wolves. Some of them traffic enthusiastically — in the male way — with women because they have strong blood vessels and marrow that burns mightily in them; however, afterwards they hate these women. Others can avoid the female gender because they do not care for women and do not wish to have them, but in their hearts they are as wild as lions and conduct themselves like bears. In practical matters, however, they are handy and skillful, and they enjoy working. The storm of desire that invades the two receptacles of these men comes as unmastered and suddenly as the wind that shakes the entire house mightily, and it lifts the stem up so powerfully that the stem, that should stand in full blossom, curves in the disgusting manner of a viper and in the evil way that a death and decay-bringing viper passes on its malignity to its offspring. The influence of the devil rages so powerfully in the passion of these men that they would kill the woman with whom they are having sexual relations if they could. For there is nothing of love or affection in them. For this reason the sons or daughters that they beget usually have a devilish craziness in their perversity and in their characters because they were begotten without love. Their offspring are often unhappy, impenetrable, and devious

66

in all their conduct. For that reason, also, they cannot be loved by people, and they themselves are not happy in the company of people because they are plagued by many hallucinations. Moreover, if they stay with people, they become envious, resentful, and bitter, and they have no satisfaction with them. However, once in a while some of their children become clever and useful. However, in spite of this usefulness, their evil and contradictory behavior is so manifest that people still cannot love or respect them. They are like ordinary stones that lie around without any shine, as if randomly scattered. Because of that, they cannot be prized among the brilliant stones, for they have no attractive gleam.

The Phlegmatic. There are also other men who have a fat, white, and dry skull, for even the small blood vessels of their skull are more white than red. They have large goggle-eyes and a womanly facial color. Their skin color is not ruddy but rather as if faded. Their blood vessels are broad and soft but still do not contain much blood. Their blood is not like blood, but somewhat foamy. They have enough flesh on their body; it is soft like woman's flesh. Their limbs are strong.

However, these men have no courage or decisiveness. They are as bold and courageous in their thoughts and in their words as a fire whose flame suddenly incandesces and then just as suddenly falls back. In their talk they show spirit, but not in their deeds. After spending time with them, one notices that it is more a matter of words than of deeds. The wind in their loins only has a weak fire so that, like lukewarm water, it is only a little warm. Their two receptacles, that should be like two bellows to arouse the fire, are retarded in their weakness and have no power to lift up the stem because they have no strong fire in them. Such men can be loved in marriage because they get along with men and women and because they are loyal. They harbor no deadly hate toward their neighbors, rather the proper enjoyment of the first begetting — from which Adam and Eve came forth without carnal embrace — while they renounce this and the other begetting. Because their seed cannot be as it is with other men, they cannot be manly in other ways, either by means of a beard or other such manly signs. Because they have no ill will toward others, they mean well and love women in their natural weakness because they are also weak and because the woman in her weakness is like a boy. Hence these men sometimes warm up a bit and grow a little beard — like the earth that brings forth a little grass. However, they do not have the full power to plow the earth because they cannot interact with women the way fruitful men can, but rather are unfruitful. Hence, in their hearts, they do not suffer very much from envy; only occasionally do their thoughts go in this direction and do they have such wishes. Because they have this bodily lack, they are also slow in thought, and the blood vessels of their sleep do not stand in full power. Rather, they have vessels that are brittle like straw and certain plants. One cannot call them men, for their vessels are cold and their semen is thin and unheated like foam. Also, they cannot restrain it until the right time.

Woman's Desire. One can compare woman's desire with the sun which softens the earth with its warmth and penetrates it slowly and continually so that it brings forth fruit. Were it to burn stronger, fixed down on the earth, it would sooner harm the fruit than bring it to ripeness. So the female's desire has a soft, gentle, but still continual warmth in order to conceive and bear offspring. If the woman were to always remain in the heat of her desire, she would not be capable of conceiving and begetting. When desire climbs in a woman, it is smaller in her than in the man because this fire does not burn so strongly in her as it does in him.

Man's Desire. When the storm of passion breaks out in a man, it whirs about in him like a mill wheel. For his loins may be compared with a forge into which the marrow dispatches its fire. This forge drives this fire forward further into the male sex organs and causes it to burn strongly. However, when the wind of desire comes out from the marrow of the woman, it enters her womb which is fastened at the navel and arouses the woman's blood to desire. Since the womb possesses a large and so to speak accessible room in the region of the woman's navel, this wind spreads out in her stomach. For this reason and also because of the moisture, the fire of desire burns there with less strength. For that reason, the woman can control her desire — either from fear or from shame — easier than the man can, so that the foam of the semen is also expelled less often from the woman than from the man, and, compared with the male seed, is as small an amount as a piece of bread compared with a whole loaf. However, it often happens that the foam of the woman is not expelled at all after the satisfaction of her desire because it mixes itself with the contents of the vessel in the womb, which is white and thick, to eventually flow out with the monthly flow of blood. What remains behind will be expelled from the womb, sometimes also divided,

68

rubbed away, and released, as in the case of relaxation of desire without contact with a man. The fertile nature of the woman is colder and bloodier than the nature of the man, and their powers are weaker than the powers of a man. For that reason, the woman does not burn with desire as much as the man does because the woman is only a vessel in which to conceive and bear offspring. For that reason, also, the wind in her is airy; her vessels open, and her limbs relax more easily than a man's do. If fertile men renounce women, they easily become sick, but not as much as women, for they pour out more seed than women do. However, infertile women are healthy if they deny themselves men; moreover, when they have men, they become sick. Just as a flood sometimes develops as a consequence of rain and storms and then rests — similarly, the fermentation in new wine now foams up and then sinks back down again — so also evil humors sometimes expand in a person and then contract again. If they were always in a high condition in their evil effects, the person could not endure it, but rather would perish in a short time. For the blood of such men thickens and thins as the moon waxes and wanes.

The Changes of the Moon and the Humors. As the moon increases and becomes full, then the blood in men also increases, and as the moon wanes, similarly, the blood in men declines. So it is always, as much with women as with men. In fact, if a man's blood increased to the full condition and if it would not then decline in the person, he would burst apart.

The Time for Begetting. Since the blood increases in this fashion in people during a waxing moon, then the person — that is the woman as well as the man — is fertile, that is capable of begetting offspring. When the blood of a person increases during a waxing moon, the man's semen is strong and powerful. When the moon wanes, the person's blood also decreases; the man's semen is weak and without power like dregs and therefore is less suited for engendering offspring. If a wife conceives during this time, the child will be sick, weak, and not powerful whether it is a boy or a girl. Thus the woman's blood, just as much as the man's, increases during the waxing moon; and as the moon wanes, the woman's blood decreases just as the man's until the fiftieth year.

The Monthly Blood Flow. When a person's blood decreases as the moon wanes, her monthly blood flow also decreases the blood in a woman. If the monthly menses begin during the waxing moon, she then suffers more during this time than she would if it started during a waning moon; for her blood increases during the waxing moon, which then will be reduced by the monthly menses. After the fiftieth year of life, a person's blood is not as strong and quickly altered by the influence of the moon's changes as was the case before. However, until the eightieth year, the blood causes human flesh to increase somewhat more than was usual before because by now the blood in a person stops increasing and decreasing. After the eightieth year both the flesh and the blood decrease in a person, the skin draws together and wrinkles develop, whereas during youth, the skin was smooth and taut because it was filled with flesh and blood. Because both the flesh and blood decrease after the eightieth year, the person himself becomes weak. For that reason he must be strengthened by food and drink like a child who also has such needs. What he now lacks in blood and flesh is made up for by food and drink. With women, the monthly menses cease around the fiftieth year. An exception are those women who are so strong and healthy that their menses continue until the seventieth year. Because their blood no longer flows as before, their flesh increases until the seventieth year because it is no longer decreased by the monthly flow. However, after the seventieth year, both their flesh and blood also decrease, their skin draws together, wrinkles develop, and they become brittle. Hence they must frequently be strengthened with food and drink like a child because they are losing flesh and blood and are weaker than men while the suffering of old age with men lasts until the eightieth year. The blood of dumb animals also increases with the waxing moon and decreases with the waning moon although to a lesser degree than with human beings. An exception is animals that come to exist out of the sweat and moisture of the earth and are nourished by it. They arise sooner from poison and decay than from blood with the exception of fish, which live in water and come forth from water and have only a little blood. It is the same with trees that become green from their roots up and put out foliage; their sap also increases as the moon waxes and decreases as the moon wanes. Thus, because of the sap and moisture that remain in them, they are sooner eaten up by termites and wood worms when they are felled during a waxing moon than they would be if they were felled during a declining moon. If they had been felled during a waning moon, they would be harder, for the sap would have flowed out of them. Consequently, the termites make less progress with them, and the wood worms inflict less damage.

Pruning Trees. With regard to their resistance, planting and pruning trees succeeds better during a waning than during a waxing moon. For when planting or pruning is done during a waxing moon, they are often bothered by rising and excessive sap, do not put down such good roots, and as a consequence do not grow as well as when this is done during a waning moon. For when it is done by a waning moon, there is a larger and stronger power hidden within the tree and the sap is somewhat reduced. For that reason, they put down better roots and have a greater resistance capacity than when there is an excess of sap, for then the sap drips out from the cut places during the waxing moon.

Pruning Grapevines. When grapevines must be pruned as part of their cultivation, the effect and fertility is better if they are pruned during a waning rather than during a waxing moon. For the more the moon is increasing when they are being cut, the more sap drips out as a result. In this way, the grapevine dries out a bit, compared with what it would have been had the vines been cut during a waning moon; then, the power stays within and the cuts grow over and heal before the moon begins to grow again.

Gathering Healing Plants. When noble, good plants are either cut or pulled up from the earth by their roots while the moon is waxing and they are full of sap, they are more powerful for the preparation of electuaries, salves and other medicines than when they are collected during a waning moon.

The Fruit Harvest. Moreover, because they are full of sap and blood, vegetables and fruits that are harvested during a waxing moon and meat from animals slaughtered during this period, have more nourishment than if they are harvested or slaughtered during a waning moon. There is an exception when one should wait longer. During the contraction of the waning moon, things to be harvested also contract. It is better and more advantageous to harvest these vegetables and fruits and to a slaughter the animals when the moon is declining, for then they can be kept longer.

The Grain Harvest. Grain, too, when it is cut and harvested during a waxing moon, produces more meal than if it is cut during a waning moon because during a waxing moon it possesses its full abundance. During a waning moon, on the contrary, this abundance has shrunk somewhat. However, the grain that is ground during a waning moon can preserve its power longer than that which is ground during an increasing moon. Grain that is cut down during a waxing moon but is sown in the earth, puts down roots sooner, grows faster, sets its grain, and brings in more straw faster, although with less yield, than if it is cut down during a waning moon.

The Time for Sowing. When what has been harvested during a waning moon is used for sowing, it germinates and grows more slowly and produces a smaller stalk, but delivers a greater yield in seed, than if it had been cut during a waxing moon. Whatever seed enters the earth during a waxing moon germinates and grows faster and produces a greater stalk than if it had been sown during a waning moon because it grows by the growing moon. If it had been sown during a waning moon, it would only come up gradually until the point when it became fully empowered and would grow further.

Adam's Sleep. Before Adam disobeyed God's command, sleep was infused in him and food was not necessary. However, after his disobedience, his flesh became as weak and frail as the decaying flesh of a dead person compared with the flesh of a living man. After this, he was enlivened by sleep as much as he was strengthened by food. And so it has been for all people since that time. For just as man's flesh grows because he eats, so his marrow grows while he is asleep.

Sleep. When a man sleeps, his marrow recovers itself and grows and when he is awake, his marrow becomes a bit thin and weakened, just as the moon grows while it is waxing and decreases when it is waning and as the roots of plants retain their growing power within themselves in winter which they unfold in the form of flowers in summer. For that reason if a man — whose marrow is exhausted by work or who has grown weak from being awake too long — is overcome by sleep, he then easily falls asleep whether he is standing, sitting, or lying down because his soul senses within him this bodily need. For when the marrow is thinned and weakened by remaining awake, then the powers of the soul draw a very pleasant and sweet breath out of the marrow that penetrates the vessels of the throat and the entire neck, goes into the temples, fills the cavities of the head, and in this way releases the life breath of men. Then it goes thus with the person: he lies there as if he were unconscious, does not know what is going on, and has no power over his body. Neither is he aware of his thoughts or feelings. Only the soul causes the life breath to flow in and out, just as it does with a person who is wide awake, because it maintains him both while he is asleep and when he is awake and because it is in him both when he is asleep and while he is awake. This is the way the person falls asleep. Later when the soul of the person has gathered its powers within itself, it causes its marrow to grow and be strengthened. In this manner it strengthens the bones, cares for the maintenance of the blood, heats up the flesh, unifies the separate members, and broadens the wisdom and knowledge in a person while he lives unconscious in sleep. Thus the soul also possesses a greater inner warmth when the person is asleep than when he is awake. For when the person is awake, his marrow becomes thin, viscous, and dark; for that reason also he falls asleep. When he sleeps, however, his marrow burns because then it grows and becomes fat and clear.

Nocturnal Emissions. In this burning heat, the marrow often arouses the blood to desire as a consequence of its excess, guides the foam of semen emissions — without the man being aware of it — into his sexual organs, and then causes it to stream out. Once in a while, also, the marrow becomes heated as a consequence of excessive indulgence in food or drink since unregulated amounts of food and drink increase the fire in the marrow and its humor disturbs the marrow and the blood into some arousal. Thus the self-heating marrow releases carnal desire into the blood and leads the foam of the seminal emission into his sexual organs without the man being aware of it. It is rare that this happens due to the summer's heat or the warmth of the man's clothing. However, since the body is then resting and doing nothing, the soul, which during waking hours is busy with many things, draws forth in dreams the knowledge of how the body works. It is as if dreams were its eyes, and it looks around itself because it is no longer restrained by the various activities of the body.

Adam's Prophetic Powers. When God caused sleep to come over Adam, his soul then saw many things in an authentic prophetic vision because it did not yet have any sins. In the same way, in sleep, a person's soul could see many things in a true prophetic vision if man were not burdened with sin.

Dreams. Because the human soul comes from God, it occasionally sees true things coming in the future while the body sleeps. The soul then knows what is coming and also occasionally what happens in that way. It also often happens that the soul, either exhausted by the devil's deception or burdened with a spiritual disturbance, cannot see clearly and becomes deceived. For very often a man is bothered in his dreams by the thoughts, impressions, and desires with which he is concerned when awake and sometimes becomes puffed up like leaven that raises a loaf of dough. In that case, it is indifferent whether the thoughts are good or bad. When men are good and holy, God's grace often shows them the truth in their dreams. However, if men are evil, the devil sees it and then often terrifies their soul and mixes lies amidst the evil men's thoughts. Thus he shows even holy men their shameful things, mocking them. Thus if a man — who is dealing with very great joy or sadness, anger or fear, domination or other such things — falls asleep, very often the devil feeds these concerns to the man in his dreams with his own deceptions mixed in, for he observed this concern in him as he was awake. However, when on occasion a man falls asleep with carnal desire, occasionally the devilish deception is presented before his eyes. It shows him the bodies of living men and sometimes also the bodies of dead people with whom he once had business or possibly whom he has never seen in his life, so that he gets the impression that he is having sinful sexual relations with them just as if he were awake or as if these dead were alive. Hence the shamefulness encounters its seed. Because the devil exercises his skill at temptation with an awake person, he also applies temptations in his dreams. Because the soul is tightly bound with the body, the body is often influenced by it while asleep — even if against its will — and also when awake, and releases various impulses in it. Just as the air in water turns the mill wheel around and causes it to grind meal, so also the soul drives the body of a waking or a sleeping person to various activities.

How the Soul Operates. As the sun is the light of the day, so the soul is the light of the awakened body. As the moon is the light of the night, so is the soul the light of the sleeping body. That is, if the body of the sleeping person has the right temperature so that his marrow warms him properly and he himself does not feel the storm of passion and the customary objection in himself, very often he sees the truth because then the knowledge in his soul is in repose. It is like the moon beaming out its light full and sharp when the night is free from the distortion of clouds and wind. However, if a storm of various contradictory thoughts takes over the body and spirit of

74

a person so that he falls into sleep during this storm, then what he sees while asleep is very often false because the knowledge of his soul is so obscured by such consternation that he cannot see the truth. In the same way, the moon cannot shine clearly during stormy weather. Since the soul is fire, it draws the breath of the sleeping person peacefully in and out so that the body will not be disturbed. In the same way, the potter pays close attention to his vessel when he puts it into the fire so that the fire does not become too hot or too cold. For if it should become too hot, the vessel would become brittle and completely break apart.

Breath. If a person did not have his breath moving in and out, his body would also not move, and his blood would not be liquid and flow, just as water does not flow without a breeze.

The Opposition Between Soul and Body. The soul is a breath that strives after good; the body, however, inclines toward sin. Only occasionally and with great effort can the soul keep the body from sin, just as the sun cannot prevent little insects from crawling onto those places on the earth that it has heated with its brilliance and warmth. However, the soul is also a breath for the body as the bellows are for fire. For if split logs and glowing coals are laid on it, the bellows ignite the fire. So the soul, which is tightly bound with the body, leads the bones, the nerves, and the flesh to all kinds of actvities and cannot refrain from them, as long as it is in the body. For it is as tightly bound with the marrow, the bones, the flesh, and all the members, as a person who is so tightly pinned to a tree trunk that he cannot tear himself loose. Yet just as water occasionally puts out a fire so that it doesn't burn too fiercely, so also the soul, aided by the grace of God and exhorted by reason, occasionally suppresses sinful habits lest they become too strong and acquire the upper hand. After the marrow of the sleeping person has increased and refreshed itself, and after the soul has put the entire organism of the sleeping body in order, it calls back the sweet wind that it had sent out from the marrow for the recuperation of the person, and so reawakens him.

However, if over a period of time he is often awake and as frequently falls asleep again, then the marrow does not retrieve its full powers, nor are his members able to fully refresh themselves. But if a person wakes up often and then falls asleep rather quickly, his marrow and his members will be refreshed in a pleasant and soft way.

In the same way, a child who often sucks and then often stops sucking again, quickly recuperates his powers over time.

Disturbance of the Soul. It sometimes happens that people sleeping on their side or on another body part become uncomfortable and pained or bothered by a bodily hurt. Because the person is sensitive, the soul — which feels and sees these hurts and oppositions from which the body suffers — gathers its powers and wakes the person from sleep immediately. If a sudden noise or sound or loud voice is heard in the area around a sleeping person so that the air echoes from it, the exterior air strikes the air that is present inside him. For the elements are also present within a person. If his soul feels this movement of air, it gathers its powers again and makes the person wake up. Thus, it often happens that a person wakes up because of a sudden noise or a disturbance or some other sudden and harsh event. As a consequence, his vessels and blood are disturbed in an unpleasant way so that he often suffers bodily aches or falls into a strong or three-day fever because his soul was inflamed through the unanticipated disturbance. However, if a man finally wakes up in the right way, he often shows himself to be refreshed and of a more cheerful disposition because now all of his members are rearranged in peace.

Too Much Sleep. When people sleep too much, they easily suffer attacks of various evil fevers and emerge with an infection in the eyes because during sleep their eyes were closed for too long a time. Similarly, when some one looks at the sun for too long a time, he acquires a disturbance in the eyes. However, if people sleep for the proper length of time, they will remain healthy. People who remain awake too long, however, will become weak in their body and, as a consequence, forfeit many of their powers and also lose a lot of their sensitivity; the flesh around their eyes will hurt, become red, and will swell up. Still, such a person does not damage the focus of his vision — the pupils — nor the strength of his vision very much. The person on the other hand who remains awake a reasonable period of time will remain healthy of body. However, it sometimes happens that people are awake and cannot sleep when their spirit is stirred up by various thoughts and problems or situations, or when they are caught up in great joy. For a person's blood becomes stirred up by the condition of grief, fear, anxiety, anger, or various other concerns; and the blood vessels that are supposed to carry up the sweet breath of sleep contract so that they cannot lift it. If, in such a situation, someone has seen or heard something or if something has happened to him over which he rejoices excessively, his blood vessels react to the joy and cannot contain the sweet breath of sleep. For this reason, he does not have the correct equilibrium in himself and so remains constantly awake until, satisfied in his thoughts with his situation, he finds peace again. If his blood vessels return to their proper condition, the person falls asleep. However, if a person is suffering from a severe disease, his blood and his humors move in contradiction to each other, so to speak, and produce in him, for example, strong disturbances so that as a consequence of these oppositions he can find no peace, but rather remains wide awake and sleepless to the damage of his health and against his will. When we are asleep, we see differently from when we are awake. Hence, we cannot see clearly immediately if we are awakened, for we are still drunk with sleep. And if we are in the dark, we cannot immediately use the same powers of sight that we had in the light of day. In a similar way, those who are in the full light of day cannot suddenly accustom their eyes to the changed conditions of darkness, but only after a while. To make a comparison, a person may give vent to words exteriorly, all the while keeping his inner thoughts hidden.

Bodily Exercise. If a person who is healthy is active for a long time or stands upright for a long time, he is not greatly damaged by the fact that he moves his body; this is only under the condition that he does not move or stand too long. However, anyone who is weak should sit, for if he worked or stood too much, he would be hurt by it. However, because the woman is weaker than the man and has a differently formed skull, she should only move about and stand in moderation, and sit more than run, lest she suffer damage therefrom. On the other hand, some one who rides a horse rarely experiences damage from it, even if he becomes tired doing so, because he is out in the fresh air. However, he should now and then pay attention to his feet and thighs and constantly exercise them by movement and stretching.

The Sanguine. Many women have a predisposition to become fat; they have soft, sumptuous flesh, soft blood vessels, and healthy blood without decay. Since their blood vessels are delicate, they have less blood in them, and their flesh grows all the more and is all the more penetrated with blood. They have a bright, white facial color; love tendernesses; are kind, exact in artistic work, and naturally in control of themselves. At the time of the monthly menses, they suffer only a small loss of blood, and their womb is powerfully developed for childbearing. Hence they are fertile and can receive the male seed. On the other hand, they do not bring that many children into the world, and if they live without a mate and hence bear no children, they easily become sick in the body. However, when they have a spouse, they are healthy. If, at the time of the monthly menses, drops of blood are perceived before the natural time and the menses do not flow, they then sometimes become melancholy or experience pains in their side; have a worm that grows in their flesh, have swollen lymph glands called scrofula; or develop a small scab.

Phlegmatic women. There are other women whose flesh does not grow so much because they have thick blood vessels and a fairly healthy, bright blood which still, however, contains a little poison whence it gets its bright color. Their facial expression is serious, their skin color is darker; they are energetic, hard-working, and somewhat masculine in appearance. During their monthly menses, the blood stream flows neither too strong nor too weak, but moderately. Because they have thick blood vessels, they are very fruitful in producing posterity and easily conceive because their womb and all of their intestines are powerfully developed. Men attract them, and for that reason men love them. For themselves, if they wish to abstain from men, they can do without union with them, and they will not thereby be very — but still a little — the worse for wear. On the other hand, if they totally avoid any union with men, they become high-strung in nature and difficult for others to bear. However, if they are together with men and do not wish to give up union with them, they become undisciplined and excessive in their passion like men. Because they are somewhat masculine, sometimes due to their inner life powers, they develop light hair on the chin. If their monthly flow of blood is interrupted, then once in a while they get a headache or a kind of craziness. They become irritable or thirsty; rampant flesh, that always appears with sores, grows in them; or boils and sores develop on one of their limbs, like a tumor or growth on a tree or a fruit.

The Choleric. Other women have delicate flesh but thick bones, moderately long blood vessels, and thick, red blood. Their facial color is pale. They are clever and charitable, men respect them, and people fear them. During the monthly menses, they experience a considerable loss of blood. Their womb is strongly developed, and they are fertile. Men love their character but still somewhat avoid them because they attract men but do not bind themselves to them. However, if they are properly bound with a man, they are modest and remain his true wife, and they remain healthy in body with their husband. If they do not have a husband, they suffer in body and on that account become sick, both because they do not know to which man they can dedicate their womanly devotion and, equally, because they do not have a husband. If their monthly menses stops earlier than is right, they easily become paralyzed and collapse in their humors so that they become sick because of these humors; they have an attack in their liver such that they become afflicted with large black boils; or their breasts swell with cancers.

The Melancholic. Other women have thin flesh, thick blood vessels, moderately strong bones, and blood that is more viscous than bloody. Their complexion is as though mixed with a dark grey color. These women are heedless and dissolute in their thoughts and of evil disposition if they are grieved by any irritation. Since they are unstable and irresponsible, on occasion they also suffer from melancholy. During the monthly menses they lose much blood, and they are infertile because they have a weak, fragile womb. For that reason, they can neither receive, retain, nor warm the male seed. For that reason they are more healthy, more powerful, and happier without a mate than with one because they become sick from relations with a husband. However, men avoid them because they do not speak in a friendly manner to men and because men love them only a little. If ever they feel a desire of the flesh, it goes away again quickly. Some of them still bring at least one child into the world if they have a powerful, full-blooded husband, even when they have attained a mature age, for example, fifty years old. If, however, their husbands are of a weaker nature, they do not conceive by them but remain unfruitful. If their monthly menses ever stops earlier than corresponds to the womanly nature, they get arthritis, swollen legs, or headaches that cause melancholy. They may have back or kidney pains, or their body may swell up a short time because the contradictory impurity, that should be expelled from their body through the monthly menses, remains closed up within. If they receive no help and are not freed from their sufferings by God's help or through a medicine, they will soon die.

Baldness. A man with large bald spots has much warmth in him. This warmth and perspiration cause his hair to fall out. The moisture of the breath of such a man is fertile and makes the flesh where the beard grows, moist, so that much hair grows there. However, a man who has little hair in his beard but much on his skull is cold and rather infertile, and if his breath disturbs the flesh around his mouth, it makes it infertile. However, if a man loses his hair, no medicine can bring it back because the moisture and the life power that he had in his scalp, that is, in his skull, is already dried out and no new growth can develop from it. For that reason, no new hair appears there. For that reason, it often happens that those who develop large bald spots also develop a larger beard, and those who have a thin and sparse beard have more hair on top.

Headaches. Sometimes strong, daily, three-day and four-day fevers — but also other fever attacks — affect the bile. When these things occur, they send a watery power to a person's head and brain and cause a strong, persistent headache.

Migraine. The migraine also comes from the bile and from all the bad humors that are in people. It attacks only one half of the human brain at a time, not the entire head, so that sometimes it afflicts the right side of the head, at other times the left. Specifically, when the humors are present in excess, the migraine attacks the right side; but when the bile has increased excessively, the left. The migraine is so strong that a person could not stand it if it attacked the entire head at the same time. It is difficult to get rid of it entirely because whatever medicine suppresses the bile also stimulates the bad humors, and what calms the bad humors causes the bile to increase. Thus its treatment is made more difficult, for it is difficult to calm the bile and the bad humors at the same time.

Headache Again. Any meal that contains juice — as for example the juice from vegetables and the sap from fruit — sometimes, if it is eaten frequently without dry bread, causes a headache in people that, however, goes away quickly for it only arises because of a weak humor. Moreover, often there is too much phlegm in people, in which case it begins to rise, concentrates in the head, weakens the blood vessels of the temple and those which strengthen the brow, and thus causes pains in the forehead.

Dizziness. If a person — without the proper instruction from his employer concerning the work to be done and not driven by his own will to be busy — constantly distracts his humor from its correct path with a great many different kinds of thoughts, it will quickly become too hurried and then again slow and without proper order. Because of this, such a person's head easily becomes dizzy so that his intellect and sensibility contract.

Madness. If the above-mentioned afflictions come together and break out in a person's head all at the same time, they bring the individual to the edge of madness; they derange the person and take away his proper understanding. A boat that is being tossed about by stormy weather breaks up in the same way. For this reason, many people believe that such a person is possessed by a demon; but that is not the case.

The demons hurry to this painful affliction and mount an attack because madness is one of their tasks. Yet they cannot decide upon his words because such a person is not possessed by a demon. For when a demon is allowed by God to control or dictate a person's words, then in place of the Holy Spirit, this demon exercises his power with words and attacks of anger until God drives him out, just as he also drove him out of heaven.

The Brain. The brain is influenced by both the good and the bad humors in a person. For that reason it is both soft and wet. If it ever dries out, it quickly becomes sick because it is naturally moist and fat. It is also the basis for science, wisdom, and human understanding. The brain receives and transmits impulses; it protects and harnesses them, however, through the power of thinking. Moreover, if the thoughts have their location in the heart, they are either sweet or bitter. The sweet ones make the brain fat, and the bitter ones make it empty. The brain has paths like the openings of a chimney by which the smoke is drawn away. These paths are located in the eyes, ears, mouth, and nose, and make themselves known. If the thoughts are sweet and pleasant, then the eyes, ears, and speech of the person betray joy. However, if they are bitter and unpleasant, the eyes show tears, and man can detect anger and grief in the hearing and in the speech. Human eyes are made similar to the firmament.

The Eyes. The eyes' pupils have a similarity with the sun. The black or grey color in the pupil has a similarity with the moon and the white, further outside, a similarity with the clouds. The eye consists of fire and water. By means of fire it is held together and strengthened so that it can endure. However, the water provides its power for seeing. If there is too much blood in the eye, it blocks the seeing power of the eye because it dries out the water that provides the seeing capacity of the eye. If on the other hand the blood is diminished too much, then the water that should make seeing possible no longer has enough force because it shrinks when it ought to support the power in the blood like a pillar. For that reason old people's eyes are short-sighted, for their water is already decreasing and becoming less in their blood. Young people see better than the old do, for their blood vessels still have the correct proportion of blood and water. Fire and water have not yet dried out or reduced the hot and the cold too much.

Grey Eyes. A person with grey eyes similar to water bases himself primarily on the air. For that reason grey eyes are weaker than other eyes because the air frequently changes through differences in warmth, cold, and moisture. Such eyes are also easily injured by unhealthy, moist air and fog. Just as these conditions damage the purity of the air, so also they injure eyes that come from the air.

Fiery Eyes. Anyone who has fiery eyes, which are similar to a black cloud next to the sun, has received them according to the order of nature from the warm south wind. They are healthy, for they originate from the heat of fire. Dust and every other evil odor damages them because the clearness does not pay heed to the dust, nor does the purity give heed to an unknown smell.

Eyes of Various Colors. Whoever has eyes that are like a cloud through which the rainbow shines has gotten them from the air with its various beams which are neither equally dry nor moist. They are weak, for they arise from the unstable air. In warmer air, they have a bad power for seeing because they do not come from fire. However, in cleaner rainy air they see sharply because they come more from moisture than from fire. All beaming light, whether it comes from the sun, the moon, the stars, gemstones, metals, or similar things, is dangerous to them because they arise from the air with its own various beams.

Cloudy Eyes. Whoever has eyes that are like a dark cloud — neither entirely fiery nor entirely dark but rather somewhat grey-blue — has received them from the dirty-colored moist earth that brings forth the various poisonous plants and earthworms. These eyes are

82

soft and cause reddish cell tissue to appear because it comes from dirty slime. They are not hurt either by moist air or dust, nor by bad smells or the brilliant light streaming from an object, from which — as was mentioned above — the vision of other eyes suffers.

On the other hand, they are sometimes damaged by certain other diseases. For just as nothing prevents poisonous plants and worms coming forth from the dirty, moist earth, so the vision of these eyes is not damaged by the aforementioned injurious elements.

Black Eyes. Whoever has black or dark eyes, as a cloud sometimes looks, has them primarily due to the earth. They are stronger and sharper than other eyes and retain their vision a long time because they come from the earth. However, they are easily damaged by the moisture of the earth and the moisture of water and swamps. In the same way, the earth itself is poisoned by injurious moisture and the moisture of water and swamps.

The White Skin of the Eyes [Cataracts]. If the human brain somehow becomes too fat, this fat sends an injurious juice and sweat to the eyes. If this juice and sweat attack and infect the eyes often, they then acquire a white skin. If this skin is not quickly taken off while it is still fresh, it becomes so thick that later it cannot be removed because it is as thick as a gallbladder. White skin develops on human eyes in this way. This white skin also develops as a consequence of cold humors and bile.

Tears in the Eyes. If too much water collects in the eyes because of an excess of bad humors, this water suffocates the fire in the eyes and absorbs it. Then the eyes become moist, as if they cried tears, and they begin to lose their power of vision.

Hearing. If people become sick to their stomach, sometimes phlegm spreads from there up to their head, attacks their ears also, and impairs their hearing. The phlegm quickly increases and decreases, and it can be easily handled and taken care of. Noxious humors also cause a vapor in people and send it into the head and to the brain. Then this vapor even draws itself into the ears, causes the person to become deaf, stays there a long time, and is difficult to cure.

Toothache. Certain extremely fine vessels surround the casing — that is, the membrane that houses the brain — and spread down to the gums and even to the teeth. If these vessels become filled with excessive and foul blood, and if they become damaged when the brain is purified of foam, they carry the foulness — together with the pain — from the brain to the gums and directly to the teeth. Thereby, the cheeks and the flesh that surrounds the teeth swell, and thus such persons have pains in their gums. If, moreover, a person does not frequently clean his teeth by rinsing them out with water, a slimy surface sometimes builds up on the flesh that surrounds the teeth and grows, and because of it, this flesh becomes sick. In this way also, worms sometimes develop in the teeth out of the slimy layer that has established itself around the teeth. Thereby the gums swell up, and the person experiences pain.

Red Face. If a person lies in bed sick and develops a red face, his sick intestines are making his blood sick and toxic, and as a result, he is red in the face. For a dangerous humor emerges out of his vessels that enters into and penetrates his flesh so that at weak points it bubbles and swells up as if he had been drilled through with tiny little holes. Such a person is not sad but rather cheerful, and he is bearable in his illness.

Pale Face. If a person is pale and thin because of his illness, the bile has joined with a paralysis so that as a result he becomes cold. Because of this coldness, his face becomes pale, and his flesh does not grow or develop. Such a person is depressed during his illness and easily inclines to anger.

The Stomach. The stomach gives moisture to the intestine, and the bladder distributes a thin fluid to them. From this, the intestines churn food this way and that, continually. Thereby, they become fat and contain various slimy humors.

The Swelling of the Spleen. If the stomach should become upset because of various spicy foods and if the bladder is attacked through various powerful drinks, the foods and drinks pour noxious humors into the intestines; in this way they send a toxic vapor into the spleen.

Heartache. Thereby the spleen becomes inflamed, swells up, and is sensitive. This painful swelling also supplies pains to the heart and builds up a slime in its area. The heart is still strong and can withstand this pain. However, if the above-mentioned humors in the intestines and the spleen gain the upper hand and have provided the heart many pains, they return to the bile and mix themselves with it. Thereby aroused, the bile rises up unwillingly with these humors, climbs with a noxious black vapor to the heart, and tires it through many sudden attacks. Thereafter, the afflicted persons, having become depressed and bitter, take little food and drink so that they waste away and sometimes can barely stand up. They also have to evacuate themselves frequently.

The Seat of the Soul. If a man builds himself a house, he constructs a door, windows, and a chimney so that he can enter and leave through the door in order to be able to receive everything necessary; get light through the windows; and also draw out the smoke through the chimney if a fire is lit. For the house should not be filled with smoke. In the same way, the soul lives in the heart as in a house; causes thoughts to enter and leave as through a door; views them as through a window; and guides their force to the brain as smoke is drawn from a lit fire to a chimney, there to test and judge them. If, on the other hand, people had no thoughts, they would also have no knowledge but would be like houses that have neither doors nor windows nor chimneys. However, thoughts are the foundation of the knowledge of good and evil, and they arrange all things. Man calls that "thinking." Thoughts ground goodness, wisdom, stupidity, and other such things. Evil thoughts also come forth from the heart, and that is the door. For that reason, a way leads from the heart to the elements with which a person does what he is thinking about. The powers of thought climb to the brain, and the brain holds them fast because the brain provides the moisture for the entire body, just as the dew covers everything. However, if evil, noxious humors develop in a person, they send a kind of noxious vapor to the brain.

Pains in the Lungs. The brain, thus aroused, guides this vapor — through certain vessels — into the lungs and infects them so that they become somewhat inflamed and can draw breath only with some difficulty, accompanied by an unpleasant sound. However, this inflamation of the lungs is not very dangerous, for it can be easily cured.

Asthma. However, there are other people whose heads are so healthy and powerful that these evil humors cannot damage their

85

brains because they cannot penetrate them. Because these humors cannot rise as far as the brain, they remain stuck in the windpipe and make people sick so that such persons can breathe only with difficulty. For if these humors remain stuck in the throat of such people, they infect their lungs with foul, sick things and cause the throat to be painful. In this way, the eyes of such a person become affected by the pain of streaming pus and boils. Thence, the lungs climb up to the throat and block the windpipe so that the affected person can scarcely breathe.

Coughing. Since decaying things are deposited in the area of the lungs, such a person coughs out much runny phlegm. Otherwise he would die soon, for this disease is sometimes dangerous.

Foul Breath during Foggy Weather. There are other people who are indisposed during foggy, moist weather. For that reason, they continually have a smelly, malodorous breath and offensive body odor. Their foul-smelling breath and the offensive humors in them reach up to their brain and afflict them with such pains that they very often, so to speak, forget themselves. If they throw out the slime from their head, they suffer less because their brain is cleaned thereby.

Conception During a Full Moon. Some persons, who were conceived during a full moon when the air was moderately warm — which thus is neither too warm nor too cold — are healthy and have a good appetite so that they enjoy all foods without distinction. However, even though they enjoy all foods without distinction, they ought still to avoid certain toxic foods. Just so, a hunter brings down the tasty wild beast yet lets the useless ones run free.

Digestive Problems with the Liver. If such persons enjoy various dishes without moderation and without discrimination, then their livers will be damaged and hardened as a consequence of the different humors from these foods so that the healing humor, which the liver must send like a salve to all their members, joints, and intestines, is ruined as a result of these various toxic humors. Thereafter, swellings, which later burst open, appear at some point on their flesh. One of their limbs can also be so damaged that later they limp on it. However, in spite of such afflictions such people can live a long time.

The Connection between Conception and Liver Failure. Some persons who were conceived as the moon was waning and the wind was changeable are always sad and subject to sudden changes of mood. As a consequence of their sadness, their livers are weakened and drilled through with many tiny holes, like a cheese that has many small holes. For that reason, such people do not eat much and are not eager either to eat or drink, but rather eat and drink only a little. Because they eat so little, their livers gradually become porous like a sponge and finally give out altogether.

The Liver as a Vessel. The human liver is like a vessel into which the heart, lungs, and stomach pour their humors. The liver causes these humors to flow back again into all the limbs, just as if a vessel is placed at a spring and the water that it takes from the spring it pours out at other sites. However, if, as was just mentioned, the liver is eaten through and porous, it is no longer in a condition to receive the good humors from the heart, lungs, and stomach.

And so these humors and juices, if they flow back to the heart, lungs, and stomach, bring about a kind of flooding. If his ailment gets worse, the person cannot live long.

Conception, If the Sun Stands Under the Sign of Cancer. Other people will conceive if the sun stands under the sign of Cancer, if it has already reached its highest position, and the air temperature stands in the right proportion. These people have a healthy liver.

Heartache. Because they have a healthy liver, they occasionally feel chest pain. For the noxious humors that flee from the liver are seeking to reach the spleen and the heart to take possession of these organs since they could not overcome the liver. If people eat unripe apples or vegetables or other unripe foods that have not been cooked over a fire or prepared with any seasoning, their stomachs cannot properly digest them because the foods were not properly prepared.

Pains in the Spleen. In this way, the noxious humors from foods that should have been prepared, scared off by being placed on the fire or fixed with seasoning such as salt or vinegar, climb up to the spleen and transform it into a painful tumor. Because it is moist and should be kept moist by juices, the spleen accepts both the dangerous and the good humors. Thus, should the mentioned noxious humors appear, they climb to the spleen and make it inflamed and sensitive.

The Stomach and Indigestion. The stomach was put into the human body to receive all the foods and to digest them. It is tough and somewhat pleated so that it can contain the foods to digest them and they will not be digested too fast. In the same way, the mason works his stones so that they accept and retain the mortar lest one of the stones slip off and fall to the ground. If, however, on some occasion many people eat too many foods including ones that are raw, uncooked, underdone and in immoderate amounts as well as excessively fat and heavy or dry and juiceless foods, then occasionally the heart, liver, lungs, and other sources of heat in a person give the stomach too small and weak a fire to fully digest these foods. Hence, they curdle and coagulate in the stomach and become hard and slimy. Occasionally, they cause the stomach to become somewhat green, blue, grey, or to contain much slime, which in German is called ''slim.'' Sometimes noxious humors and disgusting smells spread out like a decaying dunghill over the whole body, and a noxious smoke develops everywhere in the body like damp green wood that has been set on fire. The fact that certain foods harden in the stomach comes from the various ailments. For if there is too much improper heat in people, they burn the consumed foods through and through. However, if there is too much improper cold in them, the foods which they have consumed cannot be digested; rather, they stiffen and congeal as a consequence of the cold in the person. Thus they remain in the person, who therefore suffers pains.

Expansion or Tear in the Peritoneum. Some people have soft flesh on their bodies, whether they are fat or thin. The inner membrane that holds their bowels together is fat and weak so that it easily tears as a result of certain illnesses, strenuous effort, a fall, or the expansion of the stomach filled with food. However, because of their womb, this membrane is thicker and tougher in women than in men. Hence this membrane tears more easily and more often in men than in women.

The Kidneys — Why There are Two. The kidneys assure heat, store up human body warmth, and hold the human abdomen together like armed soldiers who are defending their lord. Therefore there are two of them so that they can maintain the fire in a strong and deliberate way. They do this in women as well as in men, for not only are they located near the male loins but they are also connected to the female womb. They are encased in fat so as not to become cold or damaged by something spoiled, but rather to maintain their power. Within the kidneys themselves there are very powerful vessels which maintain them and through which the entire human body is also supported. If a person develops kidney pains, this comes from a weakness in the stomach.

Intestinal Pains. Pains in the side develop from stomach pains, and pains in the bowels develop from pains in the side. That is, if the stomach becomes ill because of bad and noxious foods so that the strong and bad food in him cannot be digested, a pain develops in his side like smoke or a fog and climbs up like a biting smoke from green wood. This smoke from the stomach spreads out like a dark cloud to the intestines, and the bowels absorb this smoke. As a general rule this smoke always seeks out the intestines, just as the smoke from wood chips is immediately drawn into the chimney. Thus very often, because of the unfortunate constant tendency, every weakness and ache in the stomach descends to that customary place and causes the person to feel pain there.

The Male Sex Organs. Two agents account for the power in the male loins, that is, for the storm of passion that comes from the marrow, and are connected with one another like two boxes next to one another. They engender the passionate glow in a man and also hold in their power the male member's fire of passion. They are encased in a thin skin so that they do not lose their power. These two organs serve to lift the member. If a man no longer has these two powers, either because he has lost them by chance in a natural way or through castration, he has no more manhood and no more masculine storm of passion that erects the member to its full strength. Hence his member cannot be raised to plow the woman like the earth because he is cut free from the storm of his power which should strengthen his member as a means to beget offspring. In the same way, a plow cannot root up the earth when it has no ploughshare.

The Swelling of the Scrotum. The manly power in the sexual organs is great, but occasionally, either because of bad humors or noxious sweat or excessive gratification of the sexual organs, an unpleasant moisture or an abscess or swelling develops, so that the sexual organs swell up and are damaged by evil abscesses.

Drops of Urine. A man who can not control his urine has a cold stomach and a cold bladder. For that reason he cannot fully digest a drink. Before it is fully digested, it flows out like lukewarm water as when water, placed on the fire, gradually warms up and overflows as it boils. It is the same way with small children who cannot restrain their urine because neither their stomach nor their bladder possesses the full warmth, but are cold.

Gout. A man with soft, luxuriant flesh on his body, who consumes large amounts of various rich foods, easily develops gout. For example, if he eats two good, healthy foods and a third one that is a bad, unhealthy food, then the two good, healthy foods combat this third, evil, and unhealthy food so that it does less harm to the person who eats it. However, if a man eats two evil, unhealthy foods and at the same time a third good and healthy one, then the two bad, unhealthy foods overcome this third good and healthy food and barely allow it to contribute to the health of the person. It often happens that men who eat different kinds of food easily become sick. Thus, if people who have soft, abundant flesh on their bodies consume excessive amounts of various rich foods, the evil humors in them gain the upper hand and so multiply that they cannot be stopped from flowing — now this way, now that way — without order in the afflicted persons, finally to descend into the lower body where they soon fall into the legs and feet. Because they can find no exit there and can no longer climb back up to the upper body from whence they descended, but rather remain there in the lower body, they transform themselves into slime and harden; such a person feels the gout in his legs and feet and suffers from it to such an extent that he can scarcely walk. The evil humors, as described above, increase in women who have soft, abundant flesh and who eat immoderate amounts of rich foods. However, they do not as easily catch gout; rather, these humors are dissolved in the monthly cleansing, and so these women are spared the gout.

Fistula. A fistula is a type of gout. That is, a fistula develops from evil, overflowing humors. For if noxious, overflowing humors gain the upper hand in a person, they pour into a certain place in the body or descend into the legs or the feet. There, through the pressure of

90

their excess, they bore a hole through the skin and flow gradually toward the outside. Because the noxius humors in such a person are constantly increasing and pouring out pus, they do not allow a healing of the skin to take place.

The Cause of the Monthly Menses. As the force of desire invaded Eve, all her vessels were opened for the flow of blood. Thus, every woman has to suffer stormy experiences in her blood so that she, in a way similar to the cyclical increase and decrease of the moon, holds and releases her drops of blood so that all of her limbs, which are bound together by the vessels, open. That is, just as the moon waxes and wanes, so also are the blood and humors of the woman cleansed at the time of the monthly menses. Otherwise she could not live for long, for she retains more liquid than the man does. She would become severely ill. The chastity of a young maiden is the protection of her undamaged condition, for she does not lie with men nor does she know them. For that reason the monthly flow in a maiden is more blood-like than with a mature woman because the maiden is still closed up. For when a virgin is seduced, because she was seduced, she has more slime in the monthly flow than before when she was still a virgin. While a maiden is still an untouched virgin, the monthly menses comes upon her so to speak drop-by-drop from the blood vessels. However, once she has had sexual intercourse, the drops flow like a small stream because they have been released through sleeping with a man. The drops of blood flow for that reason like a small stream because the blood vessels have been opened through such sleeping. That is, if the protection of virginity is broken off, this invasion releases the blood. For the woman is so constructed that she receives and conserves the male seed with her blood. For that reason also the woman is weak and cold, and the humors in her are weak. As a consequence, she would be continually sick if her blood were not periodically cleansed through menstruation. In the same way, food cooking in the pot is cleansed when it throws off its foam from itself.

The Seduction of Eve. If Eve had remained in paradise, all of woman's blood vessels would have remained undamaged and healthy. But when she looked on the serpent favorably, her power of sight, through which she could spy heavenly things, was wiped out; and when she listened agreeably to the serpent, her hearing, by which she could listen to heavenly things, became deaf. As she enjoyed the apple, the brilliance that illuminated her whole being was darkened.

Just as the sap starts in the tree roots and strives upward into the tiniest twig of the tree, so it is with a woman at the time of the monthly cleansing. For at the time of the blood flow, the vessels that hold her brain together and contain the powers of sight and hearing are opened to bleeding. The vessels that contain the neck, the back, and the loins also draw the vessels of the liver, the intestines, and the navel to themselves; and each individual vessel pours itself out into another, just as the life force of the tree causes the twigs to bloom. The vessels which hold the loins together relax the circle in which the loins are inserted, contract it, and then release it again like the talons of a bird which have been cut off, open and close by means of the veins.

The Cause of the Monthly Menses. Just as a strong wind on a river foretells the coming of a storm, in the same way, a stormy movement develops in all the humors of a woman in such a way that these humors mix themselves with the blood and become thereby somewhat bloody and finally become cleansed with the blood. This is what constitutes the flow of blood in a woman. Hence, during this period the woman experiences headaches, her eyes become dim, and her whole body is weak. Still, her eyes do not become cloudy because of this if the bleeding proceeds at the right time and in the proper amount. Before the start of this bleeding, her members that are supposed to receive the male seed open themselves so that they more readily conceive now than during other times. In a similar way, a woman easily conceives once the monthly menses have stopped and are over, for then her members are still open. At other times, however, she does not so easily conceive, for then her members are somewhat closed up tight. It is the same way with a tree that spreads out its life force during the summer in order to bring forth buds, but retracts them in winter.

Conception. If the woman unites with a man, a delightful experience of heat in the brain announces both the enjoyment of this desire and the deposit of semen on the occasion of this union. If the semen has reached the right place, it draws the afore-mentioned very strong heat in the brain to itself and holds it fast. At that point, the loins of the woman contract and all the members, which at the time of the monthly flow were ready to open themselves, quickly close themselves up tight, as when a strong man closes something in his hand. Then the monthly blood mixes itself with the semen, makes it bloody, and causes it to become flesh. If the semen has turned to flesh, this blood then surrounds it with a vessel just as an insect larva spins a little house out of itself. The blood works on this vessel from day to day until a person takes shape within and this person receives the breath of life. This vessel then grows with this person anchoring him so securely to that place that he cannot budge until his birth.

Eve. The first mother of mankind was made similar to the ether. For just as the ether carries all the stars within itself, so did she carry all mankind within herself, undisturbed and untarnished and without any pain until it was said to her: "Increase and multiply!" But this proceeded with great pains.

Conception. For the woman is like the earth which must be tilled by the plow. She accepts the seed of a man, encloses it with her blood, and heats it with her warmth. In this way the seed develops until the breath of life is sent into it and until the time is ripe for it to come into the world.

Birth. When it is time for the child to come forth, then a terrible fear comes over her and such a great trembling that every woman shakes when in this terror, her vessels release large amounts of blood, all the joints of her members ache, and she breaks out in screams and tears. For so it stands written: "With tears shall you bring forth!" That means such pains as these will appear when, at the end of time, the earth will be destroyed. The blood of women is mixed with more slime than the blood of men, for they are open like the wood on which strings are stretched to make a zither; they are also as open as a window and as unstable as the wind. For that reason, the elements are more active in them than in men, and the humors are more abundant in them than in men.

Fertility. The bleeding at the time of menstruation is a sign for a woman of her power to beget life and to bloom. For she blooms in her children. Just as a tree blooms because of its life force and brings forth leaves and fruit, in the same way, in the fruit of her body, the woman brings forth blood and foliage out of the life force of her monthly flow. Just as a tree without its life force is named an infertile stump, in the same way, a woman in her prime who has no life force for her further blooming is called infertile. Just as a young tree possesses life power, but as yet carries no blooms or fruit until, when it has developed strong branches, it brings forth blooms and fruits and finally at the end of the whole time since it has put down roots, its power decreases so that its wood becomes partially hard and somewhat brittle and rotten, so is it also with a woman. For a girl has the force of life to grow to maturity, but has not yet the blood to bloom further. When at her maturity her limbs become strong, her blood has the power to bloom further through children. In ripe old age, her blood decreases so that the blood loses the power to bloom further; her flesh contracts, becomes harder and sharper, but also weaker than it was before. Young maidens do not yet have the flow of blood and hence cannot conceive a child because their limbs are not yet completely developed. In the same way, one cannot speak of a finished construction where only the foundation of a house has been laid and the walls have not yet been erected. However, when a girl has reached her twelfth year, her limbs, from that point on, will be continually strengthened until her fifteenth year. In the same way, a wall is finished when it reaches its full height on the foundation. From fifteen until twenty, the entire organism becomes finished with its individual organs. It is like a house whose rafters and roof have been finished and in which all possible furnishings are then placed. In the same way, the woman, who has fully matured in her vessels and in her entire organism, can now accept, enclose, and warm the male seed. However, if a woman has conceived a child before her twentieth year, this comes either from the excessive heat of her passionate nature or that of her husband, or from their frequent sexual intercourse. Moreover, the child she brings into the world is usually sickly and somewhat weak.

Menopause. From the fiftieth or sometimes also from the sixtieth year, a woman develops complications in the region of her womb openings and dries out so that the monthly menses retract into the sexual organs. In the same way, soil, after much effort and tilling, no longer receives, germinates, or causes seed for fruit or grain to ripen, apart from flowers or other good grasses. So it is with a woman until the eightieth year of life. At about that point, she fully loses her powers. From the age of fifty or sometimes with some women from sixty on, the monthly menses stop entirely, and the womb begins to contract and wrinkle so that she can no longer produce offspring. Only occasionally does it happen that a woman, as a result of her extraordinarily good constitution, can have a child once again up until her eightieth year. However, in such a situation, a bodily deformity sometimes results, as also often happens when a young maiden in her fragility conceives and bears a child before she is twenty years old.

After her eightieth birthday, however, a woman loses her power, and she withers away like a day that is drawing to a close.

Complications in the Monthly Period. With a few young women, as a result of grief, the drops of blood so shrink the flow that the vessels that channel this blood and cause it to flow contract and dry out because of the sobbing. Just as a tree blooms and puts forth leaves in summer because of the activity of the sun, so — often — is a woman's monthly flow of blood opened again by joy; and as cold wind, frost, and winter cause the leaves and twigs of the tree to wither away, in the same way grief makes a woman's normal flow of blood dry up.

On the other hand, humors in other women, as a result of a disease-related excess, may gain the upper hand, flow out, and thereby induce another suffering; the vessels that guide the flow of blood in these women are so narrow that their monthly periods give out because the stormy complications in their humors release an improper cold and a changeable heat so that their blood is sometimes cold and sometimes hot. Hence, for them, the blood flows now and then as the temperature changes. For the vessels that should open at certain times become narrow because of the dryness that they have within themselves, and the blood does not flow out. There are also other women who have weak and thick flesh that increases more as a result of their weakness and their poor constitution than as a result of the power of proper growth. This flesh overwhelms the vessels and constricts them. They become so narrowed that their blood flow is blocked and cannot flow out at the proper time.

For the mouths of these vessels are so encumbered and closed up that they do not allow their blood to flow out. As a result, the wombs of these women become so excessively fat that the way into them is severely hemmed in like a bottle that is closed up so that its contents cannot flow out. And so this severely retarded blood cannot flow out at the proper time.

The Cranium. The cranium in the head of a woman is split. This situation allows the vessels that flow out to be able to open themselves when they are supposed to carry away the monthly blood. At this time, the cranium opens itself and gives the vessels a free path so that the monthly cleansing of the woman can take place. However, when this purification is over, the cranium closes itself up again and holds the vessels fast so that they allow no more blood to flow out. In the same way, a pile of wood and stones holds back a stream so that it doesn't flow overpoweringly. Many women occasionally have pains from various attacks of fever, stomach pains, pains in the side or the abdomen, and these pains interfere with the proper closing of the cranium. In the same way, many storms create a flood that flows over a dam. Thus the blood channel of such a woman does not flow in a measured, regular cycle toward the exterior. This kind of woman suffers the same kind of pains as a man who is wounded by a sword. Therefore she should at these times prudently pay attention to herself, so as not to suffer even more injuries therefrom. For one should give a medicine only with great precaution.

Conception and Birth. Women who have gout and, as a consequence, have sick humors with stabbing pains, endure a torture because the humors cause great difficulties when the casing opens that encloses the child. The birth channel becomes blocked thereby either through a swelling or an inflamation. In the same way, water torrents that exceed the bank and rage around suddenly block the normal path of a small stream so that this small stream can no longer flow in its normal bed and one can no longer recognize where it runs. Thus the birth channel for the baby may be blocked by this obstacle until through God's grace the breath of life, that is the soul, presses itself out together with the body, whether the child now still lives or is dead. If the woman is very fat, then the birth channel of the baby swells as a result of the fat flesh of the mother and becomes thereby blocked, so that those late in a pregnancy have a lot to suffer until through the grace of God the breath of life in the child presses itself out together with the body. However, if the woman has a properly proportioned constitution so that she is neither too fat, too thin, nor too weak, then her birth channel will not be impeded by a difficult complication. Still, from the very beginning, both mother and child suffer the unavoidable exertions, but her exertions are normal. In women who are neither too fat nor too weak, the birth channel is not impeded, even if they are very thin. Still they must undergo the birth pangs laid down from the beginning. Many children choke and die as a consequence of the tumult of the humors and the obesity of the mother because the correct way is blocked. However, it is dangerous to give a woman who is having such a difficult time and is on the point of giving birth any medicine from the ground because she suffers either from excessive humors, obesity, or from some other painful disease. For that reason one should not give any medication which fights noxious and excessive humors during the birth of the child because of the danger to the child. For just as someone would die of asphyxiation if he were buried in the earth, so will the baby suffocate as a result of the strong action and smell of the aromatic plants and medicaments if they are applied when the birth of the child is imminent.

Postscript to Conception. If a woman has conceived the male seed, the conception of this seed has such a powerful impact on her that it draws toward itself the entire monthly flow of the woman as though through a straw or a cupping glass which the surgeon places on the flesh of a man and which draws much blood and pus to itself. At first, the seed in the woman is milky; then it congeals and turns to flesh. In the same way milk curdles and turns to cheese. And in this way the child lies in the regular blood flow and is nourished from it until birth.

Postscript to Birth. When the birth begins, the child emerges with much blood. In the same way, high water carries stones and wood with it in its flood. However, the foul-smelling slime of the monthly flow remains behind in the mother, for it cannot be separated from her so quickly, but will only come out later. The cleansing of the woman who is naturally dry and does not have too many humors completes itself in a short time after the birth while, in contrast, the cleansing of a woman who is naturally moist and has abundant humors draws itself out longer than for a woman who is dry and does not have many humors in herself.

The Fragility of a Baby. The fact that newborn babies cannot immediately run comes both from the fact that man is conceived from thin, weak seed and his flesh and his bones are thus not very strong while he is still young and that a man needs great strength when he finally stands upright to walk. It is not so with the other creatures, for shortly after their birth they can walk on their own feet. This comes from the fact that their forequarters are down on the earth. In the same way, the baby crawls around on its hands and feet before it can stand up to move. Even though other newly born creatures can stand on their own legs, still they cannot sit up as a baby sits when it cannot yet stand on its own legs. Because animals have their power in the legs and in the feet, they can run soon after birth. However, because man has his power above the navel and, as long as he is a baby, is weak in his legs and his feet, he cannot move about at that age.

Why Man Does not Swim. Because man's body is heavy and because he works with his hands, walks with his feet, holds his body upright, and also has little of the essence of air or water, he cannot naturally swim in water, and he must therefore teach himself to do this. Animals, however, have power in their legs, move with their upper body inclined toward the earth, and are moved on their legs as if by the wind. Hence, some of them can swim naturally; just as they move about on land inclined forward, they also swim in the water inclined forward. Man does not do this, for he moves about fully upright. In order to swim, he must bend over and stretch himself out.

The Female Breast. In the region of the navel of the woman, that is, above and below the navel, certain vessels are connected with one another from which some reach up to the breasts and some lead below to the womb. They take all their content from the juices of food and drink and are nourished from them — more, however, to those that lead to the breasts than those that lead below to the womb. However, as long as the woman is still a virgin, her breasts grow until the vessels that lead to the womb lead the monthly blood flow in that direction. Then they stop growing, except that later they fill up like a sponge.

Postscript to Conception and to Milk. Conception draws the monthly flow of the woman's blood to itself so that the channel that leads from the woman to the outside is now redirected toward the conception. When the development of its flesh and bones begins and the fetus receives motion from the spirit of life, the vessels that lead to the breasts open themselves under the influence of the lively movement of the womb's fruit and the activity of the elements, and lead the milk to the breasts from the humors of the food and drink by which the body of the woman is nourished. The milk has a white color.

When a pregnant woman takes food and drink, these divide themselves into two groups: one takes care of the womb and the other brings the milk to the breasts. In the same way, the blood is of two different sorts: it is red if it is in a peaceful condition; it takes on a white color when it is set into excitement during sexual relations between a man and a woman. The white color contains the milk from grain production and other cooked foods because grain produces a white meal and food gives off a white foam when it is boiled. In the same way, food and drink — through their juices — bring something like a white foam to the breasts of a pregnant woman. However, when the child is born and the woman is cleansed, these same fine vessels that lead to the womb contract and redirect the monthly flow of blood toward the exterior while those delicate vessels that lead to the breasts are opened for the milk. The fact that there is sufficient milk in the breasts while the new baby sucks comes from the fact that the baby, while it is sucking, draws milk into the breasts through the afore-mentioned fine vessels and keeps the passage through these vessels continually open through its sucking.

Nursing. When the child stops sucking, the milk decreases in the woman and dries up entirely. Then the fine vessels that lead to the womb open up again and redirect their channels to this new destination. If the woman becomes pregnant again while she is still nursing a first child, she can keep nursing without any danger to the baby until the conception inside her is formed into flesh and bones. Then she should stop nursing her first child, for the power and the health in the milk sinks down to the embryo through her monthly flow so that from that point on the milk from the breasts of this woman contains more slime than health.

Digestion. When a man eats, the fine vessels that are sensitive to taste distribute the taste throughout the body. The inner vessels — that is, those of the liver, heart, and lungs — take the more delicate humor of the food away from the stomach and distribute it throughout the whole body. In this way the person's blood is increased and the body nourished. It is like the way a fire flares up through a blast from the bellows, and the grass turns green and grows because of the wind and the dew. Just as the bellows blows the fire into a flame and the wind and the dew bring forth the grass, so also the humors from food and drink cause the blood, the humor, and a person's flesh to grow and increase. However, just as the bellows is not the fire and the wind and the dew are not the grasses, so also neither is the juice from food the blood, nor the liquid from drink the humor, but rather the juice from food takes on the color of blood and is located in it, and the liquid from drink takes on the color of a juice and remains in it. So the two build up the blood to a humor and send it up just as yeast does to the entire loaf of dough, and so they remain within it, connect themselves in this manner with it, decompose with it, and are expelled with it.

Bowel Movements. What cannot be used from the consumed foods and drinks descends into a person's lower intestines and changes itself into excrement. When it has been transformed into excrement, it is evacuated by the person. In the same way, the grapes are pressed, the wine is bottled, and what remains — that is, the vines and stems — is thrown out.

The Blood. When a person drinks, the more delicate humor that is in the drink increases the fluid of the blood. What cannot be used descends with the drink and leaves the person after it has decomposed. In the same way with wine, the liquor rises higher in the barrel, and the dregs lie on the bottom. The blood is strengthened by the juices from foods and made liquid by drink. The blood cannot endure without this liquid, any more than food can sustain a man without drink. In fact, if the blood had no liquid, it would become hard and could not flow. The person would also dry up and could not live if he only ate and did not drink. For that reason, the person who eats bad food or excessive amounts develops a bad blood, and the one who drinks bad drinks or excessive amounts increases the bad liquid in himself. For the bad humors in the food and drink join themselves with the blood and its liquid.

Nourishment. When a person eats and drinks, then a vital, rationally controlled power in the person leads the taste, the fine humor, and the smell of the food and drink upwards to the brain and warms it, in that it fills up its fine vessels. The remaining parts of this food and drink that reach the stomach warm the heart, the liver, and the lungs; from this, they draw the taste, the fine humor, and the smell into their fine vessels so that the latter are filled with them, become warmed and nourished as when a man places a fully dried piece of intestine in water and it becomes soft, swells up, and becomes full. Thus, when a person eats and drinks, his vessels become filled and warmed with the juices from the food and drink. This humor warms the blood and the liquid in the vessels, and the blood that is in the flesh draws its red color from the juices that are in its vessels.

Hunger. As the consumed nourishment decays and dries out, the vessels become emptied of their juices, and the blood in the flesh loses its red color and becomes watery. At this point, the vessels seek to be replenished again, and the blood in the flesh demands its red color. In that consists the hunger which a person experiences.

Thirst. As a person eats, he works at eating just like a mill works by grinding. Through the work of eating, the person becomes interiorly warm and dry. So he begins to dry out interiorly, and that is thirst. Then he must drink something and again eat something. When he again becomes dry because of the warmth of eating, he again becomes thirsty, and then he must drink again. Thus he must restrain himself while he is eating, for if a person who was eating, that is, consuming something, did not drink, he would develop spiritual and bodily ills, and would neither develop a good blood liquid nor have a good digestion. However, if he drinks excessively while eating, he causes an evil, stormy flooding through his bodily humors in such a way that the good humors lose their effectiveness in him. In the meantime, the foods are decaying and drying out; as a consequence of this warmth the vessels and the blood seek after moisture, and in that consists thirst. Then the person must drink something and moisten his inner dryness; otherwise, he will end up in a severe spiritual and bodily slowness. A person who has vital life in himself and nourishes himself from various foods has a greater need for drink while he eats than animals that feed on hay and grass.

Sleep. A person should not sleep immediately after a meal before the taste, the juice, and the smell of the foods have reached their place. Rather, he should resist sleep for a short time after a meal, for if he sleeps immediately after eating, this sleep leads the taste, the humors, and the smell of the foods to improper, upside-down body places and distributes them like dust here and there in the vessels. However, if a person has put off sleep for a short while and then reclines to sleep for a short while, his blood and flesh increase thereby; and he becomes healthy because of it.

Night Thirst. It often happens both by day and night that a man wakes up as a consequence of the warmth and dryness of foods and feels thirst. He should, however, avoid drinking immediately while he is still half asleep, for he thereby attracts illnesses and arouses his blood and his humors into an injurious uproar. After waking up, he should wait a while before drinking until sleep is fully wiped away from him, even when he is very thirsty.

Drink. If he is thirsty after sleep, whether he is healthy or sick, he should drink wine or beer, but no water; for water would rather harm than help his blood and his humors.

The Suffering of Lameness. A person who is plagued by a gout-like lameness has misguided humors in himself which are stirred up unpeacefully like waves in water. For that reason, such a person cannot be peaceful and moderate in his being and behavior. Hence, he should drink mild wine or, if he cannot hold wine, drink moderate barley or wheat beer. When he cannot endure that, boil water and bread, strain it through a cloth, and drink this water lukewarm. He should do this each day, and the waves of strong gout attacks will be brought under control. If such a person quickly loses bodily weight, he should, as was said, drink only a little of something moderate. However, if he is sound of body, he should drink a moderately sufficient amount of wine, beer, or water that has been cooked with bread, and the gout will leave him in peace.

Daytime Fever. If a person has daytime attacks of fever that come from different dishes, he should not drink on an empty stomach because he is dry inside. For if he were to drink soberly, the drink would rush through his body and do him more harm than good. He should eat beforehand, so that his vessels might be warmed through the previous intake of humors from the food. Then he may take a draught of wine, and it will not hurt him. If he has no wine, he should drink beer; if he has no beer, he should take mead. If he has no mead, heat water, let it cool, and then let him drink it.

Three-Day and Four-Day Fevers. If a person has a three-day or four-day fever, he should not drink on an empty stomach except in an emergency if he becomes extremely thirsty. However, he can also drink a little cold water on an empty stomach. At breakfast he should drink wine; that is healthier for him than drinking water.

If he has no wine, he should drink barley beer; if he has none of that, take mead or, if he has none of that, boiled water that has been allowed to cool. No man should drink on an empty stomach unless he is forced to do so by fainting attacks. Then it is healtheir for him to drink wine rather than water. If someone drinks wine on an empty stomach with no necessity, it makes him desirous of food and drink and irrational and foolish in his thoughts.

Nourishment and Food. If a man is empty, he should first eat food prepared from fruit and meal, for such food is dry and bestows healthy power to a person. He should first make a warm dish for himself, nothing cold, so that his stomach becomes warm; for if he should take something cold first, he thereby makes his stomach cold so that later he can barely warm himself through warm foods. He should eat something warm first until his stomach becomes warm through and through. If he then eats something cold, the warmth that already penetrates his stomach overpowers the cold food which follows. At first, he should avoid eating any type of fruit or anything that has juices or liquid within, such as vegetables, for they bring him a slimy liquid and would upset his own fluid condition. He can eat these later after he has already eaten something else; then it does him more good than harm.

Breakfast. For a person who is of sound body, it is good and healthy for his digestion for him not to break his fast until shortly before noon. However, for someone who is sick or weak in body, it is good and sound that he eat something in the morning so that he might derive from such nourishment the power that he no longer has. A person may also eat the same foods and drink the same drinks at night as he has during the day if he so chooses. But he should be certain to leave enough time after his evening meal to take a walk before retiring for the night.

The Different Kinds of Drinks. If a person drinks a noble, strong wine, it arouses the vessels and the blood in an improper way, draws the humors and all the moisture in the person to itself as purging drinks do, and sometimes discharges the urine prematurely and dangerously. Hunsrücker wine does not do this because it is not so strong that it could set a person's humors in excessive excitement. For that reason, the strength of a noble wine should be tempered by dipping bread into it or adding water because otherwise it is good neither for a healthy nor for a sick man to drink if it is not so mixed. However, one does not have to mix Hunsrücker wine in this manner because it is not so strong. However, if one adds water to it or dips bread into it and then drinks it, it is all the more pleasant to drink, but not healthier. Wine by its nature has something liquid about it, for it is nourished from the dew and the rain. That is the reason why a person who drinks wine, even if he drinks it continually without water, still has watery humors in his blood.

Postscript to Blood. If the blood did not contain watery slime, it would be completely dry and would not flow, just as the marrow does not flow. If blood were not fluid, flesh could not endure but would become like earth.

A Different Diet in Winter. A person who eats very cold foods during the extremely cold periods of winter when he himself is cold on the inside easily develops bile problems. However, a person who eats very cold foods when he himself is cold on the inside keeps fevers away. However, a person who eats moderately warm foods, that is, neither too cold nor too hot, during the cold periods of winter when he himself is cold on the inside is only slightly nourished by them for they generate no good blood for him. However, if anyone eats moderately warm foods — neither too hot nor too cold — in a very hot room during the cold season, these foods do him no harm; but the room's heat, that he himself then has, weakens him.

The Proper Temperature During Cold Periods. If a person intends to eat during the cold periods of winter, he should seek out a room that is neither too hot nor too cold, but the proper temperature. He should also eat dishes that are neither too hot nor too cold, but of a moderate temperature. In this way he will remain healthy through his nourishment. However, while he is eating, he should not sit in a cold room, for the cold air will make him sick if he breathes it in while he is eating. If the heat from the glowing coals begins to climb up the back of a person while he is eating, that is better for him than when the heat of the fire glows in his face.

The Connection between Extreme Summer Heat and the Various Foods. If a person eats cold dishes in summer when he is very hot inside, he easily develops gout. Moreover, if he eats very cold dishes in summer when he is very hot, he builds up phlegm in himself. For that reason, a person should eat moderately hot and cold dishes in summer, and these will give him good blood and healthy flesh. If a person eats a lot in summer when he is very hot within, his blood will become excessively warm because of the great quantity of food; his humors will degenerate, and the flesh of his body will swell up and become unnaturally distended because the air is warm. However, if he eats only moderately, this does him no harm; rather, he remains healthy. However, if during winter when a person is very cold on the inside, he eats a lot, it brings him health and makes him fat. However, at every season a person should avoid eating boiling hot and steaming foods; rather, he should wait after they are cooked until their hot steam has left them. If he eats steaming foods right off the fire, they stir up his stomach, cause it to swell, and easily cause mange. However, if a person is suffering under great grief, he should eat enough of the foods offered to him so as to regain his strength from the food; for at that time his grief is a burden to him. However, when he is overjoyed, he should eat only moderately, for then his blood is scattered by the widening of the blood path. Otherwise, the humors release strong fever attacks into his blood if he eats a lot at that time.

A man should not drink a lot in winter, for then the air enriches his humors with moisture at the same time. Then, if he drinks a lot, he ruins his inner humors and attracts diseases to himself. In winter, he should drink wine or beer and avoid water, where possible; for during this season, the water is not healthful because of the moisture of the earth. In summer, however, he should drink more than during winter, and that according to the amount and type of nourishment he takes in; for his humors dry out then. The water that he drinks in summer harms him less than in winter because of the dryness of the earth. A person who is healthy of body should drink lukewarm water in moderate amounts in summer when he is very warm on the inside and then go for a walk for a while so that he becomes warm. That is more advantageous for his bodily health than if he drinks wine. However, if someone is sick in summer, he should drink wine or beer mixed with water, for that does him more good than drinking plain water. However, at every season, summer and winter, a person should avoid drinking too much. Just as, for example, too much rain floods and does damage to the earth, so the person who drinks excessively sets various noxious humors loose in his body. However, a person should not refrain entirely from drinking, for if he makes himself dry through his continency, he attracts spiritual and bodily evils to himself. In that situation, no food he eats can bring him a good digestion and bodily health. In like manner, the earth becomes heavy, hard, and dry and does not bring forth good fruit when the watering by the rain has been withdrawn from it. If, however, a person's belly is full of food and drink, it is necessary that he cleanse himself through digestion.

Bloodletting. If a person's vessels are full of blood, they must be purified of damaging slime and digestive humors through a cut. If an incision is made into a person's vein, his blood becomes so to speak frightened, and what comes out first is blood, and at the same time, the decay and digestive juices flow out together with it. That is why what flows out from this point has different colors because it is made up of corruption and blood. After the blood and decay have flowed out, clean blood comes out, and then one should stop the bloodletting. If people have the intention to perform a bloodletting on a person who is healthy and strong of body, they should draw off only as much blood as a strong, thirsty man could drink in one gulp were it water. However, if someone is weak, the bloodletter should take only as much blood from his vein as an egg of normal size could contain. For an excessive bloodletting weakens the body, just as an excessive downpour of rain on the earth damages it. A properly measured bloodletting gets rid of noxious humors and heals the body. In the same way, a rain that falls gently and moderately on the earth waters it and enables it to bring forth fruit.

The Different Kinds of Bloodletting. The first thing that comes out of the wound and the incision in the vein, as mentioned above, is blood, and at the same time, poisonous and disease-carrying humors flow in it. If the out-flowing liquid takes on the proper color of red with another color, blood and humors stand in equal proportion to one another. If still more blood comes out, the good and evil humors follow at the same time with the remaining blood. At that point, one should stop the bloodletting, for otherwise the slimy humors in the remaining blood would gain the upper hand and cause bile problems and other diseases if more blood is drawn off. For anemia cannot muster an opposition to them. Just as hunger weakens the strength of the body, in the same way an excessive bloodletting makes the body weak. On the other hand, a moderate bloodletting bestows health on a body, just as moderate eating and drinking bring the body back to strength.

When a Bloodletting Should be Undertaken. A person who is strong, healthy, and fat should be bled every third month; when the moon has waxed twice and waned twice, the blood in a person has then already returned to its old condition. For then his veins are full again. If before that time he allows himself to undergo a bloodletting, he weakens himself; for his blood has not yet reached its full strength. If he postpones it too long, however, then his excessively abundant blood will be corrupt; that is, it transforms itself into dirty scum. He should be bled by a waning moon, that is, on the first day that the moon begins to decline, or on the second, third, fourth, fifth, or sixth day, and then no more, for an earlier or a later bloodletting is not as profitable. If the moon is waxing, a person should not be bled, for such a letting causes damage; at that time the humors mixed in with his blood can only be separated from it with difficulty. That is, under a waxing moon the blood and noxious humors flow, so to speak, only moderately together in a person and are then difficult to separate. In the same way, a river keeps to its channel during a moderate flow. However, during a waning moon the blood becomes agitated by increasing excitement and flow and also causes too much noxious liquid to flow out, just as happens during a severe flood that causes foul-smelling flotsam to be seen in the water and throws up foam. A bloodletting is more suitable for older rather than younger people, for the blood in the vessels of older persons is more mixed with decay than the blood in vessels of younger people. When it is necessary, one can submit a boy of twelve to a bloodletting, for his blood is already strong enough. However, only so much blood should be taken from him as can be held in the shell of a nut. Before the fifteenth year, one should only undertake a bloodletting once a year. However, because a person's blood already has its power and his veins are full in the fifteenth year, one may then, if he is healthy, remove an amount of blood equal to the amount of water a thirsty man could take in one gulp, as was mentioned above. One can carry on in this fashion until the fiftieth year. After the fiftieth year, if the blood and the phlegm of a person are already beginning to decrease and his body to dry out, again one should only undertake a bloodletting once a year, and one should then take only half as much blood as was removed before during a bleeding. One can carry on in this fashion until the eightieth year. After that, bloodletting is no longer profitable for a person but rather harms him, for the strength in his blood is already decreased, unless it happens that a great flood and infection of his humors arises. In case of such an urgent necessity, a small amount of blood may be taken. Because a man's vessels are already becoming weak after eighty years and the removal of blood no longer does him any good, he should rather apply some black carline thistle or other similar healing herb to his body to cause pustules to arise, so that in this fashion the noxious fluids that lie between the skin and the flesh can flow out through an outbreak of pustules. A woman has a greater number of damaging fluids and a more damaging corruption in her body than a man.

Bloodletting in the Case of a Woman. For that reason, women, from their twelfth year, should avail themselves of the same method and the same frequency of bloodletting as a man, with the exception that in their case bloodletting may be extended until their hundredth year. A greater exigency exists for them than for men because of their noxious fluids and poisonous corruptions. That also manifests itself in menstruation. If they were not cleansed of the damaging liquids and corruptions during menstruation, their whole body would swell up and become bloated and not be able to remain alive. After one hundred they should not be bled, for they are already cleansed from blood and the outflowing humors. However, if later a woman notices some fluid or other about her, she should then cause pustules to grow specifically at the very places on the body on which burning irons are normally set on men.

Blood Vessels. It is well known that more liquids flow in the head vein than in the middle vein or in the liver vein, because more vessels lead off the head vein than from the middle vein or the liver vein. Thus it is more advantageous to extract blood more often from the head vein than from other veins. For example, a person who has much phlegm in his head or in his chest or who has a severe headache so that thereby his powers of hearing are disturbed, should have blood taken from his head vein, yet with the precaution that too much blood is not extracted. Otherwise, his eyes could become worse since very delicate vessels that lead to the eyes and depend upon this vein would be emptied of blood and thereby would make a person's eyes worse from whose head vein much blood was taken.

Bleeding. Whoever has eyes that are impaired or ulcerous as a result of noxious humors, or flesh that has become swollen in the area of the eyes, should have a little blood taken from behind the ears and on the neck with cupping glasses or cupping horns, and this three or four times a year; or if he is driven to bleeding more often, he should take less blood so that he does not thereby suffer injury from taking too much blood. He should have blood extracted from the place on the body where he experiences pains. If people have pains in their tongue, whether because it is swollen or ulcerous, they should scratch it a little with a small bleeding knife or with a thorn so that the slime can come out at that point, and they will get better. If a person has a toothache, he should take a small bloodletting knife or a thorn and make a small cut in the flesh around the affected tooth, that is, in the gum, so that the pus can come out and he will feel better. However, a person who has a downcast heart or a depressed mood, if he has pains in his side or in the lungs, should have blood taken from the middle vein, but only a little, so that he maintains the strength of his heart; otherwise the heart may give out if too much blood is removed. If someone feels pains in the heart, he should have blood taken from the right arm before being bled in the middle vein, and it will relieve the pain in his heart. If people have pains in their liver or spleen, if they have difficulty breathing in the neck or the throat, or if they suffer weakness in the eyes, they should have blood taken from their liver vein, and they will improve. If a person is bled sufficiently from the liver vein or the head vein, the sick person will experience fewer pains thereafter than if he had taken a lot of blood from the middle vein. Both in winter and in summer, a person can take blood from either arm in the mentioned vein, as he chooses, according to the illness. Bloodletting should take place principally on these three veins, namely the head vein, the middle vein, and the liver vein because these veins are like the head and foundation for the other veins and because all the other delicate vessels lead to them and are connected with them. For that reason, the other delicate vessels should seldom be cut. They should not be cut except for an exceptional and urgent necessity, for otherwise they might dry out. If one of these main veins is cut and bleeds profusely, then the delicate vessels that are connected to it are substantially emptied of the injurious humors that are in them. However, if one of these delicate vessels is cut, the main vein and the other delicate vessels with which it is connected are not much affected by such bloodletting. For just as when many small streams lead off of a large river, all the small streams that branch off from the main stream begin to feel the withdrawal of water if men erect a water wheel on this principal river. However, if a water wheel is placed on a small stream connected with the river, this river and the other small streams that branch off from it do not feel much removal of water; rather, only the small stream over which this water wheel was placed decreases and dries out.

The incision in the above-mentioned main vein should take place at the bend of the elbow, for if the vein is cut there, the humors collect there sooner than at a point where there is no bend. If because of a disease a small blood vessel is cut over a joint, on the foot, on the thumb, or someplace else on the human body with the exception of the bend of the elbow, it can be rather profitable for the affected person, but no bloodletting can have as much worth as that which takes place on the above-mentioned three main veins in the bend of the elbow. However, nobody — whether man or woman — should proceed with a bloodletting as long as they are still young and growing in height or weight according to the natural process, even if it seems necessary. For if someone cuts these veins and releases blood — as long as the veins and the blood in the person are still naturally increasing — this weakens the person in body and creates in his character and in his sensibility, so to speak, a large vacuum. If it is absolutely necessary, burning irons can be placed on him and some blood can be removed through cups. For there is more liquid corruption in the blood of younger men than in the blood of older men. However, once a man has passed a certain age, his body no longer increases according to nature. This normally happens after twenty years; then, he may go ahead with a bloodletting if it seems necessary because of a disease. However, he should allow only a small amount of blood to be taken. If, however, he is sound of body, he should not cut into his veins but have cups and hot irons placed on his body, for his veins and his blood have not yet reached their full strength. However, when he has reached the mature age of thirty, then he may proceed with a bloodletting as he chooses, whether he is sick or well, because his veins and his blood are now fully developed. Then he will remain healthy in body.

Differences in Blood. If the blood taken from a man — like the breath of a man — has a cloudy color and black flecks in this discoloration and looks like wax on the outside edges, that person will soon die if God does not intervene. The cloudy color of the blood indicates that the humors are dying off in their cold, the black streaks in the blood show that the bile is dying off, and the waxy edges indicate that the gall has already died. If the color of a person's blood is cloudy and waxy but shows no black flecks, that person can resist death; however, he will become very sick. Even though his bodily humors are already dying off in their cold, the black streaks of the bile have not yet appeared, and thus he can resist death. However, if the blood is black, cloudy, and without a waxy color, then the person is in a hopeless condition so that now only God can help him. However, he will elude death, for even though the bile and the bodily humors are already dying off, the gall remains working at its station, and for that reason this person will not die. If these colors can be seen simultaneously when cutting the vein, it is dangerous, and the affected person cannot resist death if God does not wake him to life because the bodily humors as well as the bile and the gall are dying off in the same way. However, if the colors are separated so that of the two, one color fails, he can still resist death, but only after many pains. One can tell this about people in advance through the blood color whether or not he knows that they are already sick. The vapor that the bile exudes is cloudy. It possesses the power of the gall and is similar to wax. It is the same way with the bile. After a bloodletting, a person should avoid both the bright rays of the sun and the bright glow of a burning fire. The person's blood would be mightily upset by the bright light during these three days, and this often brings harm to the heart.

Correct Behavior and Eating Habits during Bloodletting. A moderate amount of daylight does not harm a person after a bloodletting if the sun's rays are not too intense. At all times, but especially after a bloodletting, the blood around a person's eyes boils as a result of the glow of the sun and the heat of the fire, and the delicate skin or membrane that holds the eyes together dries out and impairs the eyesight. After a bloodletting, a person should avoid various foods roasted that contain certain humors, raw fruit, and uncooked vegetables because they will increase more slime than blood in the vessels. One should also avoid strong wine, for it excites the blood and would deafen a man. Rather, a person should eat a moderate amount — at most one or two dishes — so that he is properly satisfied, and one should also drink sweet, pure wine. A person should do that for two days, for his diluted blood remains in an excited condition. By the third day, however, his blood will have regained its full strength and distributed itself throughout his arterial system. One should also avoid cheese and dairy products after a bloodletting, for they introduce slime into the blood that does not build up a clean, proper blood, but rather enriches it with disease-inducing fat. Thus if someone has a lot of blood and his veins are full of it and he does not cleanse his blood through bloodletting or a cupping, his blood will become somewhat waxy and weak, and such a person will become sick.

When Should a Person Let Blood? If a person is going to undertake a bloodletting, he should do it on an empty stomach. For when a person is empty, his humors are still a bit separated from his blood, and his blood flows according to the correct, properly measured speed just as a small stream flows peacefully and properly in its bed without a push from the wind or air. However, once a person has eaten something, his blood begins to flow more powerfully, and so the

111

humors mix themselves with it a bit, and then the humors and the blood can only be separated from one another with greater difficulty. For that reason, a person should be empty when he lets blood so that the humors, separated from the blood, may flow out all the more easily. One should only make an exception for a person who is very sick or weak. He should eat something before letting blood so that he does not become faint.

Bleeding. Whoever lets himself be cupped should do this on an empty stomach, for then the slimy humor that has been separated from the blood can flow out. For after one has eaten, the blood mixes itself with the slimy humor, and when a person then lets himself be cupped, the blood flows out together with the slimy humor. However, to make sure that the person does not suffer a heart attack, he should eat a little bread and wine before the cupping. Cupping is good and helpful on all occasions, as the noxious liquids and slimy humors in a person are decreased by it. For the slimy humors are located between the skin and the flesh, and they do particular harm to a person. Cupping is more appropriate for younger people than for older ones, for the young have more humors than their elders. Cupping is more useful in summer than in winter. In summer, people eat more fresh foods and fresh, green juices than they do in winter. From that they acquire fresh body humors. However, whoever has soft, fat flesh should allow blood to be taken twice in a month. On the other hand, thin people, should it be necessary, only once a month. Whoever have pains in their eyes, their ears, or in their entire head should place the cup or the small horn at the border between the neck and the back. If people have pains in their chest, they should place the cup between the shoulder blades. People who have pains in their side should place the cup on both arms and there where the hand stops. Persons who have pains in their legs should place it on the abdomen. Whoever has abdominal pains should place it between the buttocks and the bend of the knee, that is, on the thigh. The cup or the horn should not be placed on the same spot more often than three or four times in the same hour in which blood is to be drawn out. A cup should be placed seldom, if at all, on the calf or the shin unless one has to do it because of an urgent attack of the humors, for more blood than humors are present there. However, one should not draw humors to that place, for the entire body is carried about on the legs. A person who has decreased his humors and his blood through cupping does not have to be as careful about avoiding bright sunlight, fire, or rich foods as someone who has let blood. Rather, they should strengthen themselves by eating according to their customary practice. For during a cupping, the delicate network of the arterial system that carries a person's life in it and holds the limbs together is not cut. For if such a network is cut, all the others notice this incision and together, they suffer from it. If blood is to be taken from a horse, a cow, or a donkey, and the animal is strong and lively, then as much blood should be taken as would fill a cup of water.

Bloodletting an Animal. If a horse, cow, or donkey is weak and thin, a half cup of blood should be taken from it, depending on its degree of corpulence or thinness. After the bloodletting, they should be given soft food and dry, fine hay to eat. The animal should then be allowed to recuperate for two weeks or one week or four days after the bloodletting until it recovers its strength; otherwise, it will be kept working. After three months have gone by — in the fourth month and not before — blood can be taken once again from the same animal unless there is a strong necessity to do it sooner as a result of disease. For with such animals, there are not as many noxious humors as with people. Man may bleed a sheep often, taking only a little blood each time, because it easily becomes sick as a result of the constant change of air. With sheep, one should undertake bloodletting during moist, moderately warm weather, for then the noxious humors are increasing in them. During dry weather, however, one should forego a bloodletting because then the [good] humors in the sheep are increasing.

Burning Irons. Burning, that is the application of a burning iron, is always good and advantageous, for when it is prudently used, it decreases the liquids and the slimy humors under the skin and bestows health upon the body. It is as appropriate for the young as for older persons: for the young because, as their flesh and blood are still increasing, the noxious humors are also increasing; for the old, however, because their flesh and blood are decreasing, slimy humors remain behind between their skin and their flesh. It is somewhat healthier for older persons than for younger ones, for the slimy humors flow here and there between their skin and their flesh because of the shrinking of their flesh and blood and the wrinkling of their skin.

It is not as healthy for young persons as for those who are older. Then, as their flesh is still increasing, their blood is hot, and their skin delicate and taut, blood that brings them health and strength very often flows out along with the noxious humors from the burn wound that is caused by the burning irons. In any case, such burning is healthier for younger persons in winter than in summer. Because of their own and the summer's heat, they must protect themselves against losing both blood and the slimy humors in summer. For that reason, they should allow themselves to be burned in winter, for in winter it is cold and moist while they themselves are warm. Thus they more easily retain their blood while releasing the humors. However, burning is recommended in summer for older people, for then they themselves are cold while the summer is hot. The humors aroused by the summer's heat easily flow out through the burning, for the elderly receive the heat they need from the summer's heat to expel the humors. It is heat which they do not have themselves. However, if a person sets a burning iron, it should barely penetrate the skin lest the flesh develop holes at a deeper level and more of the person's health flows out with his blood than just the slimy humors and the noxious fluids. People grown obese should only let themselves be burned once in the course of a year and then wait a half-year after that until the next. Then they may repeat the process if they like at a different place on the body. Thinner persons may allow themselves to be burned at intervals of a half-year. After the passage of a half-year, they may if they wish allow themselves to be burned again, but on a different part of the body. For if the same part of the body is burned repeatedly and for a long time, the flesh develops much pus there, becomes sick thereby, and becomes hard. If burning is undertaken uncautiously and for too long a time with a particular person, then, because of the blunder, that person loses blood together with the noxious fluids and slimy humors. With younger people, a ten-week interval should be enough for healing. For the burning to succeed, a special sponge, the core of a spindle tree, or a knotted linen cloth should be pressed upon the wound, but not, however, an iron, because this attracts many humors indiscriminately. Also, the person should not use sulphur, for it causes the flesh to rot and makes it smelly. Neither should he use incense, for it flames up and causes the skin to dry out. The special sponge, the heart of the spindle tree, and a linen cloth burn more attractively than other kindling; they only penetrate the skin and leave no holes in the flesh. Where only the skin is damaged, then only humors come out, and the person's health remains unaffected. However, if the flesh together with the skin receives holes, both the person's health and the slimy humors flow out and are lost. If someone wants to burn himself longer and wrap the burn wound with a cloth, he should take the core from a hazelnut branch, wrap a little oakum from flax around it and place it on the spot. However, if he wishes to leave the burn open without a bandage for only a short time, he should sprinkle oakum from flax or rabbit hair on it.

If necessary, a person can be burned starting from his twelfth to his sixteenth year; after that, however, he should avoid it, for then it does him more harm than good unless of course a pressing emergency because of sickness forces him to it. If a person has pains in the eyes, the ears, or in the entire body, he should only be lightly burned behind the ears and apply no bandage to it. A person who has back pains should be burned lightly between the shoulder blades or on the arms with a glowing iron where a bandage can be applied. If a person has abdominal pains, he should be burned on his backside between his back and his buttocks. If a person has many humors distributed throughout his entire body, he should be burned on the tibia in front between the calf and the shin-bone and wrap a bandage there. Just as someone who has let blood should pause for a while, so also should people act who undergo a burning. If much of the day's time is used up, he can still let himself be burned one more time. Whoever lets himself be burned, however, should take a hemp cloth, dip it in wax three or four times, and lay it on a gorse rind because it fuses with the wax over the burn wound; then he should place the cloth over the burn so that the cloth reaches over the rind at every corner. In this way, the cloth binds the burn wound. For the more the smell is held back in the burn wound so that it cannot spread itself out, the more slime, but not blood, will be drawn out. If, however, the burn smell spreads further and if it is not bound fast, then more blood emerges from the burn and more slime remains within. If the bark of a cypress is placed on the wound, it does not help at all because the sap from the cypress damages human flesh. However, if the small cloth that is laid over the burn becomes full of slime so that the cloth has become warm because of the slime, then the cloth should be taken off the wound and another laid on. For if it is allowed to lie on the burn any longer, the humors that were drawn there will dry out. If the small cloth is taken off before it has become warm because of the slime, it harms the sick person, for the slime that has collected beneath it goes back into the flesh.

Clearing One's Throat. Just as the earth is continually moist and much useless, smelly garbage flows out of it, so man, whose interior flesh is also moist, gets rid of what is foul-smelling refuse within himself by clearing his throat. He is made from the clay of the earth. If the earth were not moist, it would not bring forth any fruit but remain dry, and so also would man, if he had no moisture within himself, be unmoving and unfit for any business.

The Fire of the Soul. The human soul is of a fiery nature. It attracts the four elements and, through them, empowers man to see, to hear, and in similar ways to move around actively. The soul is a certain power in men like fire in water; man could not live without a soul, just as water could not flow without fire if it did not retain fire within itself.

Spit (Saliva). The soul makes use of a power in human beings, namely that of saliva, for water moistens the reason and makes it ready for speaking just as strings are rubbed with wax or resin so that they will produce a pleasing sound. Saliva would be clean and pure if the soul did not possess a fiery essence. However, because of the fire of the soul, saliva is like a foam, just as water develops a foam through the activity of its fire and the sun that is heat. Because the soul has a fiery essence, for that reason it also has a watery essence. She seeks the path to reason, so that this reason may lift up its voice in human beings. Specifically, the soul draws water from the brain and from the intestines to make spit so that man can speak. For if man had no moisture within himself but was entirely dry, he would not be able to express himself nor bring forth a single word. For just as the consecrated oil used for anointing brings health, in the same way, saliva in human beings makes possible and preserves their powers to see, to hear, to smell, to speak, and to do all that is necessary for the proper functioning of the body.

A Chill in the Stomach. A person who has a cold stomach expels much spit because he is not warm; for that reason he is also sickly. However, a person who has a warm stomach only brings up a little spit, for he is somewhat dry within. For that reason, he easily gets attacks of fever.

Flesh. All flesh is fresh and has its slime from this freshness. This is clearly manifest in the flesh of cattle when they are slaughtered. For when the carcass is hung up, drops of slime fall out. A person who has thin, weak flesh more easily sweats out the slime than someone whose flesh is weighted down with much fat. For a person who has

116

thin, weak flesh on his body is like a cheese that is riven with myriad tiny holes and has not been pressed together hard. Air and the other elements easily penetrate it. For that reason, he easily attracts humors within himself and for the most part separates them out again because he has thin flesh. For the warmth and the taste of his food and drink rise out of his stomach, smoke like a poison, and climb up to his liver, to his heart, and to his lungs. However, the warmth of the liver, of the heart, and of the lungs cannot endure this slime, but rather drives it out into the chest and the throat like food that is placed on the fire to cook causes foam to climb up.

Blowing One's Nose. A person who has a cold, weak stomach and weak intestines sends a cold, moist vapor into the brain because of this weakness. These impurities turn into something like a boiled toxin and are expelled from the nose and the mouth. In the same way the stars in the air purify themselves, and the earth also throws up certain dirty, foul-smelling objects.

The Cleansing of the Brain through Spit and Nose Blowing. The brain has orifices that are continually open to the air and through which it remains constantly moist and soft. These are a person's eyes, ears, nose, and mouth. The cold, moist, foul-smelling humors collect at the entrance to the nose and the throat, for the brain cannot tolerate them but rather releases them to cleanse the person and throws them out with a pulse of air. If, for some reason, a person could not maintain this process, he would lose his mind and dry out, for the stomach would perish and the brain would putrify. They could not endure this smelly refuse. In the same way, the sea does not tolerate garbage and refuse for long, but throws them up on the shore. If a person has flesh that is taut, his flesh is as hard as a cheese that is pressed so hard that fluids can no longer run out of it. For that reason, the powerful slime in his flesh remains behind, and in that manner the flesh becomes hard within, for it can no longer evacuate this foul excrement. The moisture from food and drink and the other humors is so much weaker in such persons that they receive no help from the humor that is in their flesh. As a consequence of the tightness and hardness of their flesh, it may not flow out.

Such persons are sick on the inside of their bodies and have ulcers and boils on the outside because the dirty slime in them remains behind and they cannot get rid of it. For that reason, they have many pains in their chest, in their veins, and throughout the rest of their

117

body. Whoever has fatty flesh on his body has an excess of various humors and coughs easily, but only expels a little thereby. For air and the other elements can only penetrate his insides with difficulty, and because of the thick, fat flesh can only, with difficulty, make their way out again, thereby bringing it about that the humors for cleansing are expelled. A person who has excessive phlegm and cannot expel it has complaints throughout his sick, weak flesh; he is thereby not healthy and cannot be healthy. A person who has phlegm to excess and is able to expel it, however, becomes somewhat thin and sound of body, for he does not retain the dirt within himself. However, the person who cannot expel his phlegm and, as we have said, thereby becomes sick, should drink purgatives and thereby purify himself.

Sneezing. If a person's blood is not fresh and lively in his veins but just lies there as if it were asleep, and also if the humors in him are not lively but only flow sluggishly, the soul naturally takes notice of this and agitates the entire body through a sneeze, thereby letting the blood and the humors of the person wake up again and return to their proper disposition. For if water were not kept in motion by storms and floods, it would become stagnant and foul; in the same way a person would become contaminated within if he did not sneeze or if his nose could not clean itself by blowing.

Nose Bleeds. If persons have great anger or self-willed obstinacy within, but cannot show or express it for some reason — whether it be a lack of courage, anxiety, or feelings of shame over their depressed situation or because they otherwise cannot do it — then sometimes the vessels in their brain, their neck, and their chest break and burst because of this harmful pressure and flow through the entrance and out through the way by which smells are led to the nose. However, there are other persons who are preoccupied with various nonsensical reflections who cannot transform them into deeds or who move from place to place in their unsteady, superficial mind and are inwardly torn this way and that because of an abnormal condition or a roaming impetuosity, and thus so to speak fall into craziness, so that they no longer have their eyes and their facial expression under control. At that point, the vessels in their brain, their neck, and their chest burst under the influence of this diseased fantasy so that blood flows from their nose, as was said above. For their senseless reflections and thoughts cause the aforementioned vessels to swell up and blood to emerge. Also, if a person has too much blood both in his flesh and in his vessels, he discovers that, because of the breath that he both takes in and expels through his nose, the exit through the nose is easier than at any other point on the body, so that the vessels of the brain and the other vessels in the region, as a consequence of the excess of blood, burst there and flow out. There are also men in whom there is too much blood so that because of this excess it becomes thick and black. But since such people are basically of sound constitution and in good health, they expel the excess blood through the nose. Through this outflow, their brain is cleansed, their eyesight is sharpened, and their powers regenerate themselves again. Other men occasionally fall prey to serious fever attacks where the inner heat puts their blood into a state of excitement like wine fermenting in the vat; thus, they cause blood to flow from the nose. Through this flow of blood, the brain is somewhat emptied of blood, the eyes are clouded, and the powers in such men are weakened.

A Stuffed-Up Head. If a person's brain is otherwise clean and healthy, then storms of air and the other elements rise into the brain, the various humors move toward the brain and away again and build a cloudy vapor on the path to the nose and the throat so that a harmful slime collects there, similar to a cloudy fog. This slime then concentrates the germs of disease from the sick humors there so that they may be expelled with pain through the nose and the throat.

Ulcers that are already ripe finally break out and set free the slimy humors that are contained within them. In the same way, no food can be boiled without the dirt that is inside it being thrown out through the purifying foam. The soul acts in the same way in the human body since all the bodily humors in the eyes, ears, nose, mouth, and digestive organs are boiled through the fire of the soul each after its own fashion, as a food is cooked by the fire when it throws up a foam.

However, if a person eats a new and unknown food for the first time and drinks a new, unknown wine or some other new drink, then the other humors in the person are excited and liquified by these new humors, and they flow along the purification path out the nose just as, to make a comparison, a new wine in its vat carries out dirt and dregs as it is poured out. If a person tried somehow to hold back such a cleansing or to block the outflow, he would harm himself thereby as much as if he retained his stools or urine within himself and they were not promptly eliminated.

However, if other humors arrive in profusion to augment those already present so that a great bodily pain arises thereby, then a medicine should be applied so that they may flow out more easily.

Purgatives. Drinks that cleanse the stomach and the intestines do not help people who are very sick and who find themselves in a miserable condition, because they are exhausted by constant paralysis. They also are of no use to those who have such disturbed humors within themselves that, like rivers in a flood, they flow this way and that in continual change because the drinks they have consumed are more harmful than helpful. When such drinks leave the stomach, they often flow between the skin and the flesh and around in the veins and so do not remain in the stomach. Thus, if such a purgative drink is placed in the stomach of such a person, it no longer finds the humors present in order to drive them out.

Lameness. People who are crippled as a result of gout and are encumbered with the above-mentioned humors, are helped by the powder of noble, good herbs and good, pleasant aromas from precious roots. For by their excellent operation they suppress, overcome, and moderate the harmful vapor that emerges from the above-mentioned humors and excites the harmful humors. People who are neither completely healthy nor totally sick should take the drink mentioned below; it will bring them health. Those who are healthy should drink it, for it preserves their health so that they do not become sick. It also takes out what is slimy, dirty, and foul from those who, because of various rich foods, have fat, slimy humors in them. Also, those who have eaten something that has given them stomach pains should take it because it moderates and drives away these pains. A person who intends to take such drinks should do so in June or July before August begins, on an empty stomach, and without any additional spices. It distances the harmful humors from the stomach and cleanses it so that the person does not become sick in August. If a person has eaten something that causes pain in his stomach, he should take the drink in October. A person can also take other healing potions with more effect in the above-mentioned months than in other months.

Diet. To maintain one's health, a person should eat naturally cold dishes after naturally warm foods and naturally warm dishes after naturally cold food, naturally moist foods after naturally dry ones, and naturally dry foods after those which are naturally moist, whether they be cooked or not, so that they are properly attuned to one another.

The Creation of Adam and The Fashioning of Eve. When God made Adam, God caused him to fall into a deep sleep and put a strong feeling of love in him. And God made a form for the love of man, and this is the way it came about that woman is the love of man. As soon as the woman was finished, God gave the man the power of begetting so that through his love, that is the woman, he could beget offspring. That is, as soon as Adam's gaze fell upon Eve, he was immediately filled with wisdom because he saw before him the mother through whom he should beget children. However, when Eve's glance fell upon Adam, she saw him as if she were looking up to heaven. For a soul that strives toward heaven looks toward what is above; and her hope was placed in the man. In this way it came about that there is only one proper love between man and woman. In the heat of passion, the love of a man reacts to the love of the woman like the fire of a volcano, that one can hardly control, to a wood fire, that one can easily put out. In comparision to the love of the man which is like a strongly burning wood fire, the love of a woman is like a mild warmth that streams out from the sun and brings forth fruit, for through her gentleness she brings forth fruit in her children. The great love that was in Adam as Eve came forth from him, and the sweetness of the sleep in which he lay at that time, transformed itself, however, into the opposite of sweetness after he fell into sin. However, because the man felt this great sweetness in himself, he hurried quickly, like a stag to the spring, toward the woman and the woman toward him. It is similar to the threshing floor of a farm that is beaten with many strokes and thereby becomes warm when the grain should be threshed out.

Concupiscence. When carnal desire stirs itself up in a man, it is released from the fire in the marrow which breaks out in men for different reasons such as unbecoming, unrestrained joy; immoderate eating and drinking; or an active but straying imagination. In this way it takes men out of themselves. The fire in the marrow awakens desire that has the tang of sin, and through this savor, then, the desire arouses a passion in the blood like a storm so that the blood builds up a foam and leads this milky foam, by a blissful feeling, into the hollow spaces of the sexual organs, for it is already boiling and ripe. Every food tastes better when it is well cooked than before it is cooked and finished. The man feels this desire at the place where the entire power of the vessels is located, for it comes out of the veins. In the same way, the aroma, the taste, and the whole power of the wine comes out at the tip of the bottle. If the man is afflicted with desirous thoughts, then without any contact, he often emits as much foam out of the sexual organs as water builds up when it is agitated by the wind. However, if he reaches the release of his desire by himself, then he squirts out a thin, cloudy, and half-cooked foam similar to skim milk, for it was not heated by the fire of another person. Just as a dish is not cooked by its own natural fire if another fire is not added to it, in the same way a man's seed is not properly finished unless the fire of another person contributes to it. Thus when a person is bound in desire together with another person or with another living, feeling creature, he then squirts out a seed that is fully cooked through both fires and is similar to fat, full marrow. If a man is united with a woman as he spills out seed, he pours his seed on the right place. In the same way, a cooked dish is taken out of the pot and put onto a plate to be eaten. However, if he is not with a woman on that occasion, but with an animal that is not appropriate for his human nature, then he pours out his seed in a shameful way on an improper spot. In the same way, some one can take food from the pot and throw it on the ground. That is the filth from which mankind is made.

Nocturnal Emissions. When a sleeping man has a nocturnal emission without the influence of a dream picture but simply on the basis of the male nature, the heat of the marrow is not aroused. Thus the seed comes out like water that as a result of moderate warmth is only lukewarm. However, with an emission that takes place as a consequence of a dream picture, the marrow of the man burns strongly so that one can compare this flow of semen with boiling water that however has not been brought to a full boil because the man at this time is not awake. If a man finds himself at the high point of desire and notices the excitement in his body without, however, pouring out the sexual foam, he will not be weakened in body by it. However, a person who finds himself in such a desirous excitement that the foam reaches the member that squirts it out but still, by some means, keeps it back in his body, such a person very often becomes sick and is afflicted with a strong or three-day fever or other ailment.

Sexual Maturity in a Male. From his fifteenth year, a man experiences lustful desires in himself and then easily produces the foam of the male seed under the influence of stray fantasies. However, his feelings of desire and his seed are not yet fully matured. Because his semen is not yet mature, the young man must be closely looked after so that he does not satisfy his lust with a woman or in some other way. For then he easily becomes irrational and unintelligent, loses his understanding, and easily turns into a passionate, undisciplined being because he is not yet mature enough to produce a mature seed. If the young man is strong of body, then in his sixteenth year he may become sexually mature; however, if he is weak of body, it may not be until his seventeenth year that he becomes sexually mature. Only then, because of his maturity, will he have reached a fully developed understanding and a better, established character than he had before his maturity. After his fiftieth year, a man gives up his childish and inappropriate behavior and takes on a fixed character. If he is strong and lively in nature, then his sexual drive lasts until his seventieth year, but if he is weak in nature, then it lessens around his sixtieth year and continues so until his eightieth year. After his eightieth year, it is extinguished in him.

Sexual Maturity in a Female. A young girl feels the sexual drive in herself from her twelfth year, and she then easily sweats out the foam of desire under the influence of roving thoughts although this desire is not yet ripe for the reception of semen. Because the girl is still immature, one must most carefully make sure that she does not fall into sensuality, for she then is more prone than at other times to these wayward fantasies. Because at her young age she is not yet sexually mature, if she is not carefully watched, she easily loses the feeling for propriety and shame and the correct insight about premature sexual activity. Due to such poor habits, sooner or later she inclines more toward animal than human behavior patterns. If she is lively and moist by nature, she will reach her sexual maturity and fertility by her fifteenth year; however, if she is of a weak or sickly nature, it may take until her sixteenth year for her to reach sexual maturity and fertility. By that time, she has developed a fully matured, fully developed reason and takes on a more fixed character than before. At her fiftieth year, the woman gives up her girlish behavior and inappropriate character and takes on a balanced, even nature. However, if the woman is of a moist, lively, and powerful nature, in her case carnal desire continues until she is seventy years old. However, if she has a delicate, sickly nature, then the sexual drive declines at sixty and is gone entirely at eighty, as was described above in the case of the man. A person in his passion who sprays out his seed like the donkey develops reddish eyes and a thick skin on his eyes and thereby substantially worsens his eyesight. However, someone who does this moderately and discretely does not hurt his eyes very much.

Marrow. The marrow in the bones of men gives stability to his whole body. This marrow is fairly solid and does not flow; it has as much power and strength in the bones of men as the heart has in the rest of the body. It burns so glowingly hot that its heat exceeds the heat of fire. For man can extinquish a fire — but not that of his marrow — as long as he lives. With its heat and its sweating it penetrates the bones and strengthens both the bones as well as the entire human body.

The Three Powers of Marrow. The warmth of the fire in the marrow is like the fire in a stone; it contains three powers. The first power ignites the blood so that it flows; the second power, in various ways, sometimes causes blood to flow out in both men and women; the third power begets the burning, sweet enjoyment and the urgent, burning storm of strongest desire and the drive to beget.

Concupiscence. Sometimes when people are not busy or occupied with some affair, this burning storm breaks out, seethes in their chest, makes them feel rather pleasurable, then climbs from the chest up into their brain and fills it, as well as all their other vessels, with a burning heat. It then grasps the lungs and the heart and finally arrives in the region of the sexual organs — in a man in the loins and in the woman at the navel. Then their consciousness goes asleep, for they no longer know what they do.

Temptation. Along with the powerful storm of passion, there also comes the temptation by the devil, and people break out in passion and forget their feelings of shame.

However, when the sun comes up, the air and the dew come to the sun's help and serve it. In this way, the air fashions some cold things and the dew some moist ones whereby the heat of its fire is moderated so that the heat, cold, and moisture fall down for the general benefit of the fruit of the earth.

The Correct Warmth of Marrow. As the sun brings warmth to the earth, so a person's marrow provides warmth to the entire body. However, the strong wind that comes out of the stomach like a draught of air cools down the fire in the marrow somewhat. And the moisture that goes out of the bladder bedews and moistens the fire so that it provides the proper warmth to the human body, for it is somewhat tempered by the cold and the moisture. Just as frightening storms and hail showers disturb the air so that on the one hand it does not bring the proper coolness in its service to the sun, and on the other hand the sun cannot bring the proper heat to it, so also on occasion the various foods so stir up the stomach that under their influence it cannot send the proper cooling to the heat in the marrow, and hence it throws the marrow into great unrest rather than into the correct warmth.

Gluttony. If a person eats a variety of meat and excessively hot, rich foods without taking into account their differences and the proper sequence, their juices throw the humors in the marrow into a harmful disturbance so that it awakens the demand for the satisfaction of desire. Hence the person who wants to eat meat dishes should eat only moderately, and the food should only be cooked with simple seasonings, prepared and set out when not too hot and with not too many spicy condiments. For its juices have a certain similarity to the humors in human flesh and easily instill in the marrow the striving for the satisfaction of desire. Just as the working of an unclean, dry wind diminishes the falling of the dew so that it cannot any longer provide the commensurate moisture to the warmth of the sun, in the same way a strong, noble wine causes the effectiveness of a person's bladder to wither so that it can no longer provide the proper power and liveliness to his marrow.

Wine. Wine is the blood of the earth and is in the earth as blood is in human beings. It has a certain commonality with human blood and for that reason, like a water wheel, funnels its warmth directly out of the bladder into the marrow and sets it into an extremely burning heat so that the marrow then bestows upon the blood a hot striving of desire. For that reason, a person who wants to drink some strong, noble wine should mix it with water, so that thereby its power will be somewhat weakened and moderated. One should also mix the wine that is called ''Hunsrücker'' wine with water until its tart, bitter taste is moderated and becomes sweet. For just as blood is dry and does not flow without moist water, so also wine, if it is drunk without being mixed with water, dries a person out, harms him, im-

125

pairs his bodily health, and awakens carnal desires in him. A person should consume each food and drink with decency, properly set and moderated, for otherwise the person will be weakened by the various humors that are contained in them, and his nature then overflows its boundaries in harmful desire. Just as the earth is impaired in its fertility if the sun beams upon it in an excessively strong fashion without the moderating influence of the air and the dew, in the same way a man does harm to his physical health and becomes aroused to carnal desire if he consumes the heat of food and drink without measure. Even if he is of sound body he should pay attention when eating and drinking so that he remains healthy; however, if he is sickly, he should strengthen himself by eating meat dishes with moderation and prudent caution. Still, he shouldn't drink wine in addition to the meat dishes unless it has been mixed with water.

Thinking. The above-mentioned burning hot wind that rises out of a person's marrow toward carnal desire sometimes awakens and promotes wayward thinking when man reflects on who he is, where he comes from, and what kind of a feeling of pleasure was at issue that Adam received because he disobeyed God's command by eating the apple, or when he sees or hears something that arouses desire in him. For through the devil's temptation, such thoughts attract as if on command the above-mentioned burning hot storm of desire out of the marrow so that it arouses itself, penetrates the chest, strongly grasps the brain and the liver, penetrates the heart, and descends into the sexual organs as was described above. So it goes with those who wish to satisfy their lust.

Nightmares. Very often the blood of sleeping men strongly heats up through the fire in his marrow, and in this way through the heat in the blood, the water in the blood is evaporated. Then the devilish cunning — that was already in play at the first temptation to the first fusion during the conception of mankind — shows itself, sometimes with the permission of God, and begets a strong disturbance in the man's surroundings so that it throws him into a strong anxiety while he sleeps. Under the pressure of fantasy, it looks as if the devil were at hand. In truth, he is not there, for man could not endure his presence. Sometimes the weather also gives this impression when it sends out terrifying peals of thunder; by these means it terrorizes men with fear so that they quake with anxiety. Still, at such times the weather does not show its full strength; however, on the last day it will show its full strength when it destroys everything on the earth.

Dreams. The devil acts in the same way when he shows himself as if in a cloud of fog and tortures a man until his soul thinks it is seeing the future in dreams and becomes disturbed because it does not know what kind of fear it has withstood. Such terrors occur easily to all men during sleep with the exception of those who are of a carefree, happy nature. The latter very seldom experience such terrors while asleep, for the great and becoming happiness that they naturally have in themselves cannot exist without the flavor of a good disposition. For they are peaceloving by nature, and their character is free from deceit and cunning.

A Difficult Constitution. There are other people whom one speaks about with blood problems. Often bile builds up in their blood, makes the blood black, and dries out the blood water so that such people are thereby sorely afflicted both while awake and while asleep.

The Connection Between Adam's Fall and Bile. Adam knew the good and yet did the bad, in that he ate the apple. As a punishment for his disordered faculties, bile developed in him, which without the influence of the devil would not exist in human beings either in a waking or a sleeping condition. The melancholy and despair that Adam inherited as a result of his Fall develop out of bile. For in the same moment that Adam overstepped the divine command, bile collected in his blood. In comparison, the brightness of a candle disappears immediately as soon as the flame is put out, and only the glowing, smoking wick with its smell remains behind. In the same way, it came to be with Adam because the bile collected in his blood at the moment the flame went out in him. As a result, melancholy and despair broke out in him. For at Adam's Fall, the devil brought bile into existence in him which makes a person into a doubter or unbeliever on occasion. But because the form of man is fixed so that he cannot leave his skin behind, he fears God and is sad. So often in his sadness, he falls into despair and does not believe that God cares for him. Because man is made after the image of God, he cannot avoid fearing God. Hence it is difficult for the devil to traffic with a man who opposes him, for man still fears God more than the devil. Hence man sets his hope upon God; the devil, however, has no hope in him. Often the devil works on the bile and makes a man melancholic and despairing so that many men so afflicted become suffocated by their doubt and are heading for destruction. Still, many are fighting against themselves in this plight so much that in their fight they are like martyrs.

Spiritual Depression. The devil may afflict a person in such a way both in his waking and his sleeping moments and may sometimes so oppress him during sleep that the person has the impression that something is pressing down upon him.

The Devil's Hate. Because the devil hates the good characteristics of mankind, he has also, for that reason, a hatred for all other creatures among the beasts and plants that have good characteristics and are pure and helpful. Thus if a person is bothered by a devilish illusion by day or night, whether asleep or awake, he should seek out the help God has set up against it. If a person finds himself in a happy, sad, or angry mood — or any other one — he cannot remain for long in this mood, but must change to another movement of the spirit. If he notices a sudden change in mood so that one gives out and another begins, the soul naturally notices this rotation and has a kind of disinclination toward the fact that a person should so often change himself, and acts like it would rather separate from its body, as it does when it leaves the dying body. This causes the person to open his mouth and he yawns.

Yawning. When a person has made a change or begun a new job, the soul gives up its opposition to this change and returns to peace. However, if some other man is still vexed and this latter sees the first man yawning, then his own soul acts naturally in the same way as if it would like to leave his body, in that he opens his mouth to yawn, too.

Stretching Out the Limbs. When a person has a serious fever and harmful humors are in danger of gaining the upper hand in him, a bodily heaviness overtakes him and difficulty in thinking. The soul naturally notices some of these changes, draws back from the body as if gripped with revulsion, rather strongly racks and stretches his body together with his vessels as it does when it must leave the body.

Forgetfulness. Sometimes harmful humors beget a vapor in certain persons that rises up to their brain and so poisons it that they stop speaking, become forgetful, and are deprived of all their faculties.

Hiccups. The painful so-called hiccups come from having a chill in the stomach. This cold makes its way to the liver and from there spreads up to the region of the lungs so that the heart's activity is also affected by it. Because a person shivers from cold and his teeth chatter when he shivers, he gets the hiccups with the cooperation of his voice.

The Bile and Its Suffering Vapor. Very often, bile builds up in a person and causes a smoky vapor to stream out of him that contracts his vessels, his blood, and his flesh until it can spread itself no futher in his body but gives up. Moreover, it also happens that the bile often gains the upper hand in a person so that its excess spreads out in the human body. Then the person has pains in his body for a long time; it is as if he were stuck with nails until the excess bile recedes.

The Connection Between Bile and Adam's Punishment. Before Adam disobeyed the divine command, what is now man's bile lighted like a crystal and had the taste of good work in it. What is now black bile in him lighted like the dawn and had consciousness and the completion of good works in it. However, after Adam disobeyed God's command, the brilliance of innocence was darkened in him, and his eyes, which previously gazed on heavenly things, were unable to see; the bile became bitter, the black bile became black like the godless, and he was completely turned around. Hence his soul became sad and soon angrily sought forgiveness for this. For anger comes out of sadness. Thus has mankind received from its ancestor the melancholy, anger, and everything else that hurts it.

Melancholy and Anger. If the soul senses something unsuitable for itself and its body, it compresses the heart, the liver, and the vessels together. Thus there builds up in the region of the heart something like a fog which encloses the heart in darkness, and the person thereby becomes sad. Further, after melancholy, anger develops. For during this period if the person has seen or heard or reflected on why he is sad, sometimes this fog of sadness that has afflicted his heart builds up a warm smoke in all his humors and in the area of his bile and throws the bile into excitement. In this way anger rises silently out of the bitterness of the bile. If a person does not allow his anger to break out but endures it silently, the bile calms down. However, if the anger has not stopped, then this smoke spreads to the black bile and irritates it. This then gives out a very black fog that again returns to the bile and draws out of it a very bitter smoke. If this fog and smoke reach the person's brain, first, the two of them make him sick in the head; they then climb down into his belly, shatter his blood vessels and bowels, and, so-to-speak, throw the person into insanity. Thus, a person lets his anger break out, for in a sense he no longer knows who he is. For a man rages in anger more than in any other disturbance to his health. Through his anger a man will very often become very sick, for over time the harmful humors make him sick if they often become stirred up in his bile and black bile. If man did not have the bitter bile and the black bile, he would always be healthy.

Causes for the Increase of Bile and Black Bile. A person whose bile has predominance over his black bile can easily control his inner anger. However, the person in whom black bile has a greater influence than the bile is prone to anger and easily flies off the handle. Just as a strong, sour vinegar develops out of a good wine, in the same way the bile increases through good, appropriate foods and decreases through bad foods. However, the black bile decreases with the consumption of good, healthy foods. On the other hand, it increases with the consumption of bad, bitter, unclean, and badly prepared foods and with the various humors that are implicated in the production of various ailments. If a person's face turns red when he gets angry, his blood boils because of the influence of the bile and then pours into his face. Such a person suddenly flies into a fit of anger, but his anger is quickly over just as a strong fire quickly falls back into itself. The person is not badly hurt by such and his body does not dry out excessively in his body. He often goes away without making satisfaction and without receiving any. However, if a person turns pale when he becomes angry, his anger is caused by the fact that his black bile is cast into an uproar that on the one hand does not upset his blood, but rather gradually brings his humors into confusion. Thereby the person becomes cooled down; his powers decrease and become weak; and hiding his anger, he turns pale. However, in the meantime, the evil resolve to avenge himself has ripened within him, and this bitterness drives him on until finally he can do no other than to allow his rage free rein.

Sighing. Because of their anger, such men often become skinny and dried up, but their soul retains its knowledge and understanding. For that reason, it sighs from the inside out when it reflects about where it comes from and what it is, without the man knowing where these sighs are coming from. However, if its body must face abuse, disease, or some other unpleasant suffering that it cannot avoid, it sighs deeply within.

Tears. As a result of sadness, a kind of smoke emerges from the humors that are in a person which spreads itself out in the area of the heart. It overpowers the humor that is called water from the heart's blood and from the blood in the other vessels. This occasions loud sighing, and leads the water, if it would be vented, upwards through the veins into the tiny vessels of the brain and through these to the eyes, for the eyes have a certain relationship to water. Then this water flows from the eyes, and that makes tears. Water for tears is drawn from human blood in this way by sighing and moaning. In the same way, human seed is drawn out of marrow and blood. Tears occasioned by sadness climb, as has been said, like biting smoke upwards to the eyes, dry out a person's blood, let the flesh waste away, damage the person like harmful foods, and cloud the eyes. However, tears that are caused by joy are milder than those that come forth from sadness. When the soul in its sadness realizes for the first time because of its powers of understanding that it is a heavenly nature — but here in the world is only a pilgrim — and when the body collaborates with her in good things so that the two form a union in doing holy works, for joy and bliss, without fog or dark smoke beneath the sighing, it sends the tear humor through the mentioned vessels toward the eyes and causes it to flow out like a spring of sweet water. Such tears do not contract a person's heart, do not cause his blood to dry out nor his flesh to waste away, and do not cloud his eyes.

Regret. If a person comes to regret and repent his sins, his tears are a mixture of sadness and joy and are poured out without smoke only because of the soul's depression. Because his tears have their cause in a spiritual depression, they partially dry out the blood, cause the flesh to waste away, and somewhat cloud the eyes until, through the improvement they cause, joy breaks out. A person who from birth has had a tendency to obesity, to clogged vessels, and a soft heart cries easily and becomes happy easily. However, a person who from birth has had a tendency to be thin and has a heart as hard as a horny callous — that is, harder than other flesh — cries seldom or not at all and has a strict, antisocial nature. If the tears that are drawn up to the eyes by sighs are not poured out through the eyes, they return to the humor that is located in the human body, make it bitter and similar to vinegar, and dry out the chest. Tears that reach the eyes but are not poured out, but rather are held back within the person, still do not do much harm to the eyes since they do not flow from the eyes.

Adam's Knowledge. Before his fall, Adam knew the angels' song and every form of music and had a voice like the peal of the bell.[1] However, as a result of his fall, through envy, the serpent infested his marrow and his abdomen with a kind of wind, and it is still present in every man. Through this wind a person's spleen becomes fat, and thereby inappropriate intemperance, hilarity, and echoing laughter are set loose.

Echoing Laughter and Hilarity. Just as at Adam's fall the pure, holy form of begetting offspring was transformed into carnal desire, so also the voice full of heavenly joy that Adam possessed changed into the opposite sound of hilarity and resounding laughter. Inappropriate rowdiness and laughter have a certain commonality with carnal desire, and the same wind that sets loose laughter, emerges from a person's marrow and disturbs his abdomen and his bowels. Once in a while as a result of excessive disturbance, laughter drives as much tear water out of the eyes from the blood in the vessels as foam of the man's seed is driven out from the blood in the vessels by the heat of his passionate desire.

Joy and Laughter. When a person's consciousness is not aware of anything sad, unpleasant, or bad in himself, this person's heart also opens itself to joy, just as blossoms open themselves to the sun's warmth. For the liver receives this joy and preserves it in itself just as the stomach retains nourishment in itself. If a person rejoices over something good or something bad that pleases him, then occasionally the above-mentioned wind that comes out of his marrow grips first his abdomen, then falls to the spleen and fills its vessels up, extends itself up to the heart, fills the liver, brings the person thus to laughter, and causes his voice, similar to the sound of an animal, to break out in laughter like a neighing horse. A person who allows himself and his thoughts to be driven as easily as the wind this way and that, has a rather thick spleen; for that reason he easily becomes happy

[1] Hildegard refers to the voice sounding like a monochord, which is an ancient, one-stringed instrument.

and enjoys laughter. However, just as sadness and anger make a person thin and weak, in the same way immoderate laughter chafes the spleen, weakens the stomach, and causes the humors to circulate incorrectly.

Obesity. If a person eats meat that has too much fat and other food or dishes that have too much red blood, this will do him more harm than good; such excessively fat dishes cannot remain in the stomach long enough to be properly and healthily digested because of the excessively greasy and slippery moisture that is in them. For that reason, a person should only eat meat that is moderately fat and full-blooded so that he may retain them until they receive a good and proper digestion.

Leanness in People. If a person is very thin in his body and his limbs, then he should occasionally eat moderately fat meat and moderately blood-rich foods so that his leanness and his dryness might be somewhat diminished and moistened. For the flesh of animals that a man eats makes human flesh fat, and wine increases the blood in a person more than other foods or other drinks.

Wine. When earth that is fertile enough for grain is used for grapes, then the resulting wine is healthier for a sick person to drink than wine that comes from earth that is used as a fruit orchard, that is, that is too poor to bring forth much grain, even if the latter wine is more expensive than the first. Wine heals and gladdens mankind with its comforting warmth and great power.

Beer. Beer makes human flesh thick, and because of its power and the good humors of the grain, it gives the face a beautiful color. Water, on the other hand, weakens a person and sometimes, if he is sick, builds up a slime in the region of the lungs because water is weak and does not possess any great power. However, if the person is healthy and then on occasion drinks only water, it will do him no harm.

Drunkenness. If a person drinks wine — or some other drink from which he can become drunk — too much and without measure, his entire blood liquifies and flows and streams this way and that in his veins without order so that in the process all this person's senses and understanding are also confused. In the same way, rivers sometimes exceed their banks as a result of excessive rainfall and cause a sudden flood. Because in such a person the human understanding becomes confused and knowledge of the good wills the good, he often brings forth holy words all mixed up and without any connection without knowing it; and because, also, knowledge of evil wills the evil, in the same way he brings forth shameful, evil words without being ashamed and without knowing it. As a consequence of his drunkenness, he has more of an ailing, unrestrained understanding than a proper consciousness because his understanding is smothered and drowned.

Vomiting. If a person eats things that are too cold, and soon thereafter consumes some hot things so that the cold things overwhelm the hot, or if he consumes liquid nourishment to excess so that the liquid exceeds the dry, then very often because of the resulting stomach upset, that person will experience vomiting because he cannot digest such nourishment. For that reason, a person should choose his foods with an eye to their having the proper temperature so that he does not harm himself by vomiting. Whoever, as a consequence of some disease or because of disorderly feeding, suffers from vomiting is cold within in his stomach so that he has nothing warm within himself whereby the foods that he eats can be broken down through digestion. The half-digested foods climb upwards, for they cannot descend in the other direction to be eliminated. As a consequence, the person suffers much through vomiting. However, if a person stimulates himself to vomit or takes purgatives for that purpose, this is not healing and healthy for him. Such an artificially induced vomiting squeezes his vessels and his blood and leaves them in an unnatural condition. For this vomiting did not take the proper route toward the exterior, and so such a person will often damage himself. For that reason, a person should not induce vomiting, for it is not healthy for him. Vomiting that happens naturally in a person is better than one that the person induces through some artificial method.

Insufficient Digestion. If our humors are disturbed by some ailment or unhealthy, disease-promoting foods so that hot is connected with cold and cold with hot, wet with dry and dry with wet, then once in a while the humors push and drive out the undigested food and drink.

If such unhealthy foods are cast out, that is good for the person with regard to his health. However, if the foods are decent and they are cast out, then it is harmful for the person in regard to his bodily health for then the vessels are emptied of the good humor of this food.

If the bad humors gain the upper hand in a person, sometimes they build up thick fumes in him that are neither cold nor hot. These fumes spread out in his bowels, in the region of the stomach, and then in the entire body. They stimulate any other disease-promoting agents to action. Nor do they allow the consumed nourishment to reach the stomach through the natural, proper way or to leave through the natural, proper way, but rather cause the nourishment to churn around as in a roadside ditch or a gutter. It dilutes the necessary, natural air in him, and as a result the nourishment in him cannot be properly and correctly digested and eliminated. For that reason, it comes out half-digested and like a thin stream.

Dysentery. Certain very delicate, blood-rich vessels surround the thin skin or membrane in which the human brain is encased. They are firmly connected with other larger vessels that lead down to the heart, the liver, the lungs, the stomach, and all his inner organs. They contribute their blood to these larger vessels as do small streams that bring their water to the larger rivers. The larger vessels are like the large rivers that carry their flow over the landscape and like the pipes that bring water into houses and lead it out again. Now, if harmful humors have gained the upper hand in a person and have aroused a still-lingering fever in him, then they precipitate an immense flood in him, so to speak, that causes a thick, black vaporish smoke to rise to his brain and excite all those delicate vessels which surround the brain to a counteroffensive. At that point, an excessive amount of blood flows out of them which sets all the larger vessels connected with them into an uproar so that they also flow in the wrong direction, cause their blood to flow through the entire body, and send it down to the bowels and the digestive brew. This blood that mixes itself in the bowels and the digestive brew causes the excrement to become bloody so that blood also comes out with the excrement.

Spitting Up Blood. If harmful, curdling, and toxic humors have gained the upper hand in a person, they throw the blood that flows through the body's veins from its proper path and force it into an incorrect path to penetrate both the organs essential for life and the intestines. As a consequence, such a person loses blood in a dangerous way through elimination or vomiting and dries out within. On occasion, also, harmful humors that are watery and thin gain the upper hand in a person, oppose themselves to the blood in the vessels in their correct path, and bring it about that one bleeds from the anus without passing feces. This is dangerous for a person, and it can go so far that his vital faculties decline. However, if these humors leave the anus with his feces, they often purify the person and restore his health. Many persons have so much bitterness in their hearts and their thoughts that their spleen contracts and dries out. As a consequence, the good humor that should nourish the spleen arrives at the lungs by an incorrect path and there forms a kind of curdle out of the blood. So often the afflicted person spits and vomits out blood in a dangerous way. Other persons have a melancholy, troubled heart, and this sadness cramps together the delicate inner vessels that transport the blood through the body so that one of them can very easily be injured. For that reason, the injury causes blood droplets to flow gradually into the digestive organs, and so once in a while such a man throws up blood. However, once he has regained a cheerful composure, his delicate vessels will become healthy again, and so such an afflicted man stops spitting blood.

Unreasonable Fasting. If people are abstemious in their eating in an exaggerated way so that they do not preserve the proper, appropriate strength in their bodies by eating, and if as a consequence some become frivolous and others are afflicted with many heavy disease symptoms, then it sometimes happens that serious disturbances arise in their bodies because the elements in them are aroused against one another. For if fire and water work against one another within the mentioned persons, it sometimes happens that these two elements fight against one another either in a joint or at some other point on the body and cause a swelling to arise there in connection with a tumor in the flesh. There are three such kinds of swelling.

The Abscess. One kind of abscess is almost black. It increases under the influence of heat, is dangerous for humans, and threatens them with death. It is to be compared with a cloudburst that destroys and wipes out what it falls upon. Another kind of abscess has a greyish color; it forms in a person through the stormy tussle of the mentioned elements that hurl things like bolts of lightning and cause an immoderate amount of rain to fall. This harms the body, but yet does not kill it; it is to be compared with hail that damages the fruit but does not destroy the roots of a tree. A third type of abscess is a whitish color; it arises in a person from a powerful welling up the ele-

136

ments, like a river that rises immoderately. Although it weakens the body, still it does not lead it to destruction. In the same way, suddenly rising and overflowing rivers flood certain stretches of land and the fruit in the fields, yet they do not sweep them away entirely. The boil that is black is dangerous and almost incurable, but the grey and the whitish ones are not nearly so bad as the black and can be healed.

Tumors. The vessels and flesh of people also swell up because of various humors, both good and bad, just as dough is driven forward by yeast and expands. Sometimes the humors that emerge from the heart, from the liver, from the lungs, from the stomach, and from the remaining inner organs become viscous, slippery, and lukewarm in the event that they should develop contrary to the correct order and gain the upper hand. If they remain in a person, they make him sick. However, if they break out of him, then they make him healthier.

An Ulcer. If a person's humors have collected at one or several places and have caused one or more ulcers, then that person should let them ripen so that they may drain naturally. Otherwise, he will suffer more if they should remain within. When the humors have become mature and drained, then the person should treat such places with healing materials.

A Rash. If harmful humors have appeared on the entire body of a person in the form of a rash, he should wait a while until they are ripe in the same way and drain until the skin between the afflicted places begins to turn red and to dry out. Then he should apply appropriate salves so that the skin does not develop a yet-more-painful pus boil if he waits longer.

Jaundice. The pestilence that is named jaundice arises from a spreading of bile which runs all over as a consequence of diseased humors, fever attacks, and powerful and numerous outbreaks of anger. The liver and the remaining inner organs absorb this flood of bile whose outpouring penetrates the entire human flesh, just as a strong vinegar penetrates a new vessel, and does harm to the person. One can recognize jaundice in people by their unnatural color.

The Connection Between Bodily Activities and Spiritual Malaise. Since the human body is not indolent and will always be doing something, in the same way the human soul, corresponding to its nature, has

137

the duty, from aversion to some of the body's activities, to leave its path and act as if it has slept. In the same way a watermill stops working once in a while if it is broken in one place or another by a huge amount of water. Similarly, the soul remains peaceful and still until the body is struck and pressed by some fear or anxiety. It then regains its powers, returns to its path, and wakes up again. For that person, it is as if he had just been born and as if he had a new being.

Anger. Some men are naturally hot tempered. If on occasion they remain peaceful and calm in the face of some irritation, once in a while in their anger they suffer an attack where their body is under stress; at that point the soul wins back its power and wakes up. However, with other persons, it can happen that, while their soul keeps its peace and calm in the face of some disturbance, their body is oppressed by some suffering or other. Then, their soul also wakes up, wins back its earlier powers, and comes back to itself. There are still other people whose body is crippled by lethargy and irresolution if their soul preserves its peace while oppressed by a strenuous activity. Then the soul awakes, that already sleeps in them, and wins back its earlier powers. There are also some people who often break out in anger because of their disposition.

Frenzy and Epilepsy. The anger that hides within them arouses all their blood so that it begins to boil over; as a result of this boiling, a sort of smoke infects their brain, causes them to go into a frenzy, and limits their consciousness. If such persons should become angry and at the same time are burdened with the usual everyday cares of life, the devil sees that and terrorizes them with his breath if he wishes to lead them astray by his suggestions. Then their soul sinks down exhausted within them and gives up. The body, however, falls unconscious and lies there until the soul wins back its powers and stands up again. A person who suffers from such an affliction has a furious facial expression and makes raging movements. If he should fall to the ground, sometimes unnatural sounds come out. The illness described here appears rather seldom and is very difficult to cure.

Epilepsy. There are still other forms of this disease. With an unreliable, thoughtless, and impatient character, the soul withdraws if it suffers too much from these characteristics and gives up. Then the body, from which the soul's powers have been withdrawn, falls down on the ground and lies there as if it were dead until the soul regains

138

its powers. Such persons have a winning facial expression and a soft essence. If they fall to the ground when afflicted with this disease, they give out doleful sounds and cause much foam to come out of their mouths; however, they can easily be healed.

Dropsy. If a person who is not fat by nature, but thin and melancholy, is occupied with many difficult thoughts, his depression dries out his blood, and his various heavy thoughts excessively reduce the phlegm in him; thereby the water that is in him gains the upper hand and dominates. If a person's blood and phlegm dry out, then they deliver their digestive products to the bladder and excrete them into the urine. However, then the bladder cannot cook the urine, for it does not have the warmth contained in the blood and the phlegm; thus it gets rid of the urine raw, uncooked, and not in the proper manner, but rather causes it to flow in an unnatural way between the skin and the flesh.

Swelling. If in such cases the blood is driven out and the phlegm diminished, the water between the skin and the flesh breaks out and causes the entire body to swell. Because their blood is dry and their phlegm has evaporated, they are always thirsty. For nothing that they drink is transformed into blood and phlegm, but into water that then sits under the skin in the tissues. If water appears under the skin of such a person, one must aid him with a drug, for if one waits too long, the water changes into a cloudy liquid and, mixed with corrupted things, takes on a bloody color. Then the person is in danger. People with a normal bodily constitution, who are neither too fat nor too thin, usually have normal water retention and are seldom bothered by this disease named ''vich.'' For the humors through which these sufferings arise are not present in them in excessive amounts.

Cramps. A person who is either too fat or too thin sometimes has an excess of harmful humors, for he does not have the proper disposition and balance within himself. For that reason, harmful humors are occasionally expelled from his heart, liver, lungs, stomach, and bowels, which reach the bile and cause it to release its vapors and in this way build up an extremely dirty sludge in the person. One can understand this situation by comparing it with standing — not flowing — water where once in a while decaying mire overflows the bank and floods. This sludge reaches either the stomach region, between the bowels, or some other place between the skin and the flesh, stays there, and afflicts the person with intense, unpleasant itching as if it wanted to bite and eat him there. However, it does not have the animal spirit that one needs to bite a person, but rather only a sort of unpleasant, sharp irritation. Something like eyes then shows itself, and it lies in the flesh of a person like a maggot in meat. Sometimes it spreads itself out lengthwise; then it rolls itself up again into a ball and can be compared with the yolk of an egg. Once in a while it excretes a foam that spreads out over the whole body and causes pains to the person.

Worms. Once this foam has penetrated the stomach, it causes certain worms to swarm there, and it also causes certain very malicious, thin, tiny lice to arise in the flesh. Wherever such sludge lies in a person's body, there also occasionally arise very thin, tiny worms called "tarmi." In the same way, worms sometimes arise in water that stays in one place and does not flow. If such little worms remain in a person and do not leave, they do him much damage.

Round worms. Out of the harmful, bad humors that have a toxic influence on people, that collect like sludge in people and change into harmful, thin liquid comparable to a tepid, spoiled wine, worms easily arise in a person, especially in babies and children because their humors are still somewhat mixed with milk. No such worms arise in a person from the usual humors, or from those that are sour like vinegar. If they should begin to grow in a person who has normal humors in himself, they quickly disappear again. However, if such worms mature in a person, they make him sick.

Lice. Some people have delicate bones, limbs, and vessels, but a fat, healthy, well-developed flesh that is neither too solid nor too porous. They have full marrow with the proper warmth and hence, also, full spiritual strength. But they still incline a bit to intemperance and are soft and sensual. Because they have a full marrow, they therefore also have a thick, but delicate, white and healthy fat and are free of lice.

However, once this fat has secreted sweat, it causes lice to develop on the skin and nourishes them. Other people have heavy bones, large limbs, thick vessels, but a weak and not very warm marrow. Because of the weakness of their marrow, they are rather dull and greedy, and they like to eat often. They can also only be busy about their work a short time and do not have perseverence because their flesh is somewhat porous and tepid and their veins are rather narrow. Because they have weak marrow, their fat is thin and weak. Once they begin sweating, their sweat quickly penetrates their flesh, for it is somewhat porous and causes many lice to arise that spring up in swarms from such a person. These men are not very sick and can live a long time. Again, other persons have large bones and limbs, thick vessels, and a thick, fat marrow so that their bones are filled with hot marrow. Because of their thick, fat, full marrow they are clever and skillful, and their flesh is powerful and rather hard and solid because it is fastened by taut vessels. Just as the threads of a net are knotted one to another, so also are the vessels in the whole body of the person connected with one another. Because the flesh of such persons is rather powerful and hard, they sweat only a little. For the thick, powerful vessels hold their flesh so tightly together that they secrete only a little sweat. Because of the fullness and heat of the marrow and the excess of humors that are in them but cannot get out, their fat takes on a little of the color of blood; it is sickly and unhealthy, and as a result many lice grow therein that cannot get out of the flesh of these people but remain in their fat, bore, and eat all through it. As a consequence, the afflicted persons have many pains within their body without knowing where these pains come from. They are sluggish and derive joy from nothing, eat only a little, suffer much from weakness of the heart and the loss of their bodily powers, and have a pale complexion. Still, this color is more green than waxy. Such persons cannot live a long time but rather die soon because their fat, as was said above, is damaged from the inside by lice.

Gall or Kidney Stones. A person of mature years who has soft, moist flesh on his body and who still indulges himself with various rich foods and good, strong wine, easily develops a gall or kidney stone. For from the mentioned foods and drink, if his flesh is still soft and juicy, a kind of dregs collects at the spot where his urine should flow out, which hardens into a small stone. As long as it is located inside the person, it is still somewhat soft because of the warmth and strength of the urine. For that reason the person can still pass some urine for a long time — however, with much difficulty. If the stone inside the man were to become hard, he would soon perish. It is the same way with a woman as with a man. A man's urine is stronger than a woman's, but in spite of that the man suffers greater pains than the woman. If a child or a baby is afflicted with such stones, this comes from the wetnurse's bad, unusable milk with which they were nourished or are still being fed. For if the nurse is sick or if she regularly consumes large amounts of different foods and drink and strong wine, then her milk loses its proper taste and quickly becomes foul smelling. Such milk builds up a foul-smelling sludge in the child or baby at that spot where the urine flows out, and hardens into a gallstone.

Gluttony. The blood of people who are healthy, powerful, and also possess strong desires, but who are drinkers and gluttons and have a desire for rich meat dishes and other such dishes and drinks, takes on a waxy color and gradually becomes thicker. Since because of its viscosity it can no longer flow properly, and also because it has not been thinned out either by fever or a disease in the afflicted person who is yet healthy, it penetrates their flesh and their skin, infects it with the noxious liquid, pollutes it, so to speak, and fills it with abscesses.

The Ulcers of Leprosy. Even poor people who are sound of body and yet have this same disposition toward gluttony, but cannot regularly indulge in such rich foods and drinks, can still, in two or three weeks, or even in one week, become afflicted with the illness mentioned above if they consume what food and drink they have in a gluttonous manner without paying attention to a reasonable sequence. One can already see this with young people and children. This disease frequently arises from meat dishes, various kinds of milk and strong wine, but not from bread, vegetables, and beer.

Leprosy. Other people have solid flesh on their body and a tendency to anger. Their anger arouses their blood so intensely that it descends to the region of the liver. The liver's toughness and blood then mix with this blood, and so it is distributed throughout the person's entire body and causes disturbances in the skin and flesh. As a result, the skin becomes torn, and the sides of the nose thicken and swell because of these cuts. Other people are without restraint in their passion. They cannot be temperate and don't want to become temperate. As a consequence, their blood is often thrown into great disturbance like a kettle that is placed upon the fire, but which is neither entirely cold nor entirely boiling, and consequently retains dirt within itself, for it doesn't have enough power to throw it out. If such people burn from passion so excessively that their blood is thrown into disturbance and it is no longer properly blood nor properly

142

water nor properly foam, then it is transformed into an evil, foul sludge that ruins the person's flesh and skin and causes abscesses.

The Symptoms of Leprosy. These diseases may be distinguished in the following ways. Scabs that develop from gluttony and drunkenness leave reddish boils and pimples to arise like those in the disease "drakunkulose." Disturbed by the liver, the disease builds up black cuts in a person's skin and flesh that go all the way to the bone. If the scab comes from lasciviousness, it causes broadly sided abscesses that resemble the bark of a tree, and the flesh beneath is red.

Gout. People who have soft flesh rich in pores and are given to excessive indulgence in strong wine are often visited by ailments called gout. People who have soft flesh retain the toxic humors from their excessive drinking, and these will suddenly attack and destroy one of their limbs just as flaming logs and sudden large floods sometimes destroy water mills and other buildings in their vicinity. In the same way, these humors would destroy the limbs that they attack if the grace of God and the spirit of life that is in mankind did not stop them. Nevertheless they destroy many a limb and render many completely unusable as if they were already dead.

The Contraction of the Sinews. It often happens that the powerful disturbances of the harmful humors attack a person's limb and in their raging block his veins so that the blood cannot flow in its vessels. As a result, these vessels dry out, for no blood flows in them. In this way the person begins to limp. Because a human being is fashioned from the elements, he is also kept alive by the elements, and he stands in connection with them.

Fever. The person exhibits these different forms of fever that come from air and the other elements, namely from the heat, the cold, and the moisture, that do not put him in bed nor do him any harm but rather bring health. Through the sweat that they cause and the urine which is expelled, they purify the chest, the stomach, and all the inner organs if they don't gain the upper hand and if the air is properly warmed. However, if an excessive and uncommon heat has developed in the air, then an ordinary fever attack that is ignited by it might be transformed, in certain people, into a serious fever. Excessively cold air so moderates them that they only cause a three-day fever. However, if the air becomes watery and foul-smelling because of a moist condition, they frequently transform themselves into such a disgusting sludge that they occasion in many people a four-day fever. People who are otherwise in good health and who have no easily moved humors in them — the kind that now move in one direction, now in another — sometimes become sick during an extended heat wave, while they remain healthy with properly warmed but more peaceful air. Sometimes they may have a strong fever and, if it is God's will that they become healthy again, they must suffer sweats for between five and seven days, but they quickly regain their health because their body was healthy before.

Lameness. A person who has changeable humors within, that is, those which have no proper constancy with regard to warmth, cold, and moisture but rather are driven now this way, now that way in the person corresponding to the changeableness of the air — like many rivers and water ways that devastate much land and like ice that is not yet fully frozen but is still brittle — will become plagued by this humor with lameness, that is gout. If he ever is afflicted with a strong fever and his life is spared by God's grace, then very often, before he sweats in pain he will lie there for up to twenty or thirty days, or even longer, in pain since before this he was frequently weak and sick. For if a person becomes sick because of strenuous exertions, stressful situations, or the variety of food and drink in him so that as a consequence of the variety of food and drink different foul humors collect in him, then his soul is shaken and defeated by this clashing and conflict so that its life power is seriously reduced.

Fever and the Critical Days. Thus the harmful humors in a person shift into movement, and the fever climbs because the soul has decreased its living potential. Then the person's blood begins to decrease, and his intestines and the other inner parts of his body dry out. The heat that is necessary for the liver and the other inner organs climbs to the outer layer of the skin, and the inner cold remains within the person. Then the soul lies depressed in the body and waits, wondering whether it should leave the body or remain in it. So it continues until the seventh day because it cannot yet free itself from its foul humors. However, if it notices that the intensity of these humors, through the grace of God, is beginning to recede somewhat, it then comes to the realization that it can free itself from these humors. And so it gathers its forces again and by sweating it drives these foul humors out of its body. In this manner, the person regains his health.

144

However, it often happens that because of their excessive heat and cold, the soul cannot completely drive out these humors by sweating. Rather, the soul, gripped by fear because of happiness or sadness, anger or anxiety, draws back and closes itself up in silence. It remains this way until the third, fifth, seventh, or thirteenth day — or more or less days, as mentioned above — until it again notices that by the grace of God it can regain its powers to fill the body with new life. If such a person regains bodily health, he will have less to suffer later than before because the humors that were in him have largely disappeared through his intense sweating. However, if the soul is drowning in such foul humors to the point that it is not able to drive them out of the person's body, then by God's decision it is defeated, expires, and leaves the body.

A High Fever. If a person has a high fever, the humors within him are thrown into a very great heat, and the heat of these humors does not permit the person to eat. However, the great dryness within him drives him to drink. Thus he should drink water so that he may suffer less. If a high fever has attacked a person, it is not healthy for him to take a potion to drive it away, for this may not enable him to come to a full sweat. Rather, it remains in him according to the specific medicament taken and allows him to remain sick so much the longer because the harmful humors were evidently not, as is necessary, driven out of him. Sometimes fever arises also from excessive eating and drinking, from excessive sleep, or from vexation and laziness, if the person does nothing.

A Changeable Fever. Daily fever comes from an excess of water, that is, phlegm, or foam, namely from unwholesome food or immoderate wine drinking. The fever that visits a person every second day comes from too much unhealthy or moist air. A three-day fever comes from excessive dryness, which means from the heat; a four-day fever, however, comes from an excess of bile. A person who has soft flesh on his body — so that the foam, which is viscous, lukewarm, and without strength, predominates in him — easily develops worms in his flesh. Because his flesh is soft and the foam within is viscous and without healthy power, small pustules easily develop on him in which a worm can develop and harm the person.

Diet. As curdling milk is constantly being added to cheese that is being pressed in its container until it is finished, so also babies and children must be constantly fed with food and drink until they are fully grown. Otherwise, a baby and a child cannot grow, but on the contrary will perish. However, one must also aid an old person with food, especially one weakened by age, for he will be helped by this food if his blood and flesh are already decreasing. For man is like the earth. If the earth receives an excess of water, it is harmed thereby; on the other hand, if it receives hardly any water, this will not contribute to its fruitful expansion, either. If it has received moderate moisture, this is good for it. So it is also with a person. If a person is suffering from a great excess of moisture flowing in himself — namely in the eyes, the ears, the nose, and the mouth — then this will sooner make him sick than healthy. If, on the other hand, he has moderate or almost no flowing moisture in his limbs, that is dangerous for him. However, if he has precisely the proper moisture, then this advances his health.

III.

The medicaments given below were prescribed by God to be used against the abovenamed ailments. Either they will heal the person or he will die if God does not will that he be healed.

To Prevent Hair Loss. As soon as a young man's hair begins to fall out, he should take bear fat and some ashes from wheat or winter-wheat straw, mix them together, and then massage this into his scalp, especially there where his hair is beginning to fall out. He should leave this salve on his scalp for some time. The hair that has not yet fallen out will be moistened and strengthened by this salve so that the hair will not fall out for a long time. He should perform this often and not wash his head afterwards. For the natural heat of bear fat normally has the characteristic of causing much hair to grow, and the ashes from wheat and winterwheat straw strengthen the hair so that it will not fall out soon. Because of the mentioned mixture, the salve protects the man a bit longer against loss of hair.

A Remedy Against Headache Due to Bile. If a depression conditioned by various fever attacks causes a person headaches, he should take mallow and twice that amount of sage, crush these into a pulp in a mortar and pour a bit of olive oil on it. If he has no oil, a little vinegar will do. He should then apply it over the skull from the forehead to the neck and wrap a cloth over it. He should do this for three days. During these three days, he should add fresh olive oil or vinegar in the evening and continue this until he gets better. For mallow juice releases the bile; however, the sap of the sage dries it up, the olive oil anoints the afflicted head, and the vinegar draws out the bitterness from the bile. In this way, this mixture alleviates such a headache.

Against Loss of Consciousness. If someone's brain becomes too cold and he thereby becomes unconscious, then take bay leaves and mash them into a powder. Then take wheat flour and blend in the bay powder. Shave the hair of the sick person, apply this paste mixed with thistle water over his whole head, and bind the paste firmly to the head with a felt cap until the head becomes warm within and the sick person falls asleep. Such a treatment brings heat to the brain. However, if this paste becomes dry, prepare a new paste again in the same way. Apply it to the sick person's head and do this often; then he will regain consciousness.

Against Migraines. A person who suffers from migraines should take aloe and twice the amount of myrrh and grind the two ingredients into a very fine powder. Then take wheat flour, add some poppy oil to the entire mixture, and make a kind of dough out of this with yeast. Cover the entire head, down to the ears and neck, with this paste, place a cap on his head, and leave the whole thing on his head for three days and nights. For the heat of the aloe and the dryness of the myrrh, correctly mixed with the gentle effect of the wheat flour and the coolness of the poppy oil, soothes this headache. A paste prepared in this way returns fatness to the brain.

Against Headaches as a Consequence of an Upset Stomach. If a food that contains a secreting humor unleashes a headache in a person, he should take sage, marjoram, and fennel in equal amounts and an amount of andorn equal to the other three combined. Once they are reduced to a liquid, give it enough butter — in case you don't have any, use grease — and make a salve out of it and rub it into the head. Then he should improve. For sage, majoram, and andorn are of a dry nature and thus dry up the mentioned humors. However, the juice from fennel is moist and thereby moderates the effect of the drying humors. For that reason, a salve that is made out of these plants and butter or grease that is healthy, soothes the mentioned headache. Take olive oil and a little less rosewater and bring both to the boil in a bowl. In the meantime, take nightshade, much less than the olive oil, grind it in a mortar, strain it through a cloth, pour the juice into a saucepan with the mentioned olive oil and the rosewater and allow the whole thing to boil together for a while. Again strain the whole thing through a cloth and pour it into a new earthen vessel. If the sick person has pains, rub this salve into the crown and the skull, on the face and the temple, and wrap his face and temple with a grease-proof, wax-impressed cloth so that the salve will not be wiped away.

148

Against Headache as a Result of Phlegm. A person who has a headache in the forehead as a result of excessive phlegm should thoroughly chew a white pea with his teeth, mix it with the purest honey, apply it to the temple, bind it with a bandage, and proceed in this way until he gets better. For the pea has a little bit of phlegm in its nature; however, the white kind grows in clean, good earth and draws out the stabbing pain if one chews it thoroughly and places it on the temple. For the blood vessels of the temple control the strength of the forehead. Also, the heat of the honey, which is gathered from blooms of different species, counters the cold of the phlegm.

What Follows Now Concerns Ailments of the Lungs. Take galgant and fennel in equal weights, twice as much muscat nut, and an equal amount of feverfew so that the muscat nut and the feverfew weigh the same; grind this into a powder; mix it up; and take this daily — as much as two coins weigh — on an empty stomach with a morsel of bread. Then immediately drink a bit of warm wine and often eat some more noble plants that smell good — as much on an empty stomach as also after having breakfasted — so that their good smell extends to the lungs and overcomes the foul-smelling breath. However, anyone who only has pains in the lungs should avoid fatty meat, blood-rich nourishment, and cooked cheese, for these foods cause tuberculosis. Also, he should not eat peas, lentils, raw fruits or raw vegetables. He should also avoid nuts and oil. If he wants to eat meat, it should be lean, and if he wants cheese, he should avoid both the cooked and unripe kind but eat only dry cheese. If he will take some oil, it should only be a little. He should not drink water, for it accumulates sludge and slime "slim"[2] in the lung area. He should not drink new, unturned cider that has not yet fermented and thrown out its sludge; on the other hand, beer does him no particular harm because it has been cooked. However, he should drink no wine, and he should take precautions against moist, foggy air.

Against Spiritual Confusion. If because of much rumination a person loses his clear consciousness and power of thought so that he becomes psychologically confused, one should take balm plant and a three-fold amount of fennel, boil it together in water, take out the plants, and then drink the remaining water after it has cooled. For the sap of the balm plant reduces the operation of the harmful hu-

[2] "Slim" means "Schleim" in Middle High German.

mors and prevents them from gaining the upper hand; further, it brings a person back to his right mind. The juice from fennel puts the patient in a proper, cheerful mood. If these plants are properly mixed with one another and boiled in mild water, they cause people to regain their correct outlook. Such a person should avoid dry foods; otherwise, the humors that are currently suppressed in him would lead him to a yet greater dryness as a result of his psychological confusion. Rather, he should eat substantial foods that help him to acquire a good humor in his blood, put his humors back in the proper condition, and free his mind from its spiritual confusion. He may eat pulp made from wheat flour that was prepared with butter or fat, but not with oil, for it again fills and warms the empty, cooled brain. Oil, however, would attract phlegm, and for that reason he should avoid it. Nor should he drink wine, for it would further separate the already-divided humors in his body. He should not drink mead either, for the power of the honey would further attack the repressed humors in him. But he should also not drink plain water because it would lead his thinking into a yet greater emptiness. He should drink the potion mentioned above and beer because they maintain both the repressed humors and his thinking in the proper condition and turn away the raging of psychological confusion. He should keep his head covered with a cap made from felt or pure wool until his brain which has been cooled down through the repressed humors again gradually and slowly warms up, but not too suddenly and excessively, so that it does not become worse for the patient because of the sudden, excessive warmth. Take muscat nut and a double dose of galgant, grind both of these into a powder, add the root of the iris and the root from plantain in equal weight so that their combined weight is still less than the weight of the muscat nut, season everything, and then pound it a bit. Out of all this — with wheat flour and water — make a thin drink that should be taken on an empty stomach, and give it to the sick person to drink.

Against Weakness of the Eyes. If the blood and water in a person's eyes have been taken away as a result of increased age or disease, he should go into a green meadow and look at it until his eyes become moist as if with tears, for the green grass overcomes whatever is cloudy in his eyes and makes them clean and clear again. Also, he may go to a brook or simply pour fresh water into a vessel, bend over it, and absorb the moisture of this water into his eyes. For this moisture again arouses the water that is in his eyes but is already drying up, and makes it clear. He can also take a linen cloth, dip it in clean, fresh water, and then lay it on his temples and eyes and bind it fast; however, in so doing he should make sure that it does not make contact with the eye itself, for it would thus develop ulcers because of the water. Moisten the eyes with a soft linen cloth and cold water so that the water in the eyes may be aroused to see again by this water. Because the eyes are of a fiery nature, the eye skin [cataract] becomes thick because of the fire, and if, as is described above, it is touched by water, this skin will be thinned by the cold and moist water.

Grey Eyes. If someone has grey eyes and in any way sees badly with them and has pains, he should, when the pain is still fresh, take and grind fennel or its seed, add the dew that he will find on high-standing grass with a little wheat meal, and knead the whole thing into a small cake. He should lay this on his eyes overnight, bind it fast with a cloth, and he will improve. The gentle heat of the fennel, properly mixed with the dew and the strength of the wheat, will vanquish the pain. Grey eyes arise from the element of air; hence, dew is used as a correcting healing element.

Fiery Eyes. If a person who has fiery eyes sees badly with them and has pains, he should take violet sap, twice as much rose sap, and a third as much fennel sap as rose sap, add a bit of wine, and massage the area around the eyes with this eye salve as he goes to sleep. However, he must watch out that his eyes are not gradually damaged by the strong action of this salve. If only a little of this gets inside the eye, it will not be too badly damaged. Because fiery eyes have their origin in fire, the mild coolness of violet and the mild coolness of the rose — if it is properly regulated by the mild action of the fennel and the heat of the wine — drive away the weak eyesight and the pain in the eyes. For all these plants mature in summer and grow when it becomes moderately warm. The violet comes up first with the warm wind; hence, when mixed with the aforementioned healing elements, it makes the eyes healthy.

Eyes with a Variety of Colors. A person who has eyes similar to a cloud against which one sees a rainbow and who sees badly with them or in some other way has pains, should take zinc, place it in pure white wine, and at nighttime when he goes to sleep take the zinc out of the wine and brush his eyebrows with the wine, all the while being careful not to get it in his eye because it could otherwise be hurt by the sharpness of the zinc and then would see even less well. Zinc has equal amounts of heat and cold within itself and removes, when regulated by the warmth of the wine, noxious humors which harm the eyes. However, if it ever comes into direct contact with the eye itself, it hurts it because the heat neither overcomes its coldness, nor does the cold overcome the warmth. Thence its sharpness causes the eyes to fester, and it weakens their sight if it ever makes direct contact with them. However, as said, zinc properly regulated so that its heat and cold do not overcome one another, heals such eyes.

Cloudy Eyes. When someone has eyes like a thick cloud — neither entirely fiery nor entirely dark, but rather blue-grey — and has poor vision and pains in them, he should take fennel in summer, or in winter its seed, grind it up, and add it to a good clear egg white. When he lies down to go to sleep, he should place this on his eyes. The mild warmth of the fennel, regulated by the cold of the egg white, reduces the weakness in the vision and the pain in the eyes. For fennel with egg white that is light blue-grey, properly mixed, is a good healing remedy for eyes which are sick as a result of the blue-grey moisture of the earth.

Black Eyes. If a person has black or dark eyes — as once in a while a cloud looks — and in any way sees badly with them and has pains, he should take rue sap, twice as much pure liquid honey, mix in a little good clear wine, place a piece of wheat bread in it, and place the whole thing securely on the eyes overnight. Because the eyes come from the earth, the heat from the rue, the honey, and the wine that its sap has drawn up from the earth is good for them if a piece of bread is placed within, which also has its powers from the earth.

If a Person Has a White Fleck in the Eye. If a person suffers from having a white fleck in his eye, when this white fleck is still fresh he should take fresh ox gall, lay it — as fresh as it is — on his eyes overnight, and tie it securely with a linen cloth so that it doesn't slip. He should do this for three days in succession because the bitterness of the gall fully removes the pain. However, he should only move around sparingly with this so as not to come to harm if he goes too far. After three days have passed, he should take fenugreek, dip it in rose oil, and lay it on his eyes because it has a soothing action; secure it firmly with a cloth, for the mild coldness of the fenugreek in combination with the mild rose oil easily removes the white fleck that has been broken up by the abovementioned gall.

For Tears in the Eyes. At that moment when the sun has already warmed it on its branch, a person who has wet or running eyes should pluck a fig leaf that has been moistened by dew during the night and then place it on his eyes while it is still warm in order to fight the wetness, until it warms it a bit. If there are no fig leaves available, he should take an alder leaf that similarly has been bedewed overnight and then warmed by the sun's rays, and place it on his eyes as described above. He should not repeat this every day, but rather every third day, and only once a day. In case neither of these leaves is available, he should take the gum from either a peach tree or an oak and press it lightly into a nut shell. If it is then warmed a bit on a hot tile or on a hot plate by the fire, he should lay it around the eyes while it is still warm.

He should do this once a day every fourth day so that he does not, by overdoing it, do more harm than good to his eyes. The heat of the fig leaf and the coldness of the alder leaf naturally draw moisture toward themselves. However, they should be wet with dew so that their power might be weakened a bit by its moderating influence; they should also be warmed by the sun which loans its mildness to their sap so that they do not harm the eyes. The gum from either the peach or the oak tree contains the strength of these trees and by its own distinctive power draws the wetness in the eyes into itself with the warmth that it has from the tile or the hearth. Still, this heat should be mild rather than strong. In this way, as has been said, the wetness in the eyes will cease.

To Prevent Hearing Loss. If a person's hearing is disturbed either through an infection or some other ailment, he should take white incense, make smoke with it over a glowing coal, and cause this smoke to climb into the stopped-up ear. However, he should do this only seldom, for if he does it too often, it will then go worse for him. The warm smoke of the white incense, which is purer than the smoke of other types of incense, drives off, when it is released by another fire, the harmful smoke that injures the brain and the hearing of people.

For Toothache. A person who suffers from toothache because of infected blood and from precipitations from the brain should take equal weights of wormwood and ironweed, boil them in clear, good wine in a new kettle, strain the boiled wine through a cloth, add a bit of sugar, and drink this wine. When he goes to bed, he should place the still-warm, cooked plants directly on the jaw where he feels the pain and fasten it with a cloth. He should do this until he has regained his health. The wine, mixed with the mentioned plants and then drunk, cleanses from within the delicate vessels that lead from the scalp down to the gums, and the plants applied to the jaw soothe the toothache from the outside. For the heat of wormwood that mixes itself with the heat of the ironweed and the heat of the wine reduces the pain. With a bleeding knife or a thorn, a person who has a toothache should make a small cut in the flesh that surrounds the affected tooth, that is, in the gum, so that the pus may leave through it, and he will improve.

Healthy Teeth. Each morning when he climbs out of bed, a person who would like to have healthy, powerful teeth should take cold, pure water into his mouth and leave it there a while so that it wipes away the slimy residue on his teeth. He should clean his teeth with this water that he has in his mouth, and do this often, and the slimy residue will not continue to accumulate, but rather his teeth will remain healthy.

For Worms in the Teeth. If worms gnaw into a person's teeth, he should take equal weights of aloe and myrrh in an earthen vessel with a narrow opening on the neck and place it over glowing coals from beech wood. Then he should guide the arising smoke through a narrow straw between his opened lips to the tooth that is causing pain. However, he should squeeze his teeth together so that not too much smoke reaches the throat. He should do this two or three times a day for five days straight, and he will be healed. When the heat of the aloe and the heat of the myrrh is called forth by the equal heat and cold of the glowing coals, the power of the resulting smoke kills the worms in the teeth.

The Uvula. If the smoke referred to reaches the throat, its strength causes the throat and the uvula to become dry.

For Chest Pains. If harmful humors in a person's bowels and spleen have gained the upper hand and have brought much pain to the heart because of bile, take equal weights of galgant and bertram, a quarter as much white pepper, or, if there is no white pepper available, four times as much pepper plant, and grind them all into a powder. Then take bean meal, add the aforementioned powder, and mix it all with sap from fenugreek or with water, wine, or some other liquid. Then make small cakes out of this mixture and allow them to dry in the sun. One must make a big batch of these pills during the summer while there is sun so that they will last the entire winter. He should then consume these small cakes both after breakfast and on an empty stomach; for the heat of the galgant, the bertram, the white pepper, as well as of the pepper plant and the bean, moderated by the cold of the fenugreek and exposed to the healthy heat of the sun, soothes heart pains. Then he should take licorice, five times as much, and sugar equal to the weight of the licorice, and a bit of honey, make a drink out of it — specifically a pure drink — and drink it both before and after breakfast to prevent chest pains. For the heat of the licorice, of the fennel, and of the sugar, mixed with the heat of the honey, removes the slime that, as we have said, causes pains in a person's heart. So take white pepper, a third as much cumin, and half as much fenugreek as cumin, grind it into a powder and eat it slowly with a little bit of bread both before and after breakfast, lest you experience a weakness in your heart or a pain begins there.

For Pains in the Lungs. If harmful, foul-smelling humors send out their vapor to a person's brain, reach the lungs, and cause pains there, the person should take lung plant, boil it in water but not in wine because this plant when boiled in wine would work too powerfully, pour the brew into a pot, strain it through a cloth, and drink it for a week. When this drink is used up, he should prepare a new batch in the same way. He should drink it each day both before and after breakfast until he is healthy. For the lungs are often weakened by heart pains and the heat of the stomach; however, the coldness of this healing plant, moderated through sweet water, removes this weakness. Take juniper berries and twice as much mullein as juniper berries, twice as much bertram as mullein and boil them in pure, good wine. Pour the brew into a pot, add raw alant cut into small pieces, strain it through a cloth, and drink it slowly on an empty stomach for two to three weeks. Also take dill, three times as much lovage as dill, and as much stinging nettle as dill; boil them in pure, good wine; and then pour it into a pot. After it has been strained through a cloth and as long as it retains its taste, you may drink it both on an empty stomach and after breakfast — but only a little and cautiously. However, there are people who were conceived during foggy, moist weather and hence continually have foul-smelling breath and sweat that stinks. Their foul breath and harmful humors penetrate to the brain and make it sick and fatigued so that very often it seems to forget itself. If they eliminate the phlegm from their head, they have fewer pains, for then their brain is purified; however, if they do not get rid of it, they suffer worse headaches because they cannot free their brain from the harmful humors. Their foul breath also reaches the lungs and occupies it so that they sometimes also have a rough voice. However, this pain is not very dangerous, for it can be quickly overcome.

To Prevent Hardening of the Liver. If someone consumes a great variety of food without moderation and as he pleases, and as a result of the various humors from these foods his liver is damaged and becomes hard, he should take some small coltsfoot, twice as much plantain root and equally as much pear mistletoe brew as small coltsfoot, cut these plants into small, thin sticks, and then pierce them with an awl or some other small tool, pour the abovementioned brew into the bore holes, and then place them in pure wine. One can also take an amount comparable to what a coin weighs from a growth that has developed to bean or pea size on the leaf or the branch of a nut tree, place it in the abovementioned wine, and then drink it — both after breakfast and on an empty stomach — not boiled, but only that which was placed in the wine. The heat and the cold of the small coltsfoot removes the swelling in the liver; however, the heat of the plantain prevents the liver from congealing and hardening. The cold of the pear mistletoe pulp reduces the slime, and the growth from the leaf or the branch of a nut tree — by its bitterness — removes the harmful humors that do damage to the liver. None of this should be boiled, only placed in unboiled wine so that it may all the more easily reach the liver. The patient may also drink mulberry wine often, for the pain in the liver often comes from too rich a blood which the heat and the sap from mulberry wine, that is somehow related to blood, removes.

The food he intends to eat should be prepared with vinegar because the heat of the vinegar and its sharpness cause the liver to shrink. He can also have wheat bread which some people who enjoy savory foods like to eat along with a piece of dried shoulder of pork over which wine has been poured. For when the dried juices of this piece of shoulder meat are extracted by the warmth of the wine and the bread is saturated, the bread prepared in this manner shrinks the liver and prevents it from swelling. However, one should take care not to drink the wine with which the meat has been soaked, for it will have absorbed whatever harmful properties the meat may have had.

For Pains in the Spleen. If a person should eat a raw meal, the humors from this food sometimes climb into the spleen and cause pains, for they have not been moderated by any seasoning. For that reason, such persons should take chervil, a bit less dill, and together with wheat bread in vinegar make something like small spice cakes out of them and eat quite a few of them. For the mild coolness of the chervil removes and heals the pain in the spleen which comes about as a result of the hotter and colder humors; on the other hand, the cold of the dill strengthens the spleen, and the wheat bread causes the spleen to grow. The vinegar, however, purifies it by its sharpness. Afterward, he should take linseed and cook it in a saucepan; then he should take it out of the saucepan, squeeze out the water, put the linseed into a small pouch, and lay it over the area of the spleen as hot as he can stand it. For the linseed is warm and slimy; it penetrates and heals the spleen when it is excited to the full unfolding of its powers by the mild effect of water.

For Stomach Pains. Occasionally, undigested foods congeal and harden in a person's stomach and cause stomach pains. He should then take peony and a quarter as much carline thistle, grind that in a mortar, and then boil it in a good, pure wine — at least twice as much wine as plant juice. Then, strain it through a cloth and fill a glass vessel or a new kettle. Pour the wine that has been mixed with the aforementioned plants into a saucepan, dip a glowing hot steel into it two or three times, add ground up galgant and a bit of pepper to this wine while it is beginning to boil because of this glowing steel. If you have no galgant, use ground bertram, and drink the wine heated with the glowing steel on an empty stomach. He should drink this wine for five days in progressively smaller amounts on an empty stomach after, however, it has been heated for a while with the glowing steel. When he has done that for five days, he should take wheat bread or wheat flour and prepare a small breakfast with the mentioned wine that has been heated by the glowing steel. Add some taste to it by using an egg yolk, but no fat or oil, and again eat this for five days on an empty stomach. Finally, until he gets better, he should again drink the wine that has been heated with a glowing steel. The peony strengthens the stomach by its warmth, the carline thistle keeps gout away, the five-finger plant strengthens him with its heat, the heat of the wine removes his slime, and the strength of the steel increases all these effects on the most persistent. In this way, the heat of the galgant or bertram and the pepper increases its effectiveness against stomach pains. The wheat bread or the wheat flour together with the wine lubricates the stomach and reestablishes its power through the strength of the glowing steel. This should be done without using fat and oil because fat corrodes the stomach and oil causes stomach ulcers. The patient should often eat hyssop that has been placed in wine and drink this wine, also, because with this ailment, hyssop is more useful for him than it is for someone with a lung problem.

For Digestive Problems. If a person cannot digest the food he has eaten, he should take the juice from the Easter lily in weight equal to two coins, the juice from burnet saxifrage to the weight of one coin, the juice from a quickly working laxative to the weight of one obolus, ginger to the weight of one obolus, and then a little fine wheat flour. With these juices, he should make a small cake the size of a coin, but a bit thicker, and bake it in the sun or in an oven that has almost cooled down. A person who suffers from the abovementioned digestive problems should eat this small cake on an empty stomach in the morning when he is warm inside and the food in him is exhausted, or he should take two or three small pill cakes on an empty stomach when he is cold inside and the food he has consumed has coagulated and is pressed together from the cold. The food that he first consumes should be a soup or a breakfast; then he should eat a good, wholesome dish. He should do this until he again feels free in his stomach. For the heat of the Easter lily which is somewhat sharp and strong, if it is moderated by the cold of the burnet saxifrage, brings a person's harmful humors into motion; the heat of the ginger releases them; the cold of the quick-working laxative leads them quickly away; and the fine wheat flour strengthens the stomach so that they do not damage it. When these ingredients are all fully baked in the sun whose heat is strong or in a warmed oven whose heat is healthy and are given to the sick person, it cleanses his stomach, as was already said. Take ginger, grind it up, mix it with a little juice from the plant that is called marigold, and then take some flour and make small cakes out of this powder. Bake these cakes in the oven when the heat of the fire has already begun to be tamped down, and consume these small cakes both before and after breakfast.

For a Hernia. If a person somehow tears the inner skin that binds up the bowels, he should take celeriac, a double amount of common bone spindle, and boil the plants in good wine. After they have cooked, let him separate them from the wine, add a little zedoary powder to the wine, an equal amount of sugar as celeriac, and ample cooked honey. Then let the wine boil a little while without the plants, strain it through a small pouch the way one clarifies a drink, drink it after a meal and at night, and do this often. When the coldness of the celeriac joins with the coldness of both the bone spindle and the zedoary powder together, they draw back the inner skin of the bowels through their beneficent coldness and good effect and make it fast. For if these plants were warm, they would dry out this inner skin. However, the moderate warmth of the wine, the warmth both of the sugar and the honey heal this torn inner skin if they are aroused by an opposing warmth. The plants mentioned, boiled in wine, make the sick person warm in that place where the intestinal wall is torn, and they cause the tear to grow back together again. Also, he should slice the root of the common bone spindle into very tiny pieces and place the raw pieces in some wine so that it may absorb their taste. He should drink this wine until he becomes healthy, for the cold of the bone spindle together with the warmth of the wine draws the torn skin back together again.

For Kidney Pains. If a person has pains in the kidney or in the loins, this often comes from a stomach ache. In this case, he should take an equal weight of rue and wormwood and a bit more bear fat, crush these before an open fire, rub this mixture on the area of the kidneys and loins, wherever it hurts. Very often the pain in the kidneys and loins comes from harmful humors. However, when the heat of the rue, the heat of the wormwood, and that of the bear fat mix with one another, they drive away the humors that have become cold in an improper way.

For Body Pains. When a foul exhalation from the stomach spreads out into a person's bowels and causes pains there, he should take sage and five times as much bryony root as sage, ten times as much rue as sage, and cook these plants in a new pot until it begins to boil over; then squeeze out the water and place the boiled but still warm plants on the places where it hurts in the mentioned ways, and bind them fast there with a bandage. For when the heat of the sage, the heat of the bryony root, and the heat of the rue are mixed with one another and are increased by adding the heated water, they drive out with their powerful effects the harmful humors that cause the body pains.

For Pains in the Side. Take linseed and somewhat less resin from a peach tree so that the resin comes out to a quarter less than the linseed, and boil this in a saucepan until it is almost a clay. Then take the mistletoe from a pear tree and grind it to a liquid in a mortar so that this liquid comes out to a bit more than the resin. Add more stag marrow to this than the liquid from the pear-tree mistletoe comes to, place the whole thing in a saucepan with the abovementioned linseed and with the resin, and let it boil a while longer as before. If you have no stag marrow, add as much suet from a young bull as should have come from the stag marrow. Then strain the whole thing through a cloth that has been perforated all over with an awl, pour it into a newly thrown earthen vessel, and, before an open fire, rub this into the patient on the side where he feels pains.

For a Swelling in the Testicles. If a swelling should arise in a man's sexual organs as a result of harmful humors from a malicious growth that causes the person pains, he should take fennel, three times as much fenugreek, and a bit of cow butter, mash it all up, and apply it, and it will draw out from the male sex organs the harmful humors that cause the pains. For the mildness of the fennel, regulated by the cold of the fenugreek and the mild heat of the butter, reduces the mentioned pain. For the heat of fennel and the coldness of the fenugreek decreases the harmful humors, and the mild heat of the butter soothes the pain. So then the man should take the small cakes from which beer is made, moisten them a bit with lukewarm water, heat them, and place them on the abovementioned growth. Then the small cakes, which are moderated by the mild heat of the water, will draw out with their sharp sap the harmful humors and will heal the person who has such pains. (Thus if someone has pains in this fashion on the male sex organs, he should take fennel, three times as much fenugreek, and a little cow fat, mash the whole thing together, and place it on the organ, and it will draw out the harmful humors; then he should take a malt cake, moisten it a bit with lukewarm water, and place it on.)

For Painful Urination. If someone cannot hold back his urine because of the coldness of his stomach, he should often drink wine that

160

has been heated over the fire, mix vinegar into all of his food, and also drink vinegar, as much as he can. By such measures he will become warm in the stomach and in the bladder. For the heat of the wine, heightened by the fire and then consumed, warms the stomach and the bladder, holds back the urine until it is properly digested, and conveys to it the proper digestion and heat. He also should boil sage in water, strain the water through a cloth, and drink it often while it is still warm. Then he will be able to contain his urine and become healthy. By its heat, the sage removes the slime that has arisen through the coldness of the humors in the stomach and the bladder and which expels the urine before it is properly digested.

For Sterility in the Male. A man whose semen is infertile should eat hasel catkins, a third as much stonecrop, a fourth as much bindweed as stonecrop, and a bit of common pepper. He should boil all that with the liver of a young male goat that is already sexually mature, with the addition of some fresh, rich pork. He should then throw the plants away and eat the meat; he should also dip bread into the broth in which the meat was cooked and eat it as well. He should often eat meat that has been cooked in this fashion until his seed achieves the power to beget by means of the juice from this meat, always presupposing that it is God's will.

For Infertility in a Woman. A woman whose womb is too cold and too weak within to conceive offspring can, if God wills, be helped to become fertile in the following way. Take the womb of either a sheep or a cow that is sexually mature yet has not yet given birth, so that it is not pregnant and has never been; boil it with bacon, with other rich meat, and with fat; and give this to the woman to eat when she is having relations with her husband or will soon be doing so. She should eat such food often.

The humor from the womb of the abovementioned animals will bind with the humor from the womb of the woman so that she will be somewhat enriched and strengthened by it and, God willing, will more easily conceive. However, it often happens that because of God's will a person's power to beget is lost.

For Gout. A person who feels gout in his legs and feet and suffers from it, should, when the pain is still fresh, place many bleeding cups at various places on his leg in such a way that he begins at the ankle, without however damaging the skin, so that they draw the humors

161

into themselves, and then remove them from that spot and place them higher, until again they draw the humors from below into themselves. So he should continue, without making a cut or tear in the skin, until he comes to his backside. Having reached that point, he should wrap a bandage around the upper part of his knee so that the humors that he has drawn out with the bleeding cups do not descend into that region again. At that point where the back and the buttocks come together, he should make a small cut in the skin with the bleeding cup so that the blood and the humors may flow out. If he proceeds in this fashion, the pain from his gout will go away. Take bertram, a third that weight in ginger, and a little pepper; grind it all up; eat it on an empty stomach; and wash it down with wine.

For a Fistula. If someone is suffering from a fistula somewhere on his body that has arisen as a result of harmful, excessive humors, he should drink large amounts of laxative to decrease the excessive humors in himself. If the skin at the painful site draws together afterwards as if it wished to heal itself, and then breaks apart again because of the humors, he should again drink a laxative so that the harmful humors in him do not gain the upper hand. If he does this often, he will have less pain. Both the fistula and gout are difficult to heal.

For a Boil. If because his humors are raging, a boil or a pustule afflicts a person he should take a linen cloth saturated in fresh wax, smear it further with olive oil, and then lay it over the boil. Thereby, the boil will more quickly become soft and more easily break open, the humors will be drawn off, and the healing will proceed more pleasantly. However, if it is a matter of a suppurating boil, commonly called a "net," then make no covering because that is dangerous. If a person's skin has broken out anywhere, but no noxious boil is present, and if drops and harmful humors flow out together, then one should take mugwort, squeeze out its juice by grinding it in a mortar, and add honey to this juice until the mugwort juice makes up a third more than the honey. He should rub this in at the place where he experiences pain. Immediately thereafter he should smear the clear liquid from an egg white over it and bind it fast with a cloth. He should do this until he is healthy.

For Difficulty in Falling Asleep. If it is summer and a person cannot sleep because of some disturbance, he should take fennel and twice as much yarrow, boil it briefly in water, squeeze out the water, and place the still-warm plants on the temple, the brow, and the head and bind them fast with a cloth. He may also take green sage, dip it in wine, and then place it over his heart and throat, and he will experience recovery through sleep. In winter, he should boil fennel seed and yarrow root in water, lay them on his temple and head as described above, lay ground sage that has been dipped in wine over his heart, wrap a cloth around it, and bind it fast since no green plants are available in winter. He will then more easily fall asleep, for the heat of the fennel induces sleep, the heat of the yarrow stabilizes the sleep, and the heat of the sage causes the heart to beat more slowly and weighs down the blood vessels in the throat so that sleep comes. When these plants have been brought to their full potency by the mild effect of the heated water, they should be placed on the temple so that they may compress its blood vessels, and also on the brow and on top of the head so that they can induce peace in the brain. The fennel and yarrow seeds are boiled in water because of the mild effectiveness of water while the sage powder, on the other hand, is placed in wine so that the healing agent may be drawn out of it.

Herbs and Medicinal Plants. Now, either the indicated healing materials that God ordained for this purpose will cure the diseases described above, or they will die, for God did not will that they should be healed. For the various noble plants, powders, and roots derived from noble plants are of no use to healthy people unless they are taken in the proper order and amount, but rather harm them much more by the fact that they dry out their blood and cause their flesh to waste away because they do not discover in them the humors on which they may work their effect. They do not increase the persons' power and do not cause their flesh to grow, but rather only reduce the bad humors that they combat. If some one consumes them, this should be done only because it is necessary and in a cautious and rational manner. The healing plants should be taken with bread or wine or with some spice, and only rarely on an empty stomach. Otherwise, they grip the chest of the person who takes them, do harm to his lungs, and make the stomach sick, if they reach it, since they were not eaten with anything else. Just as the dust of the earth is harmful to man if he takes it into himself, so these agents harm a person more than they make him well if they are not taken in the right order. For that reason, a man should take them primarily with a meal or right after a meal, for then they thin out the humors of the foods and enable the person to digest the food he has just eaten, unless a man has such difficulties that in order to do this he must take noble, strong herbs or an expensive medication on an empty stomach.

IV.

For a Failure to Menstruate. A woman who suffers from a failure to menstruate should take aniseed and feverfew in equal weight and somewhat more mullein than either of the two-named plants; boil them in water from an open, flowing river because it is regulated by the sun and the air; then take bricks, place them in the fire, and take a sweat bath with the water referred to and the mentioned plants. As women go into the bath, they should place the still-warm plants on a foot stool, sit down on it, and place the still-warm plants on the genitalia and around up to the navel and all around the navel. If they have cooled down in the meantime, they should warm themselves up again in the water mentioned above and place themselves on the same stool and do this as long as they sit in the bath so that by means of the humors from the plants placed on them, their skin on the outside and their womb on the inside will become soft and their closed passageways can open. For the heat of the aniseed puts the humors into motion. Moreover, the heat of the feverfew heals, and the heat of mullein causes the blood to flow. When these plants are properly mixed with one another and their heat is increased by being placed in the mentioned river water — this water is healthier and milder than water from a living spring, for it flows in the open and has been worked over by the other elements — and when they have also been excited by the hot bricks — these are not similar to other bricks, for they were baked in a fire, whereby they have healing powers — they then, as was said, relax the monthly flow of blood by the gentle working of the bath.

Then the woman should take heidelberries, a third as much yarrow, a third of that amount of rue, and as much long Easter lilies as heidelberries and yarrow and much diptam; grind these all in a mortar; boil it with good, pure wine in a new pot; pour it into a small pouch after cooking; add open cloves to it, as many as you can get, then somewhat less white pepper than cloves; mix them with one another; add sufficient new, fresh, pure honey; and boil it in very good wine. Then pour the whole thing into the pouch with the plants mentioned above and prepare a plant wine from it. You should drink this every day both on an empty stomach and after breakfast, however not in the bath mentioned above; for the bath somewhat impedes digestion. When the coldness of the heidelberries is moderated by the heat of the yarrow, the rue, the long Easter lily, the diptam, the increased heat of the wine, and the heat of the open cloves that are better suited for this disease than other spices, and by the heat of the white pepper which also releases the monthly bleeding, and the heat of the fresh honey that also accomodates this, then, as we said, the closed womb of the woman opens up, and the hardened mass of blood breaks up. The woman may also prepare a light snack of eggs and sufficient lard with the addition of juice and should take some of both before and after a meal. For when the coldness of the eggs and of the lovage is countered by the heat of the wine and the lard, the mass in the woman is broken up. She should proceed thus from five to fifteen days long or until the breakup is achieved. In the meantime, during which she must suffer from the abovementioned difficulty in menstruating, she should avoid eating beef or other heavy foods because these have a blocking effect upon her; however, she should eat light foods and drink wine. If during this period she wants to drink water, she should drink well water but avoid water from a spouting, flowing spring for it is somewhat harder than other water. She may boil spring water and let it cool before she drinks it because it becomes soft by this procedure.

For an Excessive Monthly Flow. A woman who suffers from an untimely, strong, or irregular monthly flow should dip a linen cloth into cold water and then wrap it around her thighs several times so that she cools herself down. For through the coldness of the linen cloth and the cold water, the untimely blood flow will be held back. She should also boil celeriac in water and while it is still hot, place it on the thigh and on the navel. The coldness and the inner, opposing influence work against the harmful, excessive blood flow in the area of the thigh and the navel. The celeriac thereby becomes cooked and while still warm is placed on these parts of the body, for by its heat it brings healing to them. The woman may also place betony in wine so that it may take on some of its taste, and then drink it frequently; the heat of the betony mixed with the heat of the wine holds down the excessive heating of the blood. Also, using soft pressure of her hands, she should frequently massage all her vessels — that is, those that are in the thighs, the stomach, in the chest and the arms — so that they contract and do not cause the blood to flow excessively. However, she should also pay attention that she does not work too hard and that she does not become tired from too much activity so that her blood is not overly excited. She should also make sure that she does not eat any hard or bitter food so that she does not upset her digestion, but rather in this condition she should eat soft, wholesome foods, so that she may get well within. She should also drink wine and beer to get stronger so that she can hold back her blood.

For a Difficult Birth. If a pregnant woman is experiencing many pains while giving birth, one should prudently and with great caution boil some mild plants, specifically fennel and hazel root, squeeze out the water, and then lay them, still hot, on the thigh and the back of the woman, wrap cloths around them and fasten the whole thing so that the pain diminishes and the blocked birth passage may open smoothly and easily. For the harmful cold humors that are present in the woman sometimes make it contract during her pregnancy and close up. However, if the mild heat of the fennel and of the hazel root has been aroused in soft water over the fire and a covering has been made over the thighs and the back of the woman — for on this occasion she suffers more than on others from constriction — these agents stimulate the body parts to open themselves.

Cleaning Saliva and Nose Phlegm. To be cleansed from saliva, coughing, and nose phlegm, one should take agrimony and twice as much fenugreek, grind them up in a mortar, press out all their juice, grind some ruprecht weed, also, and add as much of its juice to that of the agrimony and of the fenugreek as an obolus weighs. Then take as much galgant as the three plants make altogether, as much gum resin as six coins weigh, and blechnum to the weight of two coins; grind it into powder; knead the powder with the abovementioned juice so that it produces a thick dough; and make pills the size of a bean from it. Afterwards, squeeze the juice out of some greater celandine, take as much of the juice as equals a quarter of the weight of a coin, dip a pill into it, roll it back and forth, and then place it in the sun to dry. Do the same with the other pills, dipping each one in the juice that weighs a quarter of the weight of a coin, and then placing it in the heat of the sun, but not close to a wood fire or the fire of an oven. In case the sun's heat is not available, one should place the pills in a light breeze or in gentle air so that they dry slowly. For the heat of agrimony and of galgant, the power of gum resin, and the heat of blechnum and of the greater celandine overcome the cold humors that arise in a person out of the phlegm; the cold of the fenugreek and of the ruprecht weed removes the cold of these humors. The greater celandine causes the humors to rage in a person, but on the other hand the other ascending plants keep them down so that they can now be easily expelled from the person. For that reason, the pills should be allowed to dry in the sun because its heat is healthy, and not by a wood or oven fire because something is missing in this heat compared to that of the sun. When a person wants to take one of these pills, he should first wrap his stomach and belly with lamb skin or other skins so that it becomes warm, for its warmth is healthy. Also one should not come too close to the fire, for thereby the vessels swell, the blood rages excessively, and the humors are led toward the exterior in an improper way. Rather, one should make use of the warmth of clothing and take the pills before the sun comes up because at this time the dawn is mild and gentle. One should take from five to nine of the pills, and in this manner, that the person dips each one in some honey and swallows it because the honey is warm and sweet. If a person does not have any honey, he should take the pills individually with a bit of wheat bread in a spoon, for then the concoction tastes good. After one has taken them, one should go for a lazy walk in the shade and not directly in the heat of the sun until one feels a breaking-up effect. For perhaps the direct rays of the sun would attract the humors of the brain toward the exterior in an improper way. Only around midday, after one has sensed a breaking-up effect or when, because of one's hardened stomach, one cannot achieve this yet, one should eat some soup or some broth made with wheat flour so that either the bowels, which have been activated by the breaking-up effect, may be healed through the mild action of the soup or the broth, or the hardened stomach become softened by these means.

For Another Type of Excessive Blood Flow. If a person has a lot of nose bleeds, he should take dill and a double dose of yarrow, and place these plants directly on the brow, the temple, and the chest. For the dryness and the cold of the dill release the heat of the blood, and the heat of the yarrow draws the blood to itself and holds it back so that it doesn't rise up excessively. These plants should be fresh, for when they are fresh, their effect is especially strong. They should be placed on the brow, the temple, and the chest because the power of the vessels that guides the blood is located there. In winter, one should grind up the plants and put the powder, when sprinkled with a little wine, in a pouch and place it on the brow, the temple, and the chest as mentioned before, for the heat in the wine bestows a power on the powder that confines the blood.

For Head Colds. If a person is suffering badly from a cold, he should take fennel and four times as much dill and place them on a stone roof tile that has been heated by the fire or on a thin roof tile, turning over the fennel and the dill until they smoke; then, he should breathe in the smoke and the fumes through the nose and the mouth. Then he should eat the fennel and the dill with bread after they have been heated on the mentioned roof tile. He should do this for three, four, or five days until the discharge in his head and nose breaks up a bit and the humors involved can be more easily eliminated. The warmth and moisture of the fennel collect humors that are not separating and flowing out in the proper way. The fennel draws the humors together, and the dry cold of the dill dries them out when, as we have said, these two plants are mixed together and warmed on a hot stone.

When One Should Take a Laxative. If a person desires to make and take a laxative, he should take ginger, half as much licorice, and a third as much zedoary, grind the whole thing up, filter it, and then weigh all the powder together. Then he should take as much sugar as this powder weighs. When he has done that, he should weigh out the whole thing to the weight of three coins. Then he should take as much of the purest wheat flour as fills half a nut shell, and as much spurge juice as a split feather of the scribe can hold in the location of the cut when the scribe dips the feather into ink. Then he should form — out of the powder, the wheat flour, and the spurge — a very thin mass of dough as though for a small cake, divide this dough into four parts, and in March or April dry them out in the sun; during these months the sun's rays are so even that they are neither too hot nor too cold and for that reason especially healthful. If during these months the spurge referred to is not available, and making the purgative must be postponed until May, then one should place the dough referred to, that is now made in May, in the May sun to dry out and so wait until the right opportunity. The heat of the ginger and the cold of the zedoary collect the humors, the heat and the moisture of the sugar keep them together and moisten them, the heat and the strength of the wheat flour keep them from flowing out in a disorderly fashion; however, by its coldness, the spurge juice draws out

169

the bad humors in a gentle, measured fashion when they are moderated as was described above. The ginger and the zedoary, the sugar and the wheat flour hold back the good humors in a person, and the spurge takes the harmful humors away. If one were to give only the spurge to a person without the other abovementioned agents, it would take out both the good and the bad humors because no proper action of the good plants would hold the good humors back. This purgative drink should be prepared in the months mentioned because then the sun and the air are well regulated. A person who wants to drink the laxative should drink a quarter of the above amount on an empty stomach. If his stomach is so hard and strong that he experiences no effect from the drink, he should again take half of the third part of the mentioned small cakes, smear them all over with spurge and, after they have dried in the sun, eat them on an empty stomach. However, before someone takes this drink when it is cold, he should warm himself by the fire and take it only then. After he has taken it, he should remain awake in bed and rest a little; then he should get up and slowly move around enough so that he does not feel cold.

Diet. After a bowel movement, he should eat wheat bread, not dry but dunked in gravy, and also young chickens, pork, and other light meat dishes, but he should avoid course bread, beef, fish, and other heavy or roasted foods. He should also refrain from cheese, raw vegetables, and fresh fruit. He may drink wine, but only moderately, and not water. He should avoid direct light from the sun and the fire and take these precautions for three days. Take the liver of the fish called catfish and place it on a piece of linden wood. Then make a fire and lay the wood, with the liver, on its glowing coals so that the liver will be dried out, but so that neither the smoke nor the flame of the fire touches the liver, and allow the liver to dry out long enough so that after the drying you can grind it into a powder. In the meantime, if you notice that the piece of wood has been burned up by the fire before the liver has become dry, then place it on another piece of wood of the same type. When it is dry, grind it into a powder. Then take muscat nut and fenugreek, dry them on a sandstone that has been moderately heated in the fire, and grind them into a powder also. Then tie up this powder and the powder that you prepared from the liver of the fish into a small cloth after you have added a little moss. Do it in such a way that the powder that you have made out of the catfish liver is more than three times the amount of the muscat nut powder, and the powder from the fenugreek is equal in amount to the powder from the liver. Keep that powder with you always; it will maintain the health of your body.

For the Harmful Holding Back of a Semen Emission. When a man is so aroused by desire that the foam has reached his member, yet for some reason is held back within the body, and when he becomes sick because of it, he should take rue and a little less wormwood, squeeze the juice out of them, add sugar and more honey than syrup to this juice, and further, as much wine as equals the juice, then pour the whole thing into a new pot or a bowl and heat it five times with a glowing piece of steel and then drink it hot after he has eaten a little. If it happens to be winter and he cannot obtain the plants mentioned, he should grind up some laurel and twice that amount of diptam; then, after the mixture has been dissolved in wine that has been heated with a hot steel, he should drink it. In that way, the harmful slime that has remained behind in the body is expelled with the urine and the feces. In summer, one can obtain these juices. The heat and the cold of the rue in combination with the heat of the wormwood drives out the thickened humors from the person, and the heat of the syrup in combination with the heat of the honey heals this type of complaint. If the heat of the wine has been moderated by the repeated heatings from the steel and the humors mentioned above, and when the whole thing has been heated five times to increase its effect, it should be taken away from the person after he has taken a little snack so that he does not experience weakness, and then he will feel better. However, in winter when the juice from these plants is not available, the heat of laurel and of diptam will, as we have said, drive the ailment referred to away from a man if their heat is regulated by the repeated warming of the wine and is strengthened through the repeated heating by the steel.

For Weakness in the Eyes. A person who has poor vision in his eyes because of excessive sexual desire, whether it be man or woman, should take the skin of the gallbladder from a catfish, empty the gallbladder, and dry the skin in the sun. In case something from the harmful liquids still remains within, it will be removed by the power of the sun's heat. For the power of this liquid would be too strong for the eyes and would harm them. Then, the skin should be dipped in the clean, best wine so that it will be tempered and softened by the mild power of the wine. When the person lies down to go to sleep, he should place the skin over his eyes and bind it fast with a cloth in such a way that the moisture of this skin does not touch the eyeballs directly; otherwise, they would be damaged by its strong effect. Around midnight, the skin should be removed and not allowed to remain on the eyes any longer, so that its strong power does not penetrate the eyes and thereby harm them. A person should do the same thing on the third, fifth, and seventh night, but not on the second, fourth, and sixth night, so that the person is not harmed because of excess. Also, when a person notices that his vision is reduced because of some other illness, he should do the same thing so that he may restore his vision by using this skin. When the skin referred to is handled in this way, it removes weakness of the eyes, unless God deems otherwise.

For Lasciviousness. To dispel sensual and carnal desire in oneself in summer, one should take dill and a double amount of stream mint, a little more cowslip than stream mint, twice as much from the root of the Illyrium sword lily as stream mint, and as much shallot as Illyrium sword lily. Cut up these ingredients and put them in vinegar, make a seasoning out of it, and then use it on every possible dish. In the winter time, one should grind up these ingredients and consume the powder with all food in the same way, for one cannot obtain these plants fresh then. For the dryness and the cold of the dill extinquishes the heat of sensual desire, the cold humor of the stream mint opposes that corrupt humor, and the cold, unwholesome juice of the cowslip removes the disordered longing after the flesh. The powerfully working cold of Illyrium sword lily suppresses carnal desire, and the toxic cold of the shallots diminishes the evil poison of lust.

For Temptations. If a person is bothered day or night, awake or asleep, by a devilish thought, he should take a belt prepared from the skin of an elk and a belt made from the skin of a roe deer, fasten these two together with four small pins of steel in such a way that one is over the stomach, one over the back and one on either side. As he fastens the pin that will go over the stomach, he should say, "By the power of almighty God I swear you to my protection." As he puts the pin in place that will go on his back, he should say, "By the power of almighty God I bless you to my protection." As he puts in place the pin that should sit on his right side, he should say, "By the power of almighty God I ordain you to my protection." And as he finally fastens the pin that should be on his left side, he should say, "By the power of almighty God I fasten you to my protection."

172

The person should be girdled with this belt at all times, both day and night, and the fiendish temptations will soften their attack upon him, and words of a magic spell will do him less harm. He is girdled and protected at every point on his body by these invocations. For steel is the foundation and ornament of the remaining things; it is like a form of completion for the human power, as strong as man already is.

There is a certain power in elk, and the roe deer is a clean animal. For that reason they turn away from devilish spirits and have a resistance to them.

For Forgetfulness. A person who is forgetful, against his will, should take a stinging nettle, pound it into a mash, and add a little olive oil to it. When he goes to sleep, he should rub his chest and his temple with it, do this often, and his forgetfulness will gradually go away. For the burning heat of the stinging nettle and the heat of the olive oil stimulate the contracted vessels of the chest and the temple which are somewhat asleep during waking consciousness.

For Hiccups. A person who suffers from hiccups should take a lot of sugar, dissolve it in hot water, and then drink this warm water because the heat of the sugar in combination with the gentle action of the heated water moistens the dryness which causes the coldness of hiccups in people.

For that reason, hot water is more suitable than wine for this complaint because water is gentle while wine is strong. Thus one should eat dry sugar and chew a lot of cloves on an empty stomach, and eat zedoary often, but only after having first eaten breakfast.

One should do this for an entire month. In such a person, sugar reduces dryness; the heat of the cloves penetrates the person, if he is empty, and makes him warm; the heat of the zedoary is strong and drives away the coldness of this ailment. One should do this for a person who has already eaten something, for if he has not, the powerful action of the zedoary would harm his empty stomach. One should use this technique for an entire month so that the person may be all the more strengthened by it.

For Poison. A powder to ward off poison and magic spells: it brings health, power, and luck to those who carry it on their person. Take the root of ruprecht weed with the leaves, two mallow roots with the leaves, and seven plantain roots with the leaves. At noon, in the middle of the month of April, pull these plants up by their roots, place them

173

on the moist earth, and sprinkle them with a little water so that they will remain fresh and green a while. As the day passes into evening, place the plants in the sunlight until the sun goes down. At dusk, take them away; place them on the moist earth, sprinkle them with a little water, and keep them this way throught the entire night so that they do not dry out too quickly. Then, at first light of the following day, just as the pink of dawn is on the horizon, again place these plants on the moist earth without sprinkling them with water and keep them there from the dawn's rays until noon, the third hour of the day, when the sun turns itself toward the south.

Pick up these plants at noon and place them facing south in the sunlight until the ninth hour of the day. Afterwards, collect them and place them on a cloth that has been slung on a wooden frame so that they are not trampled upon or scattered, and allow them to remain this way until just before midnight. Then, when the wheel of the North has turned like a mill wheel and travels back into the darkness because it can obtain no light and because then all nightly evils flee since now the night must give way to the day, that is, just before midnight place these plants either in a high window, on the threshold, or in a garden so that they have lukewarm air and can be affected by the air. Thus you must leave them lying there until shortly after midnight. Once midnight is past, pick them up from the place where they are lying, rub them a bit with the fingers, place them in a new bundle and add a little musk to it, but in such a way that the aroma of these plants is not overcome by the odor of musk. The musk will keep them from spoiling for a while. Daily, from this point on, the person should place the plants prepared in this way for defense against sickness and for the maintenance of health on the eyes, the ears, the nose, and the mouth in order to take in the aroma of these plants. If a person has a strong sexual urge, he should wrap these plants in a cloth and apply it from his loins to his member. A woman on the other hand should place it around the navel; then she will experience a cooling down. If a person has eaten something and feels pains because of it, he should put these plants into the neck of a narrow vessel filled with wine in such a way that they make no contact with the wine, but only so that the wine can take on their aroma. A person can prepare a small breakfast drink, namely "suffen," with such a wine and then drink it. However, if a person has taken poison or is visited by magic, he should drink this aromatic wine, and he will feel better. A person who carries these plants on his person when they have been prepared in the above manner will maintain his health and power, for these plants were prepared at any time and at any temperature, nights as well as days.

For a Cramp. If a cramp afflicts a person anywhere on his body, he should take olive oil and rub it on the place where he feels pain or, in case he has no olive oil available, massage himself there with some other precious salve. If he cannot obtain some sort of tree oil or other salve, he should then take his hands and powerfully massage back and forth on the place where he feels the cramp, and the pain will go away. For the heat and the power of the olive oil or the power of some other salve will drive away the vapor of the bile, and when the painful place is gently massaged with the hand, the pain will be driven away.

For Pains in the Body Like Cramps. A person who suffers from colic should take feverfew, pound it forcefully into a mash, then add a bit of cow butter and rub it into the painful place, and he will be be healed, for heat and the strength of the feverfew in combination with the heat and the gentle action of the butter drive away and alleviate this pain. (Take sage, less than zedoary; and fennel, more than the sage and zedoary. Then take water lentils, a double amount of fig root, and mustard that grows in the fields in the same weights as the fig root and less than the water lentils, from a plant on which burs grow.)

For Anger and Melancholy. If a person is overcome by anger or melancholy, he should quickly heat some wine on the fire, mix it with cold water, and drink it. In this fashion the vapors from his bile, which has led him into anger, will be suppressed.

For Anger. A person who becomes so agitated in his anger that he experiences pains should take bay leaves and dry them on a hot tile (the same with sage and marjoram), dry these plants in the sun, and then grind them up. Then he should put this powder together with the other powder made from bay leaves that was mentioned above, into a can in such a way that the powder from the bay leaves constitutes more than the powder from the sage, and the powder from the sage more than the powder from marjoram. Then one should put it up to one's nose because of its good aroma. One should also place a small amount of this powder in some cold wine, mix it up, and rub it into the brow, the temple, and the chest. The bay leaves possess a considerable, hot dryness; the wine moistens the humors that dry up those of a person's anger; the heat of the marjoram soothes the brain that has been stirred up by anger; and the dry heat of the sage gathers together again the humors that the anger has scattered. When the bay leaves are dried upon a hot tile and absorb the health that emanates from it and are laid, as said, in the sun together with the marjoram and the sage, that because of their powerful action are laid in the sun and are thus moderated, they alleviate the abovementioned sufferings through their wholesome heat. Because of its naturally gentle action, the powder that is mixed with the unheated wine also soothes, as said, the vessels of the forehead, the temple, and the chest which have been agitated by the anger.

For the Clouding of the Eyes Through Crying. A person who has poor vision because he often pours out tears should take some yarrow or its root, mash it into a soft pulp, rub it together, and place it on his eyes overnight in such a way that it does not come into contact with his eyes. Until about midnight, he should hold it on his eyes with a cloth and then take it off. Then he should smear his eyebrows with a little of the best, purest wine. For the heat of yarrow heals. Its sap is somewhat sharp and cleans wounds; because the wine is also hot and a bit sharp, it removes the sharpness of the yarrow sap. In this way the eyes are healed.

For Immoderate Laughing. A person who is seized and shaken by excessive laughter should grind up some muscat nut, add half as much sugar, shake this in some heated wine, and drink it both on an empty stomach and after having eaten something. For immoderate laughter dries out the lungs and shakes up the liver. But the heat of the muscat nut has a healing effect on the liver, and the heat of the sugar that has become liquid restores the lungs. If these two agents are regulated with the heightened heat of the wine and then consumed, they restore the good humors to their proper order which, through immoderate laughing, have become unbalanced.

For Drunkenness. To get a drunkard to regain his senses, take wild brier, place it in cold water, and moisten his forehead, temple, and throat with this water. When he regains his senses, he will feel better because the cold of the wild brier combines with the cold of the water and relaxes the powerful heat that is located in the vessels of the forehead and the temple. In the fall, one should take a grape vine with fresh leaves, place it on the forehead, the temple, and the throat of the drunkard, and thereby he will cool down. For at this time of year, the grape vine has greater power than at other times, and thereby it has a soothing action on the violent flooding that the wine calls forth in the vessels of the forehead, the temple, and the throat. If the agents referred to are not available, one should eat fennel or fennel seed, and one will feel better because the mild heat and the gentle action of the fennel suppress the unwholesome action of the wine in him.

For Vomiting. A person who suffers from vomiting should take caraway, a third as much pepper, and a fourth as much burnet saxifrage; grind them all up; take clean wheat flour; add the powder to the wheat flour; and, after adding an egg yolk and a bit of water, make some small cakes, either in a hot oven or under hot ashes. He should eat these small cakes, but he should also spread the powder referred to on bread and then eat it. When the cold of the caraway, the cold of the burnet saxifrage, and the cold of the egg yolk is tempered by the heat of the pepper and the wheat flour and is combined with the gentle action of the water, as described above; cooked by the gentle heat of the oven, they suppress the hot and cold humors that have become out of balance and that vomiting releases in a person. (Also take caraway, about a third as much pepper, about a fourth as much burnet saxifrage as caraway, grind it all up, take a little finely ground wheat flour, add the powder to the flour, and with an egg yolk and a little water bake small cakes in a hot oven or on the hearth. Eat these small cakes, but also eat the powder referred to, sprinkling it over bread.)

For Dysentery. Someone who suffers from dysentery should take an egg yolk from which the white has been separated, place it in a bowl, and stir it up. After he has done that, he should add caraway and a little ground-up pepper to the egg shells, cook it over the fire, and give it to the patient to eat after the latter has already eaten something. For the egg yolk is dry and mixed with slime; it draws everything toward itself and gathers together everything that is scattered. Also, a chick comes to be out of it, and hence it can draw the freed humors together. By its cold, the caraway also draws together what has been released. The pepper, by its heat, counters the action of these two agents so that they, as said, draw the scattered humors together all the more strongly. One should also take more egg yolks, press the fat out of them in a pan over the fire, prepare small cakes with them and with pure, fine wheat flour, and eat them after having a little something else. For the fat of the egg yolks, mixed with the heat and the strength of the fine wheat flour, removes the diarrhea. In the meantime, whatever such a patient eats should be hot, for his stomach, bowels, and humors are chilled. If something is soft and has a pleasant taste, he should eat it — also small chickens and other soft meat like fish. However, he should avoid herring and salmon, also beef, cheese, raw vegetables, and leeks. He may eat no rye bread and no barley bread and nothing roasted except roasted pears. For all these foods, because of their hardness and the difficulty of digesting them, worsen the toxicity of his intestines, and the water builds up sludge there. For that reason, a person must avoid them for the time being. Wine, however, by its heat, binds the sludge together.

For a Hemorrhage. If someone has a hemorrhage, he should take two egg yolks, beat them, add some juice from feverfew to half of one egg yolk and as much vinegar as can be contained in two egg shells. Then he should add a little cinnamon powder and less zedoary powder than cinnamon powder, and once he has mixed one with the other, prepare, with a little water, a rather thick drink from all that and serve it to the person who suffers from the hemorrhage. He should drink it moderately hot, both on an empty stomach and also after he has eaten something. Repeat this often, and the patient will improve.

For Bleeding From the Anus. A person who has such a hemorrhage should take blackberry and twice as much blood root, mash them up a bit until the sap comes out, place them in wine in this condition and drink it during the meal and after the meal, but not on an empty stomach. For blackberry and blood root have a juice that is similar to the liquid of blood; consequently, when tempered with wine, it halts the outflow of blood by its heat and coldness. These ingredients are normally consumed after something else has been eaten so that they may contain the blood, which then tends toward the stomach to digest the food consumed. He should also take some wheat flour and, with honey and a little salt, make small cakes and eat them. For by its heat and strength, wheat flour causes a person's flesh to increase and closes off the improper path of the blood. By its heat and its humor, honey calms blood that has been stirred up, and the heat of the salt dries it out. When each ingredient is moderated by the others, the blood that would otherwise flow out improperly is contained. As long as a person suffers from this ailment, he should eat wheat bread, but avoid rye and barley bread. He should not eat beef, pork, or fish that have no scales, cheese, raw vegetables, or raw fruit nor anything that has been roasted, either. He may eat other kinds of soft meat and the usual kinds of fish, and also sip some pea soup; however, he should avoid peas, lentils, and beans. He should eat nothing hot — only what is lukewarm — so that his food is neither too hot nor too cold. He may also drink mild wine, but he should avoid drinking water because it harms a person who is suffering from this ailment, as was already said concerning dysentery.

For Vomiting Up Blood. If harmful, curdling, and toxic humors have gained the upper hand in a person and he vomits and spews out blood for a time, he should apply no medication at first so that the blood, aroused by the medicine, does not cause an inner abscess and more than usual flows out. When the blood has stopped treating the person so harshly, he should add a little olive oil or butter sage to a mild, sweet wine that has been mixed with a little water. After having cooked it, he should strain it through a cloth and then take a little, but not until he is satisfied, and not on an empty stomach, but only after he has eaten something. The sage combats the inner decay of the humors, the wine enlivens and strengthens the sick person since it is moderated by the gentle action of the water, and the olive oil or the butter heals him within.

For Hemorrhoids. If harmful, watery, or thin humors have gained the upper hand in a person and have caused blood to flow from the anus without digested nourishment, the person should not try to hold back such a flow of blood within himself, for then the blood will become more disturbed and will flow out all the more.

Postscript to Blood. If a person's blood is disturbed by harmful and watery humors and he has begun to bleed from the anus with the digested nourishment, he should not try to hold it back, for it purifies him and aids his cleansing. However, if blood goes through him with his feces in an excessively strong fashion, he should mix gamander with vegetables and other good plants, prepare a meal from them, and then eat moderately. The gamander reduces the blood flow and blocks it; the vegetables and the other plants give strength back to the sick person.

Postscript to Vomiting Up Blood. If a person's spleen and lungs become damaged as a result of his embittered heart and thoughts so that the person, depressed thereby, becomes compelled to spew out blood and vomit, he should not abruptly block this release of blood lest he thereby develop an inner abscess and then vomit up more blood. After he has stopped vomiting up blood for a time, he should let the thumb of his right hand be pricked and give up some blood so that the blood that causes the suffering on the left side of the body may stream toward that point. Thereby he will be healed.

Postscript to Blood. If a person's small inner blood vessels so contract because of melancholy that he now and again vomits up blood, he should not immediately try to hold the blood back, but wait in peace until it stops by itself so that it does not do him more harm than good if he tries to quell the blood too quickly. For vomiting up blood will eventually stop by itself.

For Erysipelas. If a person experiences the eruption that is called "freislicha" in combination with an abscess, one should catch flies and, after having cut off their heads, grind them up. Then one should make a circle around the abscess because the poison of flies opposes the poison of this eruption and keeps it from spreading further. Then one should take the red slug that has no house on its back, grind it up, and make a circle around the first circle that one made with the flies. The slime from the slugs overpowers the purulent slime of the abscess mentioned above so that it stops; for what is evil opposes what is evil. Then one should take lily sap and with it massage the skin around the circle that one has made with the slug because this juice drives away the pains and brings healing. Then one should take a leaf from the milk thistle, place it on the eruption, prepare a small cake from wheat flour, place this on the leaf and over the entire abscess, fasten it with a cloth, and wait until the abscess becomes soft and breaks apart by itself. The cold and the sap from the milk thistle are not dangerous but, together with the heat of the wheat flour, turn the hard abscess soft. If the abscess does not break apart by itself, one should open it either with a dry wooden thorn or with a dry splinter, but not with a hot or cold iron or a needle, for the blister and the sore could become infected from a hot or a cold iron or needle so that it could easily become dangerous. However, as long as the person suffers from the sores of this eruption, he should protect himself from heat and cold, from wind and moist air, decline all hot,

180

roasted, heavy meats and also wine, and also avoid raw vegetables and raw fruit because all these things would increase and strengthen the harmful humors in him. He should eat only good wheat bread in water and only drink water because its gentle action is not dangerous for such a person at that time. If the person is a gourmet, he should prepare for himself a simple wheat-meal soup with pure egg yolks, but without fat and without cheese, and eat it after it has cooled. He should attend to this until he notices that the pain has decreased and gone away. In the meantime, he should avoid wine because wine congests his vessels and would aggravate any swelling. He should not eat hot foods. The excitement of its heat would disturb his humors, and thus any swelling would increase.

For Crabs, Any Kind of Abscess, and Headache. Take violets, squeeze out their juice, strain it through a cloth, weigh out some olive oil, specifically a third of the weight of the first juice, and then as much goat suet as the violet juice weighs, bring these all to a boil in a new pot and make an ointment out of it. Apply this ointment on all the body parts where the crabs or other little beasts are bothering the person, all over and even on top. They will die when they have tasted it. Apply it to other abscesses which are causing pain, also, and if someone has a headache, apply it cross-wise on his forehead.

For Itching. Someone who suffers from various sores and itching should take some chervil, three times as much blechnum as chervil and five times as much elecampane as chervil and boil these in water. Then squeeze out the water, strain it through a cloth, and pour it into a pan. Add a bit of fresh incense, sulphur, and very fresh hog fat, even more than the other components make up together, so that the whole thing will thicken, over the fire, into an ointment. One should rub this salve into the patient on and around the sores. One should also place the boiled herbs we have mentioned (on the skin and the sores), while they are still warm and the water has been squeezed out of them. However, the person must do this for five days so that his skin and his flesh are thoroughly penetrated by them. Afterwards, the sick person should wash himself in a bath so that both the slimy humors and the bad smell are removed from him. The chervil has as much heat as cold, and if it is tempered by the heat of the blechnum and the elecampane, by the gentle action of the water, by the sulphur, by the incense, by the hog fat, and by the other heat, the harmful humors in the person will be driven out. Because the chervil possesses both heat and cold, it removes the improper heat and cold of the sores and of the itching. The heat of the blechnum dries out the harmful humors, the heat of the elecampane drives them away, the heat of the incense has a healing effect on them, and the heat of the sulphur a lessening action on them. The heat from hog fat, while it is still fresh, heals the sores and the itching in a gentle way.

For Jaundice. A person who has jaundice should take ironweed, twice as much garlic as ironweed, three times as much penny royal as ironweed or, in case there is no garlic, saxifrage to the same weight as the ironweed. He should place these plants in good wine in a deep pan almost closed on the top. He should drink this wine for nine days on an empty stomach, but only a little after having eaten something else. With the same wine he should prepare for himself a fat egg soup and drink it. When he goes to sleep, he should heat the wine with a hot steel, drink it, and then cover himself with a thick cover so that he will sweat. He should do this until he is healed. The heat of the ironweed, of the garlic, and of the penny royal as well as the cold of the saxifrage have rather sharp humors. When they are moderated by the heat of the wine and consumed in a drink, and joined with the heat of the wine or of the fat and with the cold of an egg for the sake of taste, as was described above, they combat the bitterness of the bile and weaken the ailment referred to. A person should take this drink on an empty stomach so that it can the more quickly penetrate his limbs than if he has already eaten something; it should also be made stronger by being heated with a hot steel, so that it may the more quickly overcome this illness.

For Epilepsy. A person who suffers from epilepsy should take mole blood and dry it. He should also take a duck's beak, specifically that of a female, and the feet of a goose, also a female, without the skin or meat, grind and grate them into powder, so that the powder from the duck's beak is twice as much as the powder from the goose, and that of the mole's blood is somewhat more than twice as much as that of the duck's beak. One should put this all together in a cloth with the mentioned blood; he should let it lie for three days on the place where a mole had kicked up dirt from the earth a little while before. He should then take it off that spot and place it on ice so that it freezes. Then he should again lift it up and place it in the sun to dry. After that, he should take part of the liver from any edible animal or bird, as much as he can get, and prepare small cakes from it and a little

182

wheat flour, add from the mentioned powder less than the amount of the liver referred to, plus a bit of caraway, and then eat it. Because the mole sometimes shows himself and then again hides himself, and because he commonly digs in the earth, his blood fights this illness which now and then is noticeable and yet now and again remains hidden. Further, because the strength of the duck lies in its beak and because a duck probes both wholesome and unwholesome things with its beak, it also combats this illness which suddenly breaks out and then just as suddenly returns to peace. In the same way, the geese feet calm the arthritic pains of this illness, for sometimes the feet of geese are completely washed by water, but they also come into contact with every possible contamination because this illness often appears with a kind of arthritis. For that reason the beak and feet should be from a female bird, not from a male, because the female keeps quiet. For a woman is more peaceful than a man, just as this illness gives the appearance of peace until the very moment when it throws the person to the ground.

Properly mixed together, the healing agents should be placed on the very place where the mole digs its hole because the earth is healthier there than elsewhere. For these agents should receive their humor and their power from the humors and the power of the earth. There, also, they will more quickly be penetrated by the humor of the earth and contract because of its icy coldness so that whatever is contrary within it is repressed. They should also be dried in the sun so that, in case there is something contrary remaining in them, it will be removed by the heat of the sun. That is why the liver of the animal as well as of the bird should be mixed with wheat flour because the liver is dry, and it has its power from the earth, and also attracts slimy humors to itself. The liver, specifically, together with the heat and strength of the wheat flour, should drive out the harmful humors of this disease. Caraway is also added because its coldness suppresses the unattractive, hot attacks of this disease. A person who suffers from this disease should eat the mentioned cakes for five days straight, and, in case he is not yet cured, keep eating them for five days more as he needs them. When he no longer needs them, he should consume them for five days longer and then proceed in the same way seven times more in succession for five days each. He may eat bread and meat in the meantime, if they have been boiled with celeriac and parsley, for such meat is then somewhat dry and does not contain any more harmful humors. The gentle coolness of both the celeriac and the parsley frees the bowels and takes away the fever attacks from the stomach; these sometimes occasion this illness. If the sick person wants to eat beef, it should be fresh and placed in water — in summer for a day, in winter for a night — for the water removes all the slime that is in the meat. Once it is boiled, he may eat the meat. He may also eat lamb, and then it is not necessary that he place it in water as he did the beef, for it is delicate. However, for the duration he should not eat pork, for it has the characteristic that it easily awakens lust in a person, and it encourages leprosy and epilepsy, as well as allowing the worm to spread that gnaws at a person's flesh. He should avoid eel and other fish that have no scales, for corresponding to their nature they contain a fair amount of toxic slime. That is the reason they have no scales. For the duration he should pass up cheese, eggs, raw vegetables, and raw fruit, as well as everything roasted. Cheese is like a poison for this illness, and eggs, raw vegetables, and raw fruit arouse the harmful humors. And something that is roasted adds arthritis to this illness. He may have wine to drink, if it is not strong but mild and mixed with water, and beer.

For Dropsy. A person who has dropsy should take a peacock, boil it with hyssop in well water, but not in water taken from an active spring, and then eat the meat. Then he should take the heart and the bone that turns in the knee joint, as well as the feet, and make a powder out of them so that the amount of powder from the feet and the heart are three times more than the powder from the bone. He should then take betony, three times as much lovage, and a bit of eel fat, cook them in wine, strain them through a cloth, add the abovementioned powder to this wine, and then drink it. This he should do for eighteen days straight. For the flesh of the peacock is dry and has a strong action against dropsy; because of its strength it must be from a male of the species. The whole thing should be boiled with hyssop because by its dryness and mild coolness it dries out the excessive moisture that is characteristic of this illness. For that reason it should be boiled with well water because it also has dry water veins and weakens the dropsy more than lively spring water which is more watery than well water. Because of its thinness it would only make this disease worse. The ground-up peacock heart smothers this disease. Because the bone that turns in the knee joint fastens the vessels of the bone, it also fastens this disease so that it cannot become worse. Moreover, the feet suppress the disease there where it sits so that it cannot break out like a broken well. The water that is characteristic of this disease withdraws before the heat of the betony; the coolness of the lovage refreshes the person's spirit since he is depressed, and the eel fat contains the disease where it reposes and threatens to break out. The heat of the wine calms the sick person more than water. If all of this is properly carried out according to presciption, this disease will wither away.

For Colic. A person who is bothered by colic should take a bit of ginge˜ and much cinnamon and grind them up. Then he should take some sage, less than the cinnamon, and more fennel than sage and less tansy than sage. He should mash the whole thing into a liquid in a mortar and strain it through a cloth. He should then boil some honey in wine for a short time and add a little white pepper or, if he has none, a little pepper plant together with the mentioned powder and liquid. After that, he should take duckweed, twice as much blood root as duckweed, and the same weight of mustard that grows in the field, and the plant on which the very small burs grow, but less than the duckweed, mash them all together into a liquid brew in a mortar, pour it into a pouch, pour over it the wine mentioned above that is mixed with honey and powder, and in this way prepare a kind of medicated wine. A person who suffers from the pains mentioned above should drink as much of this on an empty stomach as he can put down in one gulp, and again at night when he goes to bed. He should proceed in this manner until he is healed. Colic arises from both hot and cold harmful humors, but comes more from the cold than from the hot humors. Thus, when the heat of the cinnamon, sage, fennel, tansy, honey, wine, white pepper or penny royal, the mustard that grows in the field, and the heat of the burs is properly balanced with the cold of the duckweed and the bloodroot, the improper hot and cold humors from which the colic arises are reduced if this drink is taken on an empty stomach when one retires for the evening. Specifically, it should keep these humors from rising up when one's stomach is empty; and after one has eaten something, it should suppress the harmful humors in the food.

For Round Worms. If worms arise in a person from the harmful, bad humors that are poisonous to a human being, he should take the juice of a stinging nettle and the same weight of sap of silkweed; as much sap from the leaves of the nut tree as these two together, or, if there are no nut tree leaves, as much sap from the bark of the same tree; add a bit of vinegar to it; cook much honey in a new pot; and

185

wipe away the foam that develops on top. After it has boiled up, he should take the brew off the fire and drink it for fifteen days straight in small amounts on an empty stomach so that he is not harmed by its powerful effect. After having eaten something, he may drink more of it since the food partially counteracts this strong action. When the heat of the nettle and the mullein is tempered by the equally strong heat and cold of the nut tree, and the drink made from them is taken following the above instructions, then the worms die off because of the ingredients' strong action in the person. Vinegar and oil are added to make the taste more attractive.

For Lice. If lice harm a person on the inside of his body and cannot be made to come out, he should take the bile from an eel, add a third as much of the strongest vinegar and as much honey as the two together constitute, and boil the whole thing in a sauce pan. Then he should take ginger, twice as much long pepper, and about the same weight of basil, and grind them all up. Besides this, he should take ivory, about a third as much as the basil, and from a hawk's beak about half as much as from the ivory, and add the latter to this powder. Immediately thereafter he should add the powder to the vinegar and let everything come to a boil. When this has happened, he should pour the whole thing into a pouch so that like a medicinal wine it may penetrate all through it; then he should keep it in a new earthen jar. A person who is being harmed within by lice which cannot be made to come out should drink this drink daily on an empty stomach, but not at night as he goes to bed. The lice within him will become sick and die off; then his body will begin to fill out again. The heat and acidity of the eel bile weakens the lice, the heat and strength of the vinegar takes away their power, the heat and dryness of the ivory dries them out, and the hawk's bill kills them because it is cold, is poisoned by contact with every kind of carrion, and is penetrated by the secretions from the brain of the eagle. These are all regulated by the heat of the honey, the strong heat of the long pepper that is stronger than the heat of other kinds of pepper, and the coldness of the basil; then it is heightened in its action by the increased heat of the fire and poured into a clay pot so that it does not become weak and spoil. One should take this drink both on an empty stomach and after one has eaten something. It kills lice; it kills them even faster if one takes a glass of it on an empty stomach. For if a person takes this drink after having eaten something, the humors from the food are diluted, and the lice arise from these.

For Round Worms. Take equal weights of the sap from a stinging nettle and from silkweed and as much sap from the leaves of the nut tree as these two together. If you have no nut tree leaves, take as much sap from the bark of the same tree, that is, the nut tree; add a little vinegar and much honey; boil the whole thing in a pot and wipe the foam off the top. After it has boiled, take it off the fire. Give the person who is suffering from worms in his stools a little to drink from this mixture for five days straight on an empty stomach. After having eaten something, he may consume a greater amount of it.

For Gallstones. If a person develops a stone, he should take the fresh bile from a young calf, twice the amount of its blood, and allow it to dry out. He should also take saxifrage, grind it up, and from the powder that results take as much as there is bile, wrap the whole thing in a fine cloth, and then place it in clear, strong wine. He should drink much of this on an empty stomach and also as much after having eaten, but not while he is eating, for then the drink will be soaked up by the food. The acidity of the bile, tempered by the heat of the abovementioned blood, the cold of the saxifrage, and the heat of the wine releases the stone that has built itself up inside the person.

For Scabs. A person who develops scabs because of drunkenness and carousing should take swallow dung and four times as much of the plant that has burs and red flowers, and make a powder out of it. He should also take stork fat and a little more hawk fat, fry it it in a pan, then mix the powder and a little sulphur with this fat and prepare an ointment out of it. He should have it massaged all over his body in a sweat bath and then lie down in bed. He should do this for five days or longer. If the heat of the swallow dung and the cold of the burs is tempered by the heat of the stork fat and the cold of the hawk fat as well as the heat of the sulphur, they remove the purulent discharge because the swallow dung breaks it up, the bur powder eats it up, and the fat from the stork and the hawk as well as the acidity of the sulphur draws it out. The sick person will get well unless God does not intend that he be healed.

For Scabs (Continued). A person who develops scabs because of his violent temper should go to a place where some horse blood lies upon the ground, where the blood has been released from the veins, and where such clean beasts have been slaughtered. He should consume some of this blood, together with the blood-soaked earth. He should heat this blood with water that has mixed with the earth over which it has flown in a thermal spring, and in this way prepare a bath for himself. Still, one should not use so much water that it dilutes the strength of the blood, but only as much as reaches to the neck of the sick person when he sits in the bath. He should pour a bit of this blood and this earth into a small pouch and place it on his face when he has pains there. After he has climbed out of the bath, he should lie down in bed and place the pouch with the warm blood and the earth over his heart so that he doesn't become weak and so that he keeps the harmful blood far from his heart. He should act in this fashion four or five times, or even more often. The heat of this blood mixed with the earth that has been permeated with this blood combats scabs, just as one enemy opposes another. However, people have difficulty believing this because human nature is completely different from animal nature and because people are repulsed by the blood of animals. However, this procedure will cure the person unless God has willed that he not be healed.

For Scabs as a Result of Dissoluteness. If a person develops scabs as a result of a pleasure-seeking, dissolute lifestyle, he should take some agrimony, a third as much hyssop, and twice as much hazel root as these two plants together, cook them in a thermal spring, and in this way prepare a bath from them. He should mix into it as much menstrual blood as he can obtain, and then place himself in the bath. He may also take as much goose fat as he likes, a double amount of chicken fat, and a little chicken dung and make a salve out of all that. After he has climbed out of this bath, he should smear himself with this salve and then lie down in bed. He should do this often until he is healed. The heat of the agrimony, the cold of hyssop, and the heat of the hazel root, countered by the warm menstrual blood, removes the purulent scab. Agrimony, hyssop, and hazel root cause him to sweat, while the menstrual blood suppresses and removes the scab as one enemy does to another, for the blood arises from the various humors of the woman. Goose fat and chicken fat soften the scab and heal it. The chicken dung draws out the unclean elements that still remain. In this fashion the sick person is healed, or God does not wish it.

For Arthritis. A person who has soft flesh and because of excessive drinking, suffers from arthritis (or gout) in any of his limbs should take parsley and four times that amount of rue and roast it in a dish with olive oil. If he has no oil, he should use goat tallow to roast it. He should place the plants, as hot as they can be, on the place where it hurts and fasten them there with a cloth. The coolness of the parsley juice suppresses the erupting arthritic humors, the heat of the bitter rue sap keeps these humors from increasing too much, the oil or the goat tallow penetrates them and breaks them up. These ingredients do this when they are applied in the manner outlined above.

For Swollen Glands. If someone has swollen glands in his neck, before they break out, he should take coltsfoot — and a lot of it — that is white on the outside and green within, tear it from the stalk corresponding to the spread of the swollen glands, throw the rest of it away, and smear what remains with honey. He should place the coltsfoot on the swollen glands in this fashion for three days and three nights. If it dries up, place a new batch of coltsfoot prepared in the same way, and the swollen glands will gradually go down. On the fourth day, he should take wheat flour and knead it with honey corresponding to the spread of the swollen glands. He should first place columbine on the glands, and then the dough over the whole thing. He should proceed in this fashion for nine days. If the dough dries out, he should make it supple again with more honey. He should proceed in this fashion until the swelling disappears.

For Symptoms of Paralysis. If someone begins to develop a paralysis in any one of his limbs, he should take some diptam herb, throw away what sits in the middle like a heart, thoroughly boil what remains in water, and while it is boiling add twice as much house root as diptam and twice as much stinging nettle as house root. He should mix the whole thing together and boil it in water. After the plants have been boiled, he should lightly squeeze out the water and place them, still hot, on the joint and vessels of the limb where the person is beginning to feel paralysis. As the plants gradually cool down, he should heat them again, again place them on these points, and repeat this procedure often. What lies in the middle of the diptam and is dry should be thrown away. The heat of the remaining diptam, balanced by the slow action of the house root, drives away the harmful humors that induce weakness in a person's limbs. The heat of the stinging nettle eats up these humors so that they release their hold as they, as mentioned above, are countered by the gentle action of the water. In this way the sick person will become well unless God wills otherwise.

For a High Fever. A person who eats little and drinks a lot should drink water if he suffers from a high fever so that he does not, should he drink wine, become even hotter and thereby acquire an even higher fever. He should drink the water cold or, in case it was heated, after it has cooled down, and he will then have less to suffer because it will refresh him and extinguish the glowing heat within him. For if the water were hot, it would further strengthen the heat of the high fever.

For a High Fever (Continued). Should a high fever afflict a person, he should avail himself of the following procedure so that he may improve and suffer less before he breaks out in sweat. He should take some dry sycamore wood and twice as much dry willow wood that is not green, and scrape off a little of it into cold water with a scraping knife. Then taking as much agrimony as willow wood, he should place it in the water and drink some of it after it has been prepared in this fashion, and he will have fewer pains. Both the sycamore and willow wood must be dry lest the powerful humors from these woods bring the sick person more harm than healing. The gentle action of the sycamore mitigates the bitterness of the willow. In this way the coldness of these woods opposes the improper heat of the high fevers. The gentle heat of the agrimony holds down the heat of the fevers so that they do not increase. These medicaments should be prepared with cold, not hot, water and also not with wine so that the heat of the high fevers does not develop into madness from the heated water and the heat of the wine. One should apply this form of treatment from the first hour or from the first day of the fever attack until the outbreak of sweating begins. If one postpones this treatment until the fever reaches its full strength or until it has almost reached its end — that is, until the fifth or sixth day, at the point where the person is either going to sweat his way back to health or lose his life — then this potion will not have much effect because the patient will quickly either regain his health or die.

For A One-Day Fever. A person who suffers from a one-day fever should take marjoram, camphor, and more bloodroot than these two together; grind the whole thing up; and when the fever begins, immediately add the powder to a warm wine and drink it. Then, one should lie down in bed and sleep. The heat of the marjoram and camphor, combined and tempered with the cold of the bloodroot and consumed with the warm wine, drives away this attack of fever at the very beginning so that it will go down all the more quickly.

For a Three-Day Fever. A person who suffers from fever every other day should take some yarrow and twice as much blechnum; boil these plants in a light, good wine; strain them through a cloth; and when the fever attack begins, drink this wine immediately. He should leave these plants in the wine for three days so that it is better affected by them. He should drink this wine for three days straight, and if it becomes necessary, replace these plants with fresh ones. The heat of the yarrow and of the blechnum, moderated by the increased heat of the wine and consumed with the drink according to the above formula, will lower the fever.

For Three-Day Fever (Continued). A person who suffers from a three-day fever should take balsam herb, small coltsfoot to the same weight as the balsam herb, and three times as much radish as the two plants together; boil the whole thing in wine; and strain it through a cloth. He should also take cloves, twice that amount of galgant, and a third of this combined amount of ginger; grind it all into a powder; and make a clear potion together with the wine mentioned above that was strained through the cloth. He should take this as the fever sets in, and on the following nine days, so that he may all the more powerfully be helped. The heat of the balsam herb and the cold of the small coltsfoot moderated by the heat of the radishes, cloves, galgant, and the strong heat of the ginger will drive away this kind of fever when consumed with the wine.

For a Four-Day Fever. A person who suffers from a four-day fever should take madder, the same weight of brier bush, and three times this combined amount of fallow root and boil them in wine. Then pour clear, very good wine into a basin and plunge a heated, glowing-hot piece of steel into it; plunge the heated steel into the wine in this basin a second time. Do it ten times with the same wine and the same steel. After that, take the wine in which you boiled the plants, pour it into the heated wine into which you have plunged the hot steel bar, cause the whole thing to boil up one more time, and when the fever begins again, drink it immediately, and keep it up until you are healthy. For when the cold of the madder and the heat of the brier bush and the fallow root are moderated by the increased heat of the wine and are again strengthened by the force and increased heat of the steel in the way described above, they lower the fever.

For Worms. A person who has a worm gnawing any place on his body should take chalk and double that amount of clay, make a thin paste out of them with sour wine, and apply it with a feather on the spot where the person feels the worm. He should do this every day up to the fifth day. After that, he should take aloe and a third as much myrrh, grind them up together, and with new wax make a poltice out of this, place it in a cloth made of hemp, and fasten it to the place where it hurts. He should wear this poltice for twelve days. The chalk is hot and the clay cold. In this way the heat of the chalk, combined with the cold of the clay and with the heat and acidity of the wine, kills the worms. The heat of the aloe, enhanced by the heat of the myrrh, draws the pus out of the ulcers and heals these places.

A Heating Bolt. So that the steel may be strong, immerse it in lion or ram's blood. If a diamond is immersed in ram's blood in order that it may be cut by the steel, the steel receives its strength from the point where it comes into contact with the ram's blood into which it is plunged and is then able to cut the diamond.

If you have noticed that cattle have become sick either because of harmful blood or through heavy labor, collect mussels from the sand that lies on the bottom of the river; grind them into a powder; put them into water together with the plant that is called betony in such a way that the powder constitutes more than the betony; and give it to the cattle to drink. In the meantime, give them dry hay to eat. However, if mucus begins to flow from the nose and they are making noise in their throats as if they had a cough, then take myrrh and incense — so that it is more myrrh than incense — place them on red-hot coals, and make the smoke pass into their nostrils. If the air is moist and warm and the cattle easily become sick, take dill and calamus, but so that there is more dill than calamus, and mix them into their feed so that they eat it, and these plants will preserve their health and the cattle will not become sick.

Sheep. If sheep become sick, take fennel and dill in such a mixture that there is more fennel than dill; place them in water so that the water takes on their taste, give this water to the sheep to drink, and they will improve.

The Horse. If mucus begins to flow from the nose of a horse and as a consequence it begins coughing, then boil some stinging nettle — and even more lovage than nettle — in water. Make this steam rise into the nose and mouth of the tethered horse, and he will be healed. If a horse develops stomach pains, introduce stinging nettle

192

and more lovage than nettle into his feed so that he eats it all together, and he will be healed.

The Donkey. If a donkey develops headaches and coughs, then take some beech ash — specifically beech ash out of which lye has already been made — make its vapor rise into the donkey's maw and nose while the embers are still hot, and he will be healed. If a donkey develops stomach pains, mix coltsfoot by scraping it off into bran that has already been placed in hot water, and he will be healed.

The Pig. If a pig suffers from some illness, take some snail shells and a bit more dill than snails, grind them all up, and put this in their feed so that the pig eats it. Also cook some stinging nettles in water and pour that water into the feed so that the pig eats it. Do this often, and the pig will get better.

The Nanny Goat. If a nanny goat becomes sick, feed her ample amounts of oak leaves; do this often, and she will improve.

The Horse and The Cow (Continued). If you would like to cut a vein in a horse, a cow, or a donkey in order to draw off some blood and if the animal is powerful and agitated, then draw off as much blood as will fill a water cup. However, if the horse or cow or donkey is weak and thin, then take only half a cup of blood, corresponding naturally to the bodily condition and reduced strength of the animal. After the bleeding, give it soft feed and dry, fine hay to eat. After such a bleeding it should rest for two weeks or ten days so that it may regain its strength; otherwise, it will keep on working. After three months have passed, take some more blood from the animal during the fourth month but not earlier, except in an extreme emergency due to an illness, because the harmful humors are not as abundant in such animals as they are in human beings.

Sheep. You should take blood frequently from a sheep, but only a little bit each time.

Take both the root and leaves of ruprecht weed, two roots together with the leaves from mallow, seven roots with the leaves from plantain, and these plants together with their roots in the middle of the month of April. . . .[3]

[3] Only a fragment of this section remains.

For Pains in the Tongue. If someone develops pains in the tongue so that it becomes swollen or ulcerous, scratch it a bit with a small pin or thorn so that the purulent matter can come out at the point of the wound, and it will improve.

The Chest. If someone develops a cough in his chest so that he begins to suffer pains within, take equal parts of sage and lovage and twice that amount of fennel, and place them all in good wine until it takes on a bit of their taste. Then throw away the plants, heat the wine, and drink it after a meal while it is still warm until you are healthy again.

Where Forgetfulness Comes From. In certain people, harmful humors sometimes build up a vapor which rises up to their brain and so pollutes it that they become forgetful. For this condition, take some stinging nettle, mash it into a liquid, and add a little olive oil. When you go to bed, rub it deeply into your chest and temple; do this often, and your absentmindedness will decrease.

V.

The Signs of Life. If a person is sound of body, if he has clear, bright, diaphanous eyes, regardless of the color, he has the marks of life. If his eyes are as bright and transparent as a white cloud through which another bluish cloud can occasionally be caught sight of, he will live and not die soon.

The Eyes. One can discern the power of the soul in a person's eyes if his eyes are clear, bright, and diaphanous, for the soul lives in the body with the power to accomplish many deeds through it. A person's eyes are indeed the windows of the soul.

Dull Eyes and the Sign of Death. However, if a person has dull eyes so that his eyes are not bright and transparent, even if he is healthy and no matter what color they are, he has the sign of death. Thus he will soon become sick and die if his eyes become as dim as a cloud that is so thick in front that one cannot see through it to see the blue behind. In this person's eyes one can no longer discern the power of the soul, for it will only accomplish a few more works in him and carries on as if it is walking in a fog, like a person who is brooding and reflecting over when he should take leave of his dwelling and go forth from his house.

The Signs of Life. A healthy person, whose cheek color, under the skin, is red or at least a little pink so that one can see this color beneath the skin as with an apple, and whose skin is diaphanous, clear, and bright, has the signs of life, if his cheeks have a reddish color, as happens with a white cloud through which one can sometimes see the blue sky behind it. Such a person will live and will not soon die. For the reddish color that is apparent on his cheeks is, as we have said, the fiery breath of life, that is, the soul, for the soul is fire. Thus the fact that the soul is living in the body and will not soon leave it shows itself in the cheeks.

195

The Signs of Death. An apparently healthy person who nevertheless has a pink or reddish color over the skin of his cheeks so that one cannot see the skin below this reddish color, has the sign of death. In this case the redness so covers the cheeks that one cannot see the skin beneath; it is the same with a red apple under whose redness no skin, only a certain redness of the exterior surface, is apparent. Such a person will soon become sick and die. This redness on the skin of the cheeks is the fiery breath of the soul. The soul is already showing itself as a bit outside the body, and shows itself in the body as weak and unsure of itself like a person who has already walked back and forth through his front door a few times as he forms the intention to leave the house.

The Omen of Death (Continued). A person's voice, which previously always sounded clear and pure, also presages death if the afflicted person was always strong and healthy before and then suddenly his voice becomes hoarse in such a way that it remains hoarse, without, however, any apparent sickness otherwise. In the same way, a golden trumpet that always gave out a pure tone becomes husky if it is somehow damaged. If a person's voice is clear and strong, this is the effect of the power of his mind. Specifically, it must have remained in its abode a long time; for this reason the person has a clear understanding. However, if a person becomes permanently hoarse, his soul is preparing itself to leave the body. The voice, too, which in an apparently healthy person becomes ever more hoarse and husky without any illness being the cause, is a sign of impending death if it suddenly becomes clear and bright so that afterwards the person's voice is permanently clear and bright without this being caused by any apparent illness. This is similar to a trumpet that was always useless and had a husky tone, somehow suddenly producing a clear, bright sound. It will give this tone for a short time, but will soon give out again and produce nothing. If a person's voice becomes hoarse, then his soul is doing something more secretly within his body than appears outwardly on his body. Hence, such a person is deceitful and wily. If the voice suddenly changes and becomes permanently clear and bright without any disease being the cause of it, then the soul is thereby indicating that it intends to soon depart from the body. For from now on it is showing itself more outside the body, whereas before it worked quietly within him.

If a person is lying in bed — no matter what disease holds him there — and if the flesh on his face has swollen up like that of a person who has just been awakened from a deep sleep and if his eyes are as clear as a cistern and somewhat watery, then without any doubt he will not recover from his disease but will die. For if a person's flesh has swollen up, that comes from the various diseased humors that show themselves in his face. However, the fact that his eyes are clear arises from the fact that the soul shows its fire in the eyes. The fact that they are watery comes from the fact that the fire of the soul is lowering its flames almost to the extinguishing point because it intends to leave this body soon. A person who presents a somewhat swollen face, like that of a sleeping person, but whose eyes are still clear and not watery, may just elude death, but with great anxiety and danger. For the harmful humors of this disease cause his face to swell up, but his clear eyes indicate that the fire of the soul is still in him. However, if his eyes are not watery, then in this case the soul does not bring its flames to the extinguishing point, but only holds them low in order to preserve his life.

The Sign of Life. If a person's eyes are very bright, but rather clouded and somewhat watery, he will soon get well and live. The fact that the eyes of such a sick person are not completely clear comes from the fact that the soul does not completely extinguish its fire in them. The fact that they are clouded is due to an excess of blood that is a sign of life. The fact that they are very watery comes from the fact that the excessive blood, by foaming up, cleanses and washes out the toxin so that the person may live.

The Sign of Death. If a person who, when he enjoys good health, is always clear and lucid suddenly loses his understanding during a sickness like a person who is mentally disturbed, and if he remains in this condition of confusion, he will die and not remain in life. If normally he was clear and could be understood, this must have come from the rational faculty of his soul; should he then, during an illness be continually irrational, the soul must have withdrawn its rational force and is preparing to leave.

The Sign of Life. If a person — who formerly was always rational and clear as long as he was healthy — suddenly loses his reason when he falls sick, then the soul is withdrawing itself from this life back to the Source of rationality. Should he in the further course of this illness suddenly find his way back to his former keenness of mind and remain there, then in this way the soul is giving a new sign of life by the display of the same rationality which it used to manifest, and so the person in question will evade death this time.

The Sign of Death (Continued). This concerns the person who, so long as he was healthy, always seemed confused and irrational; the soul was not allowing its rational faculty to appear in its completeness. If such a person during an illness when he is lying in bed, should suddenly become clear and lucid and remain in this condition for some time, he will die and not remain among the living because the soul is already exploring and manifesting the insight and the path it would travel in another life. However, when a person who while bodily sound was normally confused and irrational because the soul did not fully unfold its rational faculty and when sick comes to rationality, the soul is already preparing itself for the insight and the path to another life. If it should then suddenly return to its earlier condition of confusion and remain there, it will escape death again, for the soul has found its way back to the customary place and the customary condition that it formerly had in this body. In this case it will not separate from it.

The Pulse and the Sign of Life. If a person — it doesn't matter which illness has put him in bed — has a regular, peaceful pulse in the artery in his right arm, like a person who breathes in and out regularly and peacefully, that person will remain alive and not die. For no matter how great the weakness in a person might be which has been induced by a high fever because of the humors, the soul is retaining its regular respiration through it all since it does not intend to leave the body. Hence, the pulse beat in the artery is peaceful and regular, for the soul is not moving the artery in the expectation of death.

The Signs of Death (Continued). However, if the the artery in the right arm shows a rapid pulse similar to a person who already is suffocating, and it does not relax its beat, then he will die, for the soul is fixed upon separation. It moves the artery only in a weak fashion and is releasing itself from it. For that reason, a person facing death has a rapid pulse.

The Signs of Life (Continued). If the artery in its haste can produce one or two regular beats and then beats rapidly as before, the soul is showing by this speed that it is having difficulties in its separation; that is the reason it is moving the artery in such a rapid fashion. By

198

means of the one or two regular heart beats, it shows that it is still mindful of the person's life and is exerting itself for the sake of the life that is still present. Hence, the afflicted individual will not die but rather remain alive. One should pay special attention to the pulse in the right arm, for the indications that announce life and death are especially evident in the right arm since the right one usually has the greater power and is used for so many things. However, the left arm is as if crippled and is used for comparatively little. The pulse beat can be clearly measured at the elbow or under the knee because the power of the soul is located there. For the soul has the joints of the limbs securely under its power, and if it intends to leave the body, it relaxes these joints. Hence the pulse shows, in its arteries, the tumultuous disturbance that precedes death. However, if the soul does not intend to leave, even though the body is experiencing many pains, then the pulse in the arteries of the joints is peaceful and regular because the soul is not preparing itself to take its leave.

Signs in the Urine. No matter what a person likes to drink — whether it be wine, beer, mead, or water — the urine will still show, no matter what it comes from, the healthy or diseased condition of the individual. One kind of urine is not better than another, for all urine comes into existence out of dross, even if one kind of drink is better than another.

Paralysis. If a person is cold and paralyzed and lies sick in bed, his urine is as white as the foam on new cider and the same consistency as wine because of the shaking that occurs when it is moved. Because the coldness and the paralysis in him are in constant movement, his urine, therefore is thick and as white as the foam from cider so long as he is sick. It is white because of the coldness. On the other hand, heat gives urine a reddish or some other color. It is thick because the humors in such a person are rotten and do not find the right path, resembling the waters that wash over the bank during a storm and thicken themselves. If he is on the point of dying, then his thicker urine falls to the earth, for in such a person the humors separate from one another and prepare themselves for death. On top, the urine is clear, for the water in the blood separates from the blood itself. The blood water rises to the top, and the blood falls to the bottom. The blood water is located between the upper, clear level and the lower, thick level like cold water that will soon freeze, and it is also like freshly fallen snow because that which is phlegm easily allows itself to be separated. For it becomes as cold as new ice and melts away or dries up like snow since it separates itself from the blood and from the humors. Those are the indications of death just as clouds that are as powerful as mountains, of a rapidly changing form, and black and grey, often portend a storm. However, the clarity, viscosity, and signs in the urine — the one like a fresh and not-yet-closed coagulation and the other suggesting freshly fallen snow — must not be isolated or separated from one another, as was described above, but rather combined with one another; then the sick person will remain among the living and get healthy. In a similar fashion there will be no storm if similar clouds, equally divided, are to be seen in the heavens. For the blood water, the blood, and the phlegm are bound together in such a person, and for that reason this person does not die. If only a little clarity is to be seen on the top of the urine and no indication is noticeable that suggests a comparison with freshly fallen snow, then the person in question will have many pains and will only barely escape death. For in this case the blood water cannot be fully separated from the blood and from the phlegm, for only a little clarity is visible on top and there are no flakes to be seen on the bottom. So this person will stay alive. However, if a person has a hot, strong fever, his urine will turn red and thick as a result of the heat of the boiling blood while the humors, due to the red glow of the blood, simply lie there as if asleep and will not carry out their tasks. Hence the dregs from these humors sink to the bottom and are bloody because they were set into motion and disturbed by the hot, red blood. A person who has such a high fever feels no appetite and has no desire for food because the humors are not fulfilling their duties. Moreover, if a person has this high fever, desires food, and eats excessively, then this fever is having more effect, for the humors are not fulfilling their duties. If he demands something to drink and drinks a lot, he does not thereby suffer any harm, for he would dry out if he did not drink anything. If he had a hot constitution before, then it harms him if he drinks wine during this illness. Thus he should not drink wine. However, if he had a cold constitution before, then it does not harm him if during this illness he drinks wine. When he is ready to die, his urine will show various streaks in it as if it were split apart like ice that becomes split during the thaw. The humors cause these changes because they separate at the death of a person, and because by means of these changes they prepare the way for death. On top, the urine is a bit clear because it is separated from the blood water and the blood. From the bottom to just below this clear layer, the urine is thick and viscous because the humors fall to the bottom at death and lie there useless. If the streaks, the clear zone, and the viscous part in the urine are not separated from one another so that one could isolate them individually, but rather are so mixed up that one cannot distinguish them, then the patient will live and regain his health again. In the same way, storms develop that are not really very dangerous if the clouds in the sky all look alike. For the blood water, the blood, and the humors are not separating from one another in this situation, but remain bound together to keep the person alive. However, if there are certain changes in the urine, but not in the whole urine, then the humors are beginning to separate from one another. However, they are not able to do this entirely. If the top layer in the urine becomes a little clear, the blood water is beginning to separate itself from the humors, and if one can discern no streaks below, then the humors are not separating from one another. Hence the afflicted individual will remain alive. However, a certain viscosity will appear which cannot be separated from the other symptoms, for the humors are not separated from one another. The individual in question will then experience many pains and will just barely escape death.

The Harmful Humors. There are people who suffer neither from stomach aches nor pains in their side who nevertheless harbor dangerous humors within themselves. When these people are ready to die, they dry out within, for they are seized by terror before the sudden very grave disease, and they thereby dry out within themselves. Their urine, caught in a urine glass, has the proper color because it was indeed healthy before. Once the urine is caught, it must be kept in a this urinal until it has cooled. Thus, if such a person is ready to die, his urine, once it has cooled down, soon becomes pale because this person is cold within due to his dryness, and it is clear on the bottom because its blood water has separated from the humors and from the blood. On top, it looks as if powder were sprinkled on it, for the person's humors are frightened and give out a type of powder as they prepare themselves for death. In the same way a person disperses powder if he is disturbed. This is a sign of death. If the urine does not soon turn pale, is not transparent on the bottom, and is not as if someone has sprinkled powder on top of it, but rather appears differentiated, then the sick person will remain alive and become healthy again (just as no serious storm will arise if uniform clouds appear in the sky). For the blood water, the blood, and the remaining humors which are in a person are not separating from one another in the expectation of death. If the urine appears somewhat reddish, clear on the bottom and from the middle upward like a noble wine, and it appears as if a small piece of fat would float on the top, then the poor fellow will certainly have many pains and will only barely escape death. For with this disease, the reddish urine indicates that the health of the individual has not been completely destroyed because health will totally penetrate the illness of the person with its heat and because such a warming has begun. That is why the urine begins to turn red. However, if the urine is transparent on the bottom, that indicates that the blood water is separated from the humors and from the blood, and if, from the middle to the top, it has the color of an excellent wine and something like a little piece of fat floats in the middle, this indicates a problem in the liver because the individual is apparently suffering from an inability to digest fat. For that reason the urine eliminates this indication, that is, the foam of this fat. Such urine is a symptom of a serious illness and great danger, but at the same time its reddish color indicates that his life is still hanging on.

A Daily Fever. If the urine of a person who has fever every day becomes thick and has a color similar to that of wine, he will soon become well again. For daily attacks of fever come from an improper movement of the humors. That is why the person's urine is thick and viscous because his humors are not in proper motion. Such fever attacks are also due to improper digestion if the feces are unusually hard or thin. That is why the urine of such a person takes on more or less the color of wine that has turned bad. However, if the urine is as clear and bright as water, the sick person will die, for the blood of this person has turned cold. For that reason also the remaining humors flow together, as when milk congeals, for there is a lack of heat and blood. For that reason also the urine is clear and bright, for it is not mixed with the humors because they are not carrying out their proper duties. If the urine is a little bit pale, thick, and somewhat watery, the person will experience many pains and will only barely escape death. Because such a person has a chill within, his urine is pale and somewhat watery; and since his humors are overflowing like a river in flood at the prospect of death, his urine is thick and viscous. Such a person will suffer a long time, but not to the point of death.

A Three-Day Fever. If the urine of a person who has a three-day fever becomes bloody and maintains the color of blood and if the urine becomes thick, then this person will not die, however, he will remain weak for a long time. For the humors in such a person have become red hot; hence his urine remains bloody and, because of the intensity of this heat, stays red. Because such a person's humors are boiling, his digestion is also upset. Hence his humor gets somewhat mixed in with his urine, and that is the reason the latter becomes thick and viscous. Due to this illness such a person will remain weak for a long time, but he will not die because his humors do not ultimately separate from one another. When the urine has been caught in a urine glass and is red and then turns a bit pale, and if different streaks like little veins appear in it and they are red, watery, and cloudy, this is an indication of death, and this person will die. Such a person's urine, which was red because of the heat and warmth of this person, possesses no more great warmth if it turns pale because the afflicted individual has cooled down inside. The variously colored streaks then appear in the urine because the humors in such a person become separated from one another, and each has a color corresponding to its job. They are red because the heat and blood become separated from one another by the chill; watery because the blood water and the blood are separated from the humors by the heat; but cloudy because the bile and similar humors separate from one another. If the urine shows the variegated streaks as a result of the various humors, but there are no red streaks to be seen therein, then blood and heat are still mixed together therein and are not separated. The urine thereby shows that life is still present. However, such a person will experience many pains, and will just barely escape death.

The Four-Day Fever. If the urine of a person who has a four-day fever is thick and red and if various streaks appear in it like veins, this person will have to suffer because he is dry inside; still he will remain alive. For if a person's urine is thick, excrement is mixed with the urine, and thereby the urine becomes thick. If it is red, the heat has stayed in the blood and has not separated from it. However, if it manifests various streaks, then the various humors still remain closely bound together. Thus the afflicted person dries out as a result of this disease; however, he can remain alive because a complete dissolution of his humors does not result.

The Prognostication of Death in the Urine. If the urine is white like tainted milk, similar to milk that has congealed and to a cloud which is crimson, white, and opaque in the middle, then that is a harbinger of death, and the afflicted individual will die. For urine that is as white as spoiled milk and similar to congealed milk indicates that the natural heat of this person has given out. That is the reason his urine is white. For that reason, also, the toxic elements that were located in the humors congeal because they don't possess the proper heat. And that is also the reason why the urine is like a cloud that is crimson, white, and opaque in its middle, for the bile is concealing itself in the middle of the humors as if protecting itself by their strength. It is crimson because it has changed its colors into the colors of a wound, and it is already in the process of dissolution; white, because its poison flows all over and because it indicates that its strength is giving out; opaque, because it is now releasing the harmful natural vapor that it kept within itself before. If a person's urine resembles a cloud that is crimson, white, and opaque and if it is also somewhat clear on the edge because it is not completely viscous, then the individual in question will suffer many pains and will just barely escape death. Nevertheless, he will heal faster than a person whose urine is red. For crimson urine indicates that the spleen is injured, white shows that it is already on the point of destruction, and opaque makes clear that it is already releasing its vapor at expiration. If the urine is viscous only in the middle and not everywhere, the clarity at its edges indicates that this person's humors are not yet fully separated from one another. Then the urine is clear at the periphery and thick in the middle because the humors are still strongly bound together. Thus this person will escape death and sooner regain his health than the person whose urine is red because he still has substantial heat within from which he cannot be freed so rapidly.

Differences in the Flow. It is noteworthy that the water in the river changes according to the condition of the air. For example, when a strong wind is blowing, terrifying storms develop over the waves. If the sun is shining brightly, the waters boil and send up foam. If the air is mild and peaceful, the waters also are still, peaceful, and beautiful. It is the same way with a person's urine; that is, if a serious illness, like a powerful wind, breaks out in a person to the extent that his soul would like to free itself from his body, then stormy disturbances build themselves up in his urine. If excessive heat similar to the burning sun afflicts a person's humors, then the urine will also change its appearance as a result of the heat. If a person's body is in a proper and peaceful condition, the urine will also show this.

Testing the Urine. To obtain a correct test of the healthy or diseased condition of people with a complaint, their urine should be collected as soon as they awake from sleep, for then the urine's consistency and color will accurately indicate their condition. For as a person sleeps and is peaceful and without movement, his perspiration and his humors flow according to their nature and the prevailing condition within the person. However, if the sick person cannot sleep, the urine that he expels during the night or at dawn should be collected for an accurate diagnosis of his condition; the temperature of the night, that is, the temperature that prevails at dawn, tends to regulate both his humors and his inner condition.

The Motionlessness of the Earth and a varied Examination of Feces. By their nature, earth and clay have no motion and for that reason cannot be moved by the air. However, they emit a noticeable odor after a heavy rain or just before it is going to rain. It is the same with a person's excrement. There are signs during a bowel movement that tell whether the person will live or die because excrement, like the earth, has no motion of itself. Still, by its odor it can provide the grounds for a limited conclusion about whether a person will live or die, but a conclusion arrived at only with great effort and only occasionally. If the feces have a strong smell, as they normally do, there is no indication of death because a warm decay displays itself in such an odor. However, if the excrement does not smell strongly and if the smell that it has is different from the one it normally has, that is an indication that death is imminent. For this warm decay is then lacking, and the heat itself changes if a person's humors change. Also, if the feces are black and dry, this warns of death because bile turns the feces black and dry as soon as a person's humors are preparing for death. If the feces are black and dry but still smell the same as usual, the man may still barely escape death although the bile indicates the person's perilous condition by the blackness and dryness of his excrement. If this odor is present, such a person, who has become somewhat black and dry within because of his bile, still has the proper warmth of decay. However, if the excrement has a different smell than is normal, that is a sign of death because the proper heat of corruption has been withdrawn from his feces by his diseased condition.

The Differences in Water and Baths. It is not conducive to good health for a person to bathe often, unless the person is thin and dry and easily becomes cold or hot, for his flesh is meager; such a person should bathe in water in order to make his body warmer and more moist. On the other hand, water baths harm a person who is fat because fat people are already warm and moist within, anyway. They do harm to their body if they induce still more warmth and moisture, unless they bathe in water only seldom simply to wash the dirt off and quickly get out again. Water that is good for drinking is also good for baths; however, it should be heated a little. Then, a person can sit a long time in it if he wants to because such an immersion will induce no disease, but rather bring a good, rich color to the person. Water that is bad to drink is also bad for bathing. If it is absolutely necessary that someone take a bath in such water, it should be properly boiled first so that any dirt that it contains will be reduced by the boiling. Also, one should remain only a short while in such a bath because such water is unhealthy. Rain water is somewhat astringent and sharp since the clouds and the air draw the rain up toward themselves from the various good and bad flowing streams and from the moist earth; for that reason it is not healthy. This water falls down through the air like lye through ashes; from this it derives its acidic and sharp taste. If it is heated for a bath, its dryness penetrates the skin and does considerable damage. Water from melted snow is also somewhat impure, and if one takes a bath in it, one may absorb harmful humors and other elements because such water runs through the raw elements, the chill and the dirt of the earth. Water from a protected cistern is somewhat softer and more suitable for bathing than water from rain or snow because it is somewhat purified. If a person takes a bath in the summertime in a flowing stream he will probably not be harmed by it, for the stream is regulated by the heat of the sun and the air so that it is neither too cold or too hot, but just the right temperature. Flowing water does not especially suppress bad or harmful humors, but neither do they increase.

The Punishments in Purgatory. There are inextinguishable fires in the air that are aroused by the various deeds of men. They ought to serve for man's glory, but because of the evil deeds of mankind they have become fires for our punishment, and so they come down from heaven to a few spots on earth. They gather themselves on the spot where several rivers spring up, flow out, and receive their warmth from these fires. Following the judgment of God, various souls are purified in these fires and in these waters. From these waters, certain streams that are always hot because they have come forth from the inextinguishable fires occasionally flow into the various lands toward mankind. Occasionally, also, fire rains down on certain parts of the earth as a punishment from God. It stands written: "It rained down fire from hot coals, and the tumult of the storm fills a part of its cup." The land, the mountains, and the rocks that this fire has touched will burn forever after until the last day. On places where it burns in this manner, small streams sometimes spring up which are permanently warm because of the same fire, and run hot. Clever people sometimes dig small channels from the places through which these streams flow, absorb its heat, and then let it flow on, using the hot water to warm themselves. These waters in no way harm a person who takes a bath in them, but rather bring him much health. Their own warmth overcomes the improper heat that is contained in this water and destroys the harmful humors within it.

The Turkish Bath. A Turkish bath, where dry rocks are heated, is not recommended for a person who is thin and parched because he thereby renders himself even drier. However, such a sweat bath is good and helpful for a person who is fat, for thereby he overcomes and reduces humors that are present in excessive amounts in himself. Such steam baths, in which hot stones are prepared, are also helpful for those who are arthritic, for the humors that are ever and again rising up in them are somewhat overcome by the sweat bath. In an ordinary water bath, on the other hand, the humors begin to collect and agitate themselves in an improper manner because the flesh, the blood, and the vessels of the arthritic person are thrown into an unstable condition. The stones contain fire and various kinds of moisture. If they are placed in a fire, the moisture in them cannot be fully driven out, and for this reason it is not healthy to prepare a steam bath with them. Rather, it is much healthier if one uses tile stones because they have already been burned and dried out. For the moisture that was in them has been completely removed by being burned in the ovens. Thus, anyone who wants to take a sweat bath should use tile stones. If he cannot get tile stones, he should then use sandstone, for it has a gentler fire and moisture in it. However, he should not use flint because flint has a strong fire in itself and has taken on various forms of moisture from water.

Different Kinds of Eyes. A person who has grey eyes is careless on occasion and sometimes rash, very unruly, lazy, or untidy; however, he completes every task he undertakes.

A person who has fiery eyes which are like a black cloud close to the sun is clever, understands things quickly, and has a problem with his temper.

The Eyes (Continued). A person who has eyes similar to a cloud in which one can see the rainbow is himself changeable, such that sometimes he is melancholic, sometimes happy; however, he behaves properly.

The Eyes (Continued). A person whose eyes resemble a storm cloud which is neither entirely fiery nor entirely dark, but somewhat grey, is inconstant, careless, and beaten down. However, he is ready to learn, so that he easily picks up and masters any job that he doesn't already know.

The Eyes (Continued). A person who has black or dark eyes which sometimes resemble a cloud is smart and follows good advice, but nevertheless feels himself confined and hemmed in by everything that he does.

Excessive Indulgence in Cherries. A person who consumes a large amount of cherries should also drink some wine so that their juice is countered by the wine and he is not harmed by their humor.

Some Points on Conception. Water draws certain people toward drowning, people who were conceived while the moon was up and it was raining heavily. A person who was conceived while the moon was shining and during the period of summer's hottest days is easily lured by fire to being burned up. A person who was conceived during "dog days" is likely to be eaten up by wild beasts because these are the "biting" days. A person who was conceived during autumn while the leaves are falling is thereafter prone to falling from trees or other high places.

The First Phase of the Moon. A person conceived during the first phase of the moon when the moon is receiving its light from the sun, will be proud and hard-hearted when he grows up. He only likes people who fear or respect him. He enjoys speaking evil about his neighbors, their pride, and all their possessions.

However, he is sound of body and will not suffer from any serious illnesses; still, he will not reach a great age. If the person happens to be a woman, she constantly wants to be highly regarded, is more loved by strangers than by her own family members, neglects herself, and loves new friends. She is mean to those around her and does not bother about them. She is sound of body. If she ever gets sick, she becomes very sick, almost unto death. She also does not live a long time.

The Second Phase of the Moon. A person conceived during the second phase of the moon, if he is a man, possesses a lively imagination, a comprehensive understanding, and a firm character. He is treated with respect by his neighbors. However, on any occasion of fear he easily slips into a panic. He is frequently sick, but not seriously, and may live longer than someone conceived during the first phase of the moon. If it is a woman, she will be smart. She inquires about many people, is industrious, and cares about herself and other people.

She wants to be loved but cannot be loved. She suffers from bile and easily becomes melancholic; however, she can live a long time.

The Third Phase of the Moon. A person conceived during the third phase of the moon, if he is a man, will be skillful. But this proficiency will be of no help to him because he will be dependent upon others. He is more concerned with the situations of others than his own affairs, is more interested in strangers than his own relations, loves God without bringing God's work to any fruition, and in his enthusiasm easily takes leave of practical restraints. His body easily becomes sick; however, he can live a long time. If it is a woman, she is unhappy and clumsy in worldly affairs, but prays to God. She frequently experiences pains in her vessels from various diseases that yet can be endured. She can also live a long time.

The Fourth Phase of the Moon. A person conceived during the fourth phase of the moon, if it is a man, will be slow and will often let himself be deceived by others. Still he has a good attitude and prospers so that he will be proud, rich, and respected. He is sound of body and can live long enough, but still will not live very long. If it is a woman, she will do a good job. She is useful and well-liked by her neighbors and gets on well with them. She becomes sick easily, and her body often feels weak. She will not live a long time.

The Fifth Phase of the Moon. A person conceived during the fifth phase of the moon, if it is a man, will be proficient and reliable, courageous and persistent as well as sound of body. He will live a long time. If it is a woman, she will have masculine traits, be quarrelsome and spiteful, but also skillful. She will not often, but now and again, be bothered by a light illness. She also can live a rather long time.

The Sixth Phase of the Moon. A person conceived during the sixth phase of the moon, if it is a male, will have a cheerful outlook and a charming, but not especially masculine nature — rather, one soft like a woman. He will easily become sick, and he will not live a long time. However, if it is a woman, she will be skillful, upright, and much loved by her companions. She is sound of body; however, she will not live a long time.

The Seventh Phase of the Moon. A person conceived during the seventh phase of the moon, if it is a man, will be slow and unintelligent. He will believe himself to be shrewd although he is not at all clever. He is not beloved by his companions. He has powerful veins and is not often sick. However, once he becomes sick, he becomes self-pitying and depressed. He will live a fairly long time.

If it is a woman, she will be bold, but slow and unintelligent, with a quick temper and a contrary personality. Her body is healthy, and she will live a long time.

The Eighth Phase of the Moon. A person conceived during the eighth phase of the moon, if it is a man, will be clever, chaste, and moderate in all that he does. He aids his companions and is sound of body. Moreover, once he becomes sick, he quickly recovers his health, and he reaches a sufficient age, although he will not become very old. If it is a woman, she will be kind, pleasant, careful about her dress, and skillful. She does not care for men. She is sound of body and will reach a sufficient age, although she will not become very old.

The Ninth Phase of the Moon. A person conceived during the ninth phase of the moon, if it is a man, easily becomes anxious. He will be unchaste, physically weak, and not live a long time. If it is a woman, she will be virtuous, loving men modestly; physically weak; and will not live a long time.

210

The Tenth Phase of the Moon. A person conceived during the tenth phase of the moon will be competent, honest, useful, successful, and sound of body, and will live a long time. If it is a woman, she will be skillful, kind, and as pleasant to her companions as a lily, honest, and successful. She will easily become sick; however, she will get well again quickly and will live a long time.

The Eleventh Phase of the Moon. A person conceived during the eleventh phase of the moon, if it is a man, will have a quick temper and will not prosper. Women do not care for him. Also, he will not enjoy good health or live a long time. If it is a woman, she will have a quick temper, be industrious and defamatory, but also competent. She will easily be put in bed by an illness, but she will also quickly regain her health. However, she will not live a long time.

The Twelfth Phase of the Moon. A person conceived during the twelfth phase of the moon, if it is a man, will be confused, and his thoughts will go in every direction. He is constantly interested in new places and new things and likes to be that way. His whole way of comporting himself is a burden to his companions. He will become melancholic and will not live a long time. If it is a woman, she will not have a definite character. She will be ignorant and will not be improved by education. She is a burden to her companions. She will not have many illnesses, but nevertheless she will not live a long time.

The Thirteenth Phase of the Moon. A person conceived during the thirteenth phase of the moon, if it is a man, will be unfriendly, anxious, and unreliable. He enjoys speaking badly about his companions and easily becomes mentally disturbed. He will not live a long time. If it is a woman, she will not be amiable, but rather cunning, and in a deceitful manner impart ''good'' advice. She will experience many signs of paralysis and will not live a long time.

The Fourteenth Phase of the Moon. A person conceived during the fourteenth phase of the moon, if it is a man, will be haughty and proud. He will work hard all his life; indeed, for the sake of his reputation he will work until his death and will have many children. He will easily become sick, but quickly regain his health. He will not live a long time. If it is a woman, however, she will be meek and not strive to be admired because she is already admired. She keeps her opinions to herself, works hard, however will not be much beloved. Although she will enjoy good health, she will not live a long time.

The Fifteenth Phase of the Moon. A person conceived during the fifteenth phase of the moon, if it is a man, will be well respected and prosperous. In all the enterprises that he undertakes he will be successful and experience no failures in them, regardless whether they be good or bad. For he was conceived during the full moon. Although he is sound of body, he will not live a long time. If it is a woman, she will be praiseworthy and interested in new things. She will be respected, but on the other hand, in what concerns her relationship with God, she will easily go astray if she does not show God proper reverence. She will easily become sick, but will quickly regain her health. She will not live a long time.

The Sixteenth Phase of the Moon. A person conceived during the sixteenth phase of the moon, if it is a man, will have a conventional character that will please nobody, but rather be unpleasant to all. He will have no success in his enterprises; however, he will have such an assuredness about himself that he will still do well with his life. He will be much bothered by illnesses; he will reach an old age. If it is a woman, however, she will be slow and have no perseverence. Still, she will live in a self-confident fashion. She is sound of body and will live a long time.

The Seventeenth Phase of the Moon. A person conceived during the seventeenth phase of the moon, if it is a man, will be foolish and have no understanding. From another point of view, however, he is useful, and people will enjoy themselves with him as they do with a child. People will like him. He will easily become sick at his core and not live a long time, but will still reach a certain age. If it is a woman, she will be slow, contentious, and hot tempered, but then often cheerful again. For that reason, people will enjoy her. She will be pained by cramps that will take away her senses. She also will not live a long time, but will still reach a certain age.

The Eighteenth Phase of the Moon. A person conceived during the eighteenth phase of the moon, if it is a man, will become a thief and have a desire to steal. Thus he will be discovered to be a thief. He will have no basic possessions, for normally he will not be concerned to eke out his living from the earth — for example, fields, vineyards, or such like — but rather will always try to take away from others what does not belong to him. He is sound of body and will, insofar as he controls it, live a long time. If it is a woman, she will be deceitful, have a character like a fox, and normally not disclose what, in her heart, she intends to do. Rather, because of her spoiled character, she deceives people with her words and, when she is able, brings upright people to their death. She is sound of body, but has periods of craziness. As far as she is concerned, she will live a long time. However, such character, whether it be in a man or woman, is averse to God.

The Nineteenth Phase of the Moon. A person conceived during the nineteenth phase of the moon, if it is a man, will be simple and straightforward, not deceitful, but amiable to other people. He will not live in luxury if he is not helped to this condition by other people. Although sound of body, he will not live a long time. If it is a woman, she will be slow and yet still well-liked by people. Her airs and snobbery will work to her disadvantage because others will not come to her assistance. She will easily get sick, but quickly regain her health. She will not live a long time.

The Twentieth. A person conceived in the twentieth phase of the moon, if it is a man, will be bold and cruel, a thief and a murderer, and he will enjoy doing it. He will not easily become sick, but once sick, he will be seriously ill. He will not live a long time. If it is a woman, however, she will be a betrayer, a destroyer, and a poisoner, and will even enjoy poisoning people. She will frequently walk in her sleep and will live a long time.

The Twenty-First. A person conceived in the twenty-first phase of the moon, if it is a man, will be without understanding or feeling, and full of foul moods. He will be unable to help himself in any situation, but rather will act like an imbecile who constantly loses his way. Such a person decays within, has shifting moods, is melancholic, and cannot be comforted. He will not become truly sick, but once in a while he will become depressed and thence sick. He will live this way a long time. If it is a woman, she will be loved by her companions; however, she will be fearful and anxious. She also is not able to help herself so that she will almost perish from fear if even a small child threatens her. Physically she will not often be sick, but her melancholic disposition will be a burden to her. It will sometimes cause her to be sick. She will live a long time this way.

The Twenty-Second. A person who was conceived in the twenty-second phase of the moon, if it is a man, will have a divided nature. In wartime, he will behave like someone who is not brave in battle. In front of other men, he behaves in a way corresponding to what he sees is to his own advantage. Just as the wind often changes, so it is with his outlook. Still, he is rather proficient, but not well-liked among his companions. He is physically sound and will live a long time. If it is a woman, however, then her character is hollow and of no worth. However, she exercises her attraction over men directly through her character, not through promiscuity. She lies without difficulty and easily falls into serious illnesses, such as, for example, mental illness and diseases of people on whom worms gnaw. She will live a long time.

The Twenty-Third. A person conceived during the twenty-third phase of the moon, if it is a man, will be good and amiable. He graciously follows good advice, but on the other hand does not know how to protect himself against injuries due to the duplicity of other people. He generally does well, but he rarely stays satisfied with what he has. He easily becomes sick, but equally as quickly regains his health, and will live a long time. If it is a woman, she will be modest and beloved by all because of her modesty. Because of her self-assuredness, she can be inconsiderate, but not deceptive. Still, she is generally happy and rarely sick. She will live a long time.

The Twenty-Fourth. A person conceived during the twenty-fourth phase of the moon, if it is a man, will tend to evil gossip, will be cautious, and ever after exert himself to make himself, alone, rich. He is a miser and helps almost no one. Physical ills do not bother him very much, and he will live a fairly long time. If it is a woman, however, she will be clever and scheming. She gives the impression of being good, but is not very helpful to others. Physically, she is not often sick but suffers occasionally from huge dragon-like ulcers. She also will live a fairly long time.

The Twenty-Fifth. A person conceived during the twenty-fifth phase of the moon, if it is a man, will be proud and outrageous, and he would be clever, also, if his pride and wantonness did not overpower his cleverness like a wind that scatters the dust. He is like those who want more than they have, thus like a boat that hardly remains in the water. His pride often works to his disadvantage, and he is burdensome to his companions. He easily comes down with repulsive diseases, and will not live a long time. If it is a woman, she will have an attractive face. She makes much of her propriety; however, her behavior is not really proper. If one looks for her decency, one finds nothing. For that reason she is disliked, and in her haughtiness she suffers a fall. Physically she is not often sick, but she will not live a long time.

The Twenty-Sixth. A person conceived during the twenty-sixth phase of the moon, if it is a man, will be clever and carefully consider everything that he does. He will be bothered by bouts with fever, but he can live a long time. If it is a woman, she will be clever, solicitous, stable, and modest; however, she will easily catch cold. Still, she will live a long time.

The Twenty-Seventh. A person conceived during the twenty-seventh phase of the moon, if it is a man, will be anxious and absent-minded. Also, he will easily become afraid. On the other hand, he is decent and useful, and he is well-liked by his companions. However, he is plagued by serious illnesses. For example, he becomes depressed because of an excess of bile. He will live long enough. If it is a woman, she will be virtuous; as a result, she will be well-liked by her companions. She will be weak physically, but she will still have a fairly long life.

The Twenty-Eighth. A person conceived during the twenty-eighth phase of the moon, if it is a man, will be twisted and warped in his thoughts, his character, and his behavior, and will behave like a fool. However, his understanding and intelligence are sufficient for him. One cannot hurt him. He easily loses his senses, but will live long enough. However, if it is a woman, she will be stupid and slow. She will have an unbearable nature, and so will not be liked by her companions. She will have frequent bouts with fever, but she will become fairly old.

The Twenty-Ninth. A person conceived during the twenty-ninth phase of the moon, if it is a man, will be curious, have an eccentric character and similar conduct. He enjoys new fashions in clothes and in ways of doing things, as well as new and untrustworthy people. He easily acquires toxic humors in his body and as a consequence is often sick. He will not live a long time. If it is a woman, she will be indolent and frivolous. Because of her nature and her behavior, she draws men in her train. She easily becomes sick to her stomach and also will not live a long time.

The Thirtieth Phase of the Moon. A person conceived during the thirtieth phase of the moon, if it is a man, will be poor, and if he is noble, he will continually fail and will never prosper. He will easily diminish in his body, his powers, and his flesh; however, he will live long enough. If it is a woman, she will be poor and indulge in malicious gossip. She prefers the company of strangers to her own relations. She will not often be sick, and she will live long enough.

Which Lands Produce Plants That Cure Which Illnesses. If someone suddenly becomes sick, one should help him (as well as the healthy) with medicinal plants that grow only in the East. A person who suffers from depression and has pains in his side needs plants that grow in the West. A person who has a paralysis or a strong one-day, three-day, or possibly four-day fever or a stomach ailment requires plants that grow in the South, and those mentally disturbed or with liver ailments do best with plants which come from the North.

Differences in Conception. A person who comes from dark blood walks early as a child and speaks early, but is slow and has a heavy nature. If he becomes sick, he is weak for a long time because his dark blood is slimy and diseased. A child who comes from red blood can walk and speak earlier than one who comes from dark blood. He can run fast and has quick reactions, but soon moves on. He does not remain sick for a long time, but quickly regains his health. He will be smart.

Red Blood Is Healthy. A child who comes from thickly flowing, properly colored blood will be plump and will walk as soon as it has enough body size. It is healthy and crawls early on its hands and knees. It does not stay sick long. It will be smart and strong. That kind of blood is healthy. A child that comes from thin, watery blood has no understanding. It can endure nothing and easily becomes sick, but does not easily lose its temper. Such blood is slimy. Further, such a child remains a child for a long time because it does not climb up on its feet and does not talk.

Why People Sleep After Having Taken a Laxative or After Having Been Bled. The fact that people commonly fall asleep after having taken a laxative or after having been bled is due to the emptiness in their blood vessels. The vessels wish to rest after they experience the emptying of their humors and their blood. That is why the person immediately falls asleep.

For Head Colds. If your nose runs heavily, you should inhale the smoke from a fire made of wood from a fir tree, and the congestion will break up and diminish. One may also burn some fir wood all the way to ashes, run water through it to make a lye from it, and then wash the person's head with it. This will reduce the harmful humors in the head and clear the eyes.

The Causes of Fever. Fever arises from sleeping too long, from excessive eating or drinking, or from boredom and idleness if a person does not work.

(Here the Revelations of the Blessed Hildegard come to an end. Here also ends the book; the Scribe has acquitted himself well. Everyone says, ''Amen!'')

INDEX

Heavens, creation of, 10; harmony
of, 9-10; limits of, 9; stability of,
13
Hemorrhage, cure of, 178
Hemorrhoids, cure of, 179
Herbs as medicine, 163-64
Hernia, for cure of, 159
Hiccups, 129; relief of, 173
Holy Spirit, 17-18
Horse, cure of, 192-93
Human beings, inner organs of, 38
Humors, four, 45-52; harmful,
201-02
Hunger, 100

Idiocy, 47
Infertility in woman, 161
Insanity, 48
Insomnia, cure of, 162-63
Instability, 50-51
Intemperance, 33-34
Intestinal pains, 89
Irons, burning, 113-15
Itching, cure of, 181-82

Jaundice, 137; cure of, 182
Judgment Day, 4, 14

Kidney pains, relief of, 159
Kidney stones, 141-42
Kidneys, 88
Knowledge, 60

Lameness, 102, 120, 144
Lasciviousness, 172
Last Day, 9
Laughter, 132-33; prevention of
immoderate, 176
Laxatives, 169-70
Leanness, 133
Leo, 11
Leprosy, 142-43

Libra, 12
Lice, 140-41, 186
Life, signs of, 195, 197, 198
Lightning, 3
Liver, digestive problems with, 86,
87; to prevent hardening of,
156-57
Loins, 63
Lucifer, fall of, 1, 10, 52-53
Lungs, 85; ailments of, 149; cure
of pains, 155-56

Madness, 46, 80-81
Male, sexual maturity in, 122-23
Male sex organs, 89
Man's desire, 68-69; hairlessness,
30-31
Marrow, 124-25
Matter, 1
Melancholic, the, 34-35, 66-67
Melancholic women, 79
Melancholy and anger, 129-30;
as disease, 35
Memory loss, 194
Menopause, 94-95
Menstruation, 91, 92, 95, 165-67
Migraines, 80
Milk, 61
Moon, 7, 8, 15-16; changes of, 69;
darkness of, 8; influence of,
17-18; thirty phases of, 208-16

Nightmares, 126-27
Nocturnal emissions, 73, 122
Nose, 39
Nose, blowing one's, 117
Nose bleeds, 118-19; cure of,
168-69
Nothingness, 5
Nourishment, 100; and food, 102
Nursing, 99

221

Wind, 4; subordinate, 5–6
Wine, 125–26, 133
Woman, subjugation of, 61

Woman's desire, 68
World, creation of, 1
Worms, 91–92, 140, 185–86, 187